COMPREHENSIVE
BIOCHEMISTRY

EDITED BY

MARCEL FLORKIN

Professor of Biochemistry, University of Liège (Belgium)

AND

ELMER H. STOTZ

*Professor of Biochemistry, University of Rochester, School of Medicine
and Dentistry, Rochester, N.Y. (U.S.A.)*

VOLUME 1

ATOMIC AND MOLECULAR STRUCTURE

ELSEVIER PUBLISHING COMPANY

AMSTERDAM · NEW YORK

1962

CONTRIBUTORS TO THIS VOLUME

PROF. J. D. BERNAL, M.A., F.R.S.

Department of Physics, Birkbeck College, University of London,
Malet Street, London, W.C.1 (Great Britain)

PROF. H. H. JAFFÉ

Department of Chemistry, University of Cincincinati,
Cincinnati 21, Ohio (U.S.A.)

KURT MISLOW, B.Sc., PH.D. (California Institute of Technology)

Department of Chemistry, New York University, University Heights,
New York 53, N.Y. (U.S.A.)

W. PARKER ALFORD, B.Sc., PH.D. (Princeton)

Department of Physics and Astronomy, College of Arts and Science,
The University of Rochester, River Campus Station, Rochester 20, N.Y. (U.S.A.)

COMPREHENSIVE BIOCHEMISTRY

SOLE DISTRIBUTORS FOR THE UNITED STATES AND CANADA:

AMERICAN ELSEVIER PUBLISHING COMPANY, INC.

52, Vanderbilt Avenue, New York 17, N.Y.

Library of Congress Catalog Card Number 62–10359

With 64 illustrations and 17 tables

PRINTED IN THE NETHERLANDS BY

DRUKKERIJ MEIJER – WORMERVEER AND AMSTERDAM

COMPREHENSIVE BIOCHEMISTRY

COMPREHENSIVE
BIOCHEMISTRY

SECTION I (VOLUMES I–4)
PHYSICO-CHEMICAL AND ORGANIC ASPECTS
OF BIOCHEMISTRY

SECTION II (VOLUMES 5–11)
CHEMISTRY OF BIOLOGICAL COMPOUNDS

SECTION III
BIOCHEMICAL REACTION MECHANISMS

SECTION IV
METABOLISM

SECTION V
CHEMICAL BIOLOGY
GENERAL INDEX

GENERAL PREFACE

The Editors are keenly aware that the literature of Biochemistry is already very large, in fact so widespread that it is increasingly difficult to assemble the most pertinent material in a given area. Beyond the ordinary textbook the subject matter of the rapidly expanding knowledge of biochemistry is spread among innumerable journals, monographs, and series of reviews. The Editors believe that there is a real place for an advanced treatise in biochemistry which assembles the principal areas of the subject in a single set of books.

It would be ideal if an individual or small group of biochemists could produce such an advanced treatise, and within the time to keep reasonably abreast of rapid advances, but this is at least difficult if not impossible. Instead, the Editors with the advice of the Advisory Board, have assembled what they consider the best possible sequence of chapters written by competent authors; they must take the responsibility for inevitable gaps of subject matter and duplication which may result from this procedure.

Most evident to the modern biochemist, apart from the body of knowledge of the chemistry and metabolism of biological substances, is the extent to which he must draw from recent concepts of physical and organic chemistry, and in turn project into the vast field of biology. Thus in the organization of Comprehensive Biochemistry, the middle three sections, Chemistry of Biological Compounds, Biochemical Reaction Mechanisms, and Metabolism may be considered classical biochemistry, while the first and last sections provide selected material on the origins and projections of the subject.

It is hoped that sub-division of sections into volumes will not only be convenient, but will find favour among students concerned with specialized areas, and will permit easier future revisions of the individual volumes. Toward the latter end particularly, the Editors will welcome all comments in their effort to produce a useful and efficient source of biochemical knowledge.

Liège/Rochester   M. FLORKIN
March 1962   E. H. STOTZ

PREFACE TO SECTION I

(Volumes 1–4)

Students and teachers of Biochemistry would not deny the importance of a sound understanding of at least certain areas of organic and physical chemistry in the comprehension of modern biochemistry. Toward this end the Editors have constituted the first section of Comprehensive Biochemistry. This section is intended neither as a textbook of organic nor of physical chemistry, but rather as a collection of chapters which seem generally pertinent in the interpretation of biochemical techniques and in the understanding of the chemistry of biological compounds and reaction mechanisms. Certain areas of organic and physical chemistry have been reserved for later presentation in context with specific biochemical topics, but the material of section 1 seems to the authors to underlie all of modern biochemistry. The choice of material for section 1 may well not agree with that of individual readers, and comments toward the construction of future sections will be appreciated.

Section 1 has been subdivided into groups of topics designated as Atomic and Molecular Structure (Volume 1), Organic and Physical Chemistry (Volume 2), Methods for the Study of Molecules (Volume 3) and Separation Methods (Volume 4). It is hoped that all may find general favour, and that the individual volumes will find a special place on the shelf of the specialist.

Liège/Rochester　　　　　　　　　　　　　　　　　　　　M. FLORKIN
June 1962　　　　　　　　　　　　　　　　　　　　　　　E. H. STOTZ

CONTENTS

VOLUME I

ATOMIC AND MOLECULAR STRUCTURE

General Preface. VII

Preface to Section I VIII

Chapter I. Atomic Structure
by W. PARKER ALFORD

1. Introduction. I
   The Bohr atom. 4
2. Atomic energy levels and radiation 10
3. Basic concepts of quantum mechanics – The De Broglie hypothesis 15
   a. Physical significance of the matter waves 16
   b. The hydrogen atom. 21
   c. Complex atoms 26

Bibliography 33

Chapter II. Electronic Theory of Organic Molecules
by H. H. JAFFÉ

1. Introduction. 34
2. The hydrogen molecule-ion and the hydrogen molecule in molecular orbital
   and valence bond theory 35
   a. The physical meaning of the wave function 43
   b. The energies 46
3. Other diatomic molecules 49
   a. Dilithium, Li_2 50
   b. The nitrogen, oxygen and fluorine molecules 52
   c. Molecules, LiH and CO 58
4. Polyatomic molecules: methane, ethane and water 63
5. Comparison of MO and VB theories. 67
6. The geometry of molecules. 68
7. Unsaturated compounds. 70
8. Conjugated and aromatic molecules. 73
   a. Butadiene. 73
   b. Benzene 85
   c. Hyperconjugation 91
   d. Substituted conjugated systems 92
   e. Small ring compounds 100
9. The role of d electrons 103

References 112

Chapter III. The Structure of Molecules
by J. D. BERNAL

A. Physical and Chemical Aspects of Molecular Structure

1. Introduction 113
   a. Biochemical implications of molecular structure 115
   b. Stages in the description of molecular structure 115
   c. Value of structural studies. 120
   d. Conformation 121
   e. Rigid and flexible molecules 123
   f. Van der Waals forces 124
   g. Hydrogen bonds 126
2. Classification of molecular shapes 129
   a. Simple and compound molecules 129
   b. Classification of simple molecules 131
      (i) Small molecules, 133 − (ii) Long-chain molecules, 133 − (iii) Monocyclic
      molecules, 136 − (iv) Polycyclic molecules, 137 − (v) Basket-like molecules,
      139 − (vi) Heteromorphous molecules, 140
   c. Compound molecules, oligomers and polymers 141
      Polymers, 141
   d. Molecular aggregates and molecular compounds 144
3. Physical properties of polymer aggregates 145
   a. The globular–fibrous G–F transformation 146
   b. Isotactic polymers 147
   c. Colloidal properties of polymers 148
   d. Long-range forces 149

B. Structures of the Major Classes of Biochemical Molecules

1. Simple nitrogen compounds 153
   a. Amino acids 153
   b. Pyrimidines, purines and porphyrins 155
2. Carbohydrates, vegetable acids and aldehydes 156
   Polysaccharides, 156
3. Lipids 157
   Carotenoids, 159
4. Sterols and terpenes 160
5. Alkaloids 161
6. Peptides and proteins 163
   a. Peptides 163
   b. Globular and fibrous proteins 165
   c. Active and structural proteins 168
   d. Denaturation 169
   e. Crystalline proteins, myoglobin and haemoglobin 169
   f. Fibrous proteins 171
7. Nucleotides and nucleic acids 174
   a. Nucleic acids 176
   b. Nucleoproteins. 178
   c. Virus nucleoproteins 178
      (i) Rod-shaped viruses, 179 − (ii) Spherical viruses, 180
8. Molecular structures in relation to cells or tissues 181
   a. Intracellular structures 181
   b. Fibres 182
   c. Chromosomes 184
   d. Flagellae and cilia 184
   e. Intracellular membranes 185
   f. Supporting structures. 188

Chapter IV. Stereoisomerism
by KURT MISLOW

Introduction 192

A. Stereoisomeric Types

1. Enantiomers and diastereomers 192
   a. Enantiomers. 193
   b. Optical activity 194
   c. Racemic forms. 198
   d. Diastereomers 198
2. Stereoisomers resulting from hindered or restricted rotation 199
   a. Conformational stereoisomers 199
   b. Atropisomers 200
   c. Geometric isomers 201
   d. Allenes 204
3. Stereoisomers resulting from asymmetric atoms 205
   a. Asymmetric atoms 205
   b. Meso isomers 206
4. Stereoisomerism in cyclohexanes 209
   a. Cyclohexane. 209
   b. Inositol 210
   c. Decalin 212
   d. Perhydrophenanthrene 214
5. Stereoisomerism in macromolecules 214
6. Configurational nomenclature 217

B. Preparation of Stereoisomers

1. Diastereomers 219
   Asymmetric synthesis, 220
2. Optical activation 221
   a. Resolution 221
   b. Asymmetric synthesis. 223
   c. Some conjectures concerning origin and maintenance of optical activity in
      nature 225

C. Determination of Configuration

1. Diastereomers 226
2. Absolute and relative configurations of enantiomers. 227
   a. Correlations by chemical methods 228
   b. Correlations by physical methods. 232
   c. The configuration of mandelic acid 234

Bibliography 238

References 239

Subject Index 245

The other parts of Section I contain the following chapters:

Volume 2. *Organic and Physical Chemistry*

Chapter I. Mechanisms of Organic Reactions by M. L. BENDER and R. BRESLOW (Evanston, Ill. and New York, N.Y.)

Chapter II. Behaviour of Molecules in Solution by W. D. Stein (Cambridge, Great Britain)

Chapter III. Diffusion and Osmosis by W. D. Stein (Cambridge, Great Britain)

Volume 3. *Methods for the Study of Molecules*

Chapter I. Crystallography by G. J. BULLEN (London)

Chapter II. X-Ray Diffraction by G. J. BULLEN (London)

Chapter III. Analysis by Emission Spectroscopy by NORMAN H. NACHTRIEB (Chicago, Ill.)

Chapter IV. Spectrophotometry in the Ultraviolet and Visible Regions by R. A. MORTON (Liverpool)

Chapter V. Infrared Spectra of Compounds of Biological Interest by L. J. BELLAMY (Waltham Abbey, Essex)

Chapter VI. Fluorescence by A. EHRENBERG AND H. THEORELL (Stockholm)

Chapter VII. Electronic Paramagnetic Resonance by S. I. WEISSMAN (St. Louis, Mo.)

Chapter VIII. Nuclear Magnetic Resonance by C. D. JARDETZKY AND O. JARDETZKY (Cambridge and Boston, Mass.)

Chapter IX. Determination of Mass, Form and Dimensions of Large Particles in Solution by CH. SADRON AND M. DAUNE (Strasbourg)

Volume 4. *Separation Methods*

Chapter I. Countercurrent Distribution by LYMAN C. CRAIG (New York)

Chapter II. Chromatography by E. LEDERER AND M. LEDERER (Paris and Rome)

Chapter III. Gas Chromatography by P. CHOVIN (Paris)

Chapter I

Atomic Structure

W. PARKER ALFORD

Department of Physics, University of Rochester, N.Y. (U.S.A.)

1. Introduction

The purpose of this chapter will be to provide an introduction to those parts of the theory of atomic structure which seem most relevant to biological problems. On the one hand, a knowledge of atomic phenomena is now needed to appreciate the possibilities and the limitations of new physical techniques and instruments being utilized in biological studies. On a more fundamental level, an understanding of many of the concepts of atomic physics is essential to the understanding of such fundamental phenomena as the structure and stability of molecules, energy transfer in molecular systems, or the interaction between atoms and radiation.

Since any problem in atomic structure can be solved, at least in principle, using the methods of *quantum mechanics*, a large part of this chapter will be devoted to examining the new ideas introduced into scientific thinking by the development of quantum mechanics. Though the formal methods of quantum mechanics will not be used to obtain a complete solution of atomic problems, we shall see that with the introduction of these ideas we are able to obtain an understanding of the physical behaviour and properties of atomic systems.

Until the beginning of this century, an essential idea in the description of natural phenomena was that of the continuity of structure and motion. While the atomic nature of matter was clearly recognized, the small size of atoms and the very great numbers involved in most observable phenomena made matter appear structureless and continuous. Even in situations in which the atomic nature of matter was explicitly recognized, as in the kinetic theory of gases, it was assumed that the motions and interactions of atoms could be described by the physical laws governing macroscopic phenomena. These were Newton's laws, describing the *motion of particles*, and Maxwell's equations describing *interactions of charged particles* with electric and

Bibliography p. 33

magnetic fields in general, and the process of *electro-magnetic radiation* in particular. During the last part of the nineteenth century, however, the quantitative investigation of several phenomena involving the interaction of radiation with matter made it clear that classical mechanics and electro-magnetic theory could not account for the experimental facts. It was the attempt to understand these phenomena which led to basic changes in our conceptions of matter and radiation and culminated in the development of quantum mechanics.

One of these phenomena was that of *thermal or "black-body" radiation*, the well-known radiation emitted by bodies when raised to high temperatures. Many general features of this radiation including the relationship between the total radiation emitted and the temperature of the body were correctly predicted on the basis of classical thermodynamics. The spectral distribution could not be deduced from classical theories, however, even though the principles employed were thought to have very general validity. A theoretical expression for the spectrum which was in excellent agreement with experimental measurements was finally derived by the German physicist M. Planck on the basis of a fundamentally new assumption. Since the spectrum was known to be independent of the nature of the radiating body, Planck reasoned that he was free to choose a convenient, though not necessarily realistic, model to represent the mechanism of energy interchange between the radiator and the emitted radiation. The radiator (*i.e.* the surface of the radiating body) was pictured as consisting of a collection of simple harmonic oscillators, each one of which was capable of emitting or absorbing radiation at some fixed frequency v. Under conditions of thermodynamic equilibrium, the rates of absorption and emission of energy by a given oscillator were equal, and could readily be calculated using standard results of electro-magnetic theory. Planck assumed that an oscillator absorbed energy from the radiation field in a continuous manner, in accordance with the theory; this new assumption was that an oscillator did not re-radiate its energy continuously, however, but only in discrete finite amounts, or quanta. The quantum of energy E was related to the frequency of the oscillator by the simple expression

$$E = hv \tag{1}$$

where h is a universal constant, now known as Planck's constant. The introduction of this new assumption represented a decisive break with classical ideas, and marked the birth of quantum theory. It is interesting to note that Planck did not regard the assumption in this light at the time. Though it led to a theoretical spectrum which agreed well with experiment, Planck noted explicitly the tentative nature of this hypothesis, and suggested that further work might show the need for a revision of his ideas.

Planck had applied the notion of quantization only to the emission of energy into the electromagnetic field, and considered the field itself to be a continuous wave disturbance in agreement with classical views. A. Einstein soon showed, however, that under some circumstances the energy in the radiation field itself could be considered as concentrated in discrete quanta, with the relation between quantum energy and wave frequency given by Eqn. (1). If this were the case, it would be expected that not only the emission, but also the absorption of radiant energy would be quantized. In confirmation of this view, he was able to apply it to explain several puzzling features of the photoelectric effect.

It had been known for some time that under the influence of ultraviolet light, electrons were emitted from metals. The maximum energy of the ejected electrons was found to be independent of the intensity of the light, in direct contradiction to classical ideas, but proportional to the frequency of the light. This result was explained by Einstein on the assumption that the incident light consisted of discrete quanta (now usually referred to as photons) of energy $h\nu$, and that the ejection of a photoelectron was caused by the absorption of a photon. The maximum energy of the electron was then related to the frequency of the light by the expression $E = h\nu - \Phi$ where Φ is the binding energy of the electron to the metal surface, and is a constant for a given metal. This relationship has been very carefully verified, particularly by the work of R. A. Millikan.

Another field which had been extensively studied was that of *atomic spectra*. Since the middle of the nineteenth century, it had been known that atoms, when suitably excited, would radiate light of certain discrete wavelengths. It had also been recognized that the radiations from a given type of atom were characteristic of that type, and that the nature of the radiating atoms could be inferred from the spectra emitted. The spectrum of some elements showed very many lines, apparently distributed more or less randomly in wavelength. In other spectra, notably those of hydrogen and the alkali metals, relatively few lines appeared, but their distribution in wavelength did not display the regularity that might be expected on the basis of classical electromagnetism.

With the discovery of the *electrical nature of matter*, it was natural to suppose that radiation was associated with the motion of electrical charges in the atom. Now, no matter how complex the motion of the charges in the atom might be, the motion could be resolved into a superposition of simple harmonic disturbances, each one of which would occur at a definite frequency which was an integral multiple of some fundamental frequency. It was also known that an electric charge in simple harmonic motion would radiate electromagnetic waves at the same frequency as its motion. Thus it was expected that the frequencies of spectral lines from a given atom should all be integral multiples of some fundamental frequency.

Bibliography p. 33

Attempts to find these simple harmonic relationships proved fruitless; most spectra consisted of a very great number of lines in the visible region, with no apparent relationship at all between the frequencies of different lines. The spectrum of hydrogen was particularly simple, however, as is shown in Fig. 1. In 1885, J. J. Balmer showed that the frequencies of successive lines in this spectrum could be represented by the simple formula

$$v = v_0 \left(\frac{1}{2^2} - \frac{1}{n^2} \right) \tag{2}$$

where v_0 is a constant and n takes on the integral values 3, 4, 5 —for successive lines.

Such a regular sequence of lines was called a *series*. Following Balmer's discovery, efforts were made to identify series in the spectra of other elements, and in many cases it was found that the spectrum consisted of not one but several different series, often overlapping one another in wavelength.

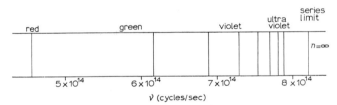

Fig. 1. Appearance of the Balmer series in the hydrogen spectrum. The spacing between successive lines becomes small as the series limit is approached and (in principle at least) an infinite number of lines will lie between the last line shown and the series limit.

Many other empirical relationships between the frequencies of the lines in the spectrum of a given element were subsequently discovered. These are summarized in the *Ritz Combination Principle*: the frequency of one line in a given spectrum can usually be expressed as the sum or difference of the frequencies of some other pair of lines in that spectrum. It was not until 1913 that a theoretical explanation of these empirical relationships was provided by the Bohr theory of the hydrogen atom.

The Bohr atom

Historically, the Bohr theory of the hydrogen atom stands midway between the older ideas of classical physics and the later development of quantum mechanics. Though many detailed predictions of the Bohr theory turned out to be incorrect, it is still of considerable interest, both for the simple, useful model of the atom which it provides, and for the insight it gives into the relationship between atomic structure and radiation. Before discussing the theory in detail, however, it will be necessary to describe the development of some earlier ideas concerning atomic structure.

Late in the nineteenth century, the study of gas discharges had demonstrated that in the discharge electrically neutral gas atoms were broken up into components bearing positive and negative charges. For the negative component the ratio of charge to mass was found to be a constant, independent of the nature of the gas in the discharge. For the positive component this ratio was smaller by a factor of about 2000 if the gas were hydrogen, and by an even larger factor if other gases were used. Thus it appeared that all atoms were made up of electrically charged particles with most of the mass and presumably the characteristic properties of the atom associated with the positively charged particles. The negatively charged particles common to all atoms were eventually named electrons, and were later recognized as the charge carriers in the phenomenon of the photoelectric effect.

The origin of spectral lines in the motion of the electrons was apparently demonstrated about 1897 by the study of the Zeeman effect. This effect is the splitting of individual spectral lines into two or more component lines when the radiating atoms are placed in a strong magnetic field. Assuming that the radiated lines were produced by the motion of electrical charges in the atom, the Dutch physicist H. A. Lorentz showed that a splitting of the lines should occur as these motions were disturbed by an external magnetic field. At least in the normal Zeeman effect, the magnitude of the observed splittings, and the polarization of the light in the different components was just as predicted by Lorentz' theory, provided that the radiating charges were electrons. The physical model on which Lorentz developed his theory was later seen to be quite unsatisfactory, but the identification of the electrons as the atomic radiators was correct.

With the above information available, a definite model of the atom was proposed by J. J. Thomson. The positive charge and most of the mass of the atom was pictured as being distributed uniformly over a volume of atomic dimensions. The electrons were pictured as concentrations of negative charge having dimensions much smaller than that of the atom. These electrons were somehow distributed throughout the volume of the atom, with enough electrons in the normal atom so that its net charge was zero.

As a test of this model, E. Rutherford made a study of the scattering of alpha particles in passing through matter. It was already known that alpha particles, a type of radiation emitted in the radioactive decay of certain substances, were the positively charged part of helium atoms. The velocity of these particles had been shown to be of the order of 10^9 cm/sec, and it was known that they could traverse thin layers of matter, such as a piece

Bibliography p. 33

of gold leaf, or a few centimetres of air. Now in a collision between an alpha particle and an atom constructed according to the Thomson model, it had been shown that the alpha particle could be deviated from its original direction of motion by only a small amount, of the order of a few degrees. To test this prediction, Rutherford used the following experimental arrangement: A collimated beam of alpha particles from a radioactive source was allowed to fall on a thin foil of gold or some other metal. With a suitable detector, measurements were made of the relative numbers of alpha particles scattered through various angles by collision with an atom of the metal foil. Contrary to the prediction of the Thomson model, it was found that many alpha particles were scattered through angles of 90° or greater.

This result led Rutherford to propose the *nuclear model of the atom*. The positive charge and most of the mass of the atom was supposed to be concentrated in a volume of radius less than 10^{-12} cm at the centre of the atom. The electrons were bound to the nucleus by electrostatic forces and were assumed to move around it much as the planets were known to move around the sun. Since most of the volume of this atom is just empty space, it is able to account for the ability of alpha particles to traverse matter. Rutherford also showed that in a close collision between the alpha particle and the massive impenetrable nucleus, the alpha particle could be deflected through any angle up to 180°.

Though this model was consistent with the known facts of atomic structure it was still unsatisfactory since it did not seem possible that such an atom could be stable. If the electrons were bound to the nucleus by the electrostatic attraction between their negative charge and the positive charge of the nucleus, then they would have to move around the nucleus in circular or elliptical orbits. As the electrons rotated in these orbits, they would be constantly accelerated towards the nucleus, and according to well established results of electromagnetic theory, an accelerated charge must radiate electromagnetic waves. If the electrons did this, they would constantly lose energy and their orbits would eventually collapse into the nucleus. Another difficulty arises from the fact that the radiation from such an atom would be expected to be continuous, with radiation at all frequencies, rather than the discrete line spectrum actually observed, with radiation only at definite isolated frequencies.

In spite of this difficulty, a new theory of the hydrogen atom based on this model was proposed in 1913 by the Danish physicist Niels Bohr. In setting up this theory, Bohr assumed that the laws of classical mechanics and electromagnetism could be applied to the atom just as to macroscopic systems. They were subject to certain restrictions, however, which were important at the atomic level, but which could be ignored in large-scale systems. Because of its importance to the further development of atomic physics, and because of the useful physical picture provided by the Bohr theory, we will discuss these assumptions, and the results of the theory in some detail.

The first assumption, as already noted, was that the laws of mechanics and electromagnetism could be used to calculate the behaviour of atomic systems. This might better be described as a philosophical point of view: that the laws of physics which had been shown to hold for large-scale phenomena could be extended to the atomic domain. We shall see later that an essential feature of quantum mechanics was the recognition of the fact that a radical change in this classical point of view was necessary before atomic structure could be fully understood. The other specific assumptions relevant to the problem were the following:

(1) The hydrogen atom is composed of a massive positively charged nucleus plus an electron. The particles are attracted to one another by electrostatic forces, and under the influence of this attraction the electron moves in a circular orbit about the nucleus.

(2) Not all orbits are possible, but only those for which the orbital angular momentum* of the electron is an integral multiple of Planck's constant divided by 2π. It may be recalled here that Planck's constant, h, first appeared in connection with the problem of black-body radiation, where to explain the shape of the spectrum Planck had assumed that radiation could be emitted only in units or quanta of energy $E = h\nu$. In the present problem the constant h appears in a new context, but again in such a way as to single out from the classically continuous distribution of possible states of the system only those discrete states satisfying certain conditions. Such states are said to be quantized and the requirement:

$$\text{angular momentum} = nh/2\pi \ (n \text{ integral})$$

---

* The concept of angular momentum plays an important role in many physical problems because of the fact that it is a constant of the motion for a body moving under the influence of a central force. For instance for a particle of mass m moving in a circular path of radius r with uniform velocity v, the angular momentum has the value $L = mvr$. Angular momentum is a vector (actually an axial vector), and in the above example points normal to the plane of the path in the direction of advance of a right-handed screw rotated in the sense of v. More generally, for a particle moving in an arbitrary path with (vector) velocity $\vec{v}$, its angular momentum about a point is defined as $\vec{L} = m \vec{r} \times \vec{v}$. Here $\vec{r}$ is the distance from the point in question to the particle. $\vec{r} \times \vec{v}$ is called the vector product of $\vec{r}$ and $\vec{v}$ and is defined as a vector normal to the plane of $\vec{r}$ and $\vec{v}$, of length $rv \sin\theta$ where θ is the angle between $\vec{r}$ and $\vec{v}$. Its direction is the direction of advance of a right-hand screw rotated through the smallest angle from the direction of $\vec{r}$ to the direction of $\vec{v}$. This is illustrated in Fig. 2. It is seen that this is equivalent to the earlier definition for the special case of motion in a circular path where $\theta = 90°$.

Bibliography p. 33

is called a quantum condition for the allowed states of the system.

(*3*) The classical electromagnetic laws do not apply to the radiation of electromagnetic waves from atomic systems. In particular, an electron can move indefinitely in one of the allowed orbits specified by assumption (2) without the emission of radiation. It is interesting to note here that while electromagnetic radiation processes are assumed different in atomic and macroscopic systems, the electrostatic forces between charges are assumed the same.

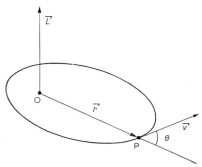

Fig. 2. Illustrating the defiintion of orbital angular momentum for a particle.

(*4*) Radiation is emitted or absorbed if the electron makes a transition between two of the states allowed by the quantum condition (2). If the energy of the electron in the higher state is E_1 and in the lower state E_2, the frequency v of the radiation is given by the relation

$$E_1 - E_2 = hv$$

It is to be noted that this is just the energy of a photon of frequency v as postulated to explain the photoelectric effect. Hence the interpretation of the above relation is that the electron can make transitions between allowed energy states with the emission or absorption of a photon of energy equal to the energy difference between the two states.

In order to compare the predictions of this theory with experiment, it is necessary to calculate the energy of the electron in the allowed states specified by the quantum condition. A straightforward calculation yields the result:

$$E_n = - 2\pi^2 me^4 / n^2 h^2 \tag{3}$$

where the symbols have the following meaning: e and m are the charge and mass of the electron, h is Planck's constant and n an integer specifying the orbital angular momentum of the electron in the given state. This is also called the quantum number specifying the state.

The negative sign appearing in Eqn. (3) indicates that the electron is bound to the nucleus, or that energy must be supplied to the atom in order to remove the electron. The magnitude of this energy for the ground state $(n = 1)$ is given by Eqn. (3) as $2.18 \cdot 10^{-11}$ erg. A more convenient unit of energy for atomic problems is the electronvolt, which is the energy acquired by an electron when allowed to fall through a potential difference of one Volt. One electronvolt $= 1.6 \cdot 10^{-12}$ erg, so that the above binding energy equals 13.6 electronvolts. This is a fairly typical value of the binding energy of the outermost electrons in an atom.

In accordance with assumption (4), the frequency of the spectral line emitted by the atom when the electron makes a transition from a state of quantum number n to one of quantum number m will be given by

$$v_{nm} = \frac{E_n - E_m}{h} = \frac{2\pi^2 m e^4}{h^3} \left(\frac{1}{m^2} - \frac{1}{n^2} \right)$$

This is seen to be just the form of the Balmer formula if we take $m = 2$ and let n take on values, 3, 4, 5. Not only does this expression have the appropriate dependence on n but the actual frequencies predicted by it agreed with spectral measurements within the accuracy of the constants

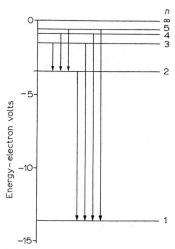

Fig. 3. Term diagram for the hydrogen atom according to the Bohr theory. The horizontal lines represent the allowed energy levels of the atom while the vertical arrows represent electron transitions giving rise to spectral lines. Transitions ending on the level with $n = 2$ give rise to the Balmer series.

Bibliography p. 33

appearing in the theoretical expression for E_n. The energy levels of the hydrogen atom predicted by the Bohr theory are shown as the horizontal lines in Fig. 3. The vertical arrows represent possible electron transitions giving rise to spectral lines. Transitions ending on the energy level with $n = 2$ give rise to the Balmer series.

2. Atomic energy levels and radiation

The physical interpretation of these results is as follows. Under ordinary circumstances, the hydrogen atom will remain indefinitely in the state of lowest energy, that is the allowed state with $n = 1$. This is referred to as the ground state. If energy is now supplied to the atom by heating in a flame or bombardment by charged particles in an electrical discharge, the electron may make a transition from the ground state to one of the excited states, or allowed states of higher energy. Subsequently this electron will spontaneously make a transition to some state of lower energy, with the simultaneous emission of a quantum of radiation. Eventually it will return to the stable gound state. The expression for the frequencies of the lines in the *Balmer series* gives these in terms of the energy difference between the first excited state ($n = 2$) and higher excited states. Hence the Balmer series arises from transitions in which the electron moves from one of the higher excited states to the first excited state. Other series would be expected and have been observed, arising from transitions leading directly to the ground state (*Lyman series*), the second excited state (*Paschen series*) and so on. The Lyman series lies in the ultraviolet region of the spectrum while all others except the Balmer series lie in the infrared.

The Bohr theory also provides an immediate understanding of the Ritz Combination Principle. Consider three energy states of an atom, of energies $E_a > E_b > E_c$. Then the frequency of radiations emitted as the electron makes transitions from higher to lower states will be given by

$$v_{ab} = \frac{E_a - E_b}{h} \qquad v_{bc} = \frac{E_b - E_c}{h}$$

$$v_{ac} = \frac{E_a - E_c}{h} = v_{ab} + v_{ac}$$

This situation is illustrated in Fig. 4. Clearly, whenever two different spectral lines arise from transitions involving a common level we may expect to find another line whose frequency is the sum or difference of the frequencies of the two lines.

A very convincing demonstration of the existence of the allowed energy states and their connection with the radiation emitted by an atom was furnished by the experiments of Franck and Hertz. Mercury vapour in a special evacuated tube was bombarded by electrons of variable energy. A means was provided for measuring the energy of the electrons after passing through the mercury vapour, and the mercury vapour itself was

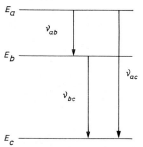

Fig. 4. Illustrating the physical significance of the Ritz Combination Principle. The frequency ν_{ac} will equal the sum $\nu_{ab} + \nu_{cb}$.

observed with a spectroscope. It was found that at low enough energies, electrons traversed the mercury vapour with no loss of energy. However, as the electron energy was increased, a critical energy E_c was reached at which point electrons lost essentially all their energy in traversing the vapour. As this critical energy was reached it was found that the mercury vapour emitted a single line of the mercury spectrum, and the frequency of the line was connected to the critical energy by the Bohr condition

$$h\nu = E_c$$

The explanation of this result is as follows: the mercury atoms can exist only in certain discrete allowed energy states, just as the hydrogen atom. If bombarded by electrons of energy less than the energy difference between the ground state and first excited state, the mercury atom cannot be raised to the excited state and the electrons will be scattered with no energy loss. However, as soon as the energy of the bombarding electrons is great enough, the electron may give up its kinetic energy to the mercury atom, thus producing a mercury atom in an excited state and an electron of zero energy. Eventually the mercury atom will return to its ground state with the emission of radiation of the frequency given by the Bohr condition above.

These first and simplest results of the Bohr theory provided an understanding of the main features of the spectrum of hydrogen. Following Bohr's original paper a number of workers refined and extended the theory to explain many of the finer details of the spectrum. Much of this work is now

Bibliography p. 33

of historical interest only, but two of these developments warrant discussion for the insight they provide into the significance of the later quantum-mechanical theory. The first of these was the extension of the theory to include the possibility of elliptical as well as circular orbits for the electron. It is well known that the orbits of a particle bound by an inverse-square force are generally ellipses with the centre of attraction at one focus. The circular orbit is simply a special case of the elliptical orbit. Bohr recognized this fact in his original paper, but was unable to use his quantum condition to specify the allowed elliptical orbits. The circular orbit corresponding to a given orbital angular momentum is unique, but an infinite number of elliptical orbits of different shapes and sizes are possible for a given angular momentum. The problem of quantizing the elliptical orbits was solved by the introduction of the *Wilson–Sommerfeld quantum conditions*. It is not possible to discuss these in detail here, but it will be sufficient to note that these new conditions apply to each independent coordinate involved in any periodic motion whatsoever (*i.e.* any motion in which the particle traverses a recurrent, closed path). The Bohr quantum condition appears as a special case of the Wilson–Sommerfeld condition, of course.

The application of these conditions yielded the result that only those elliptical orbits are allowed for which the length of the semi-major axis is equal to the radius of one of the Bohr orbits. Corresponding to a given circular orbit of radius r_n, energy E_n, and angular momentum $nh/2\pi$, there would be a number of allowed elliptical orbits. The energy of the electron was the same in each of these, while the angular momentum could take on any one of the values $nh/2\pi$, $(n-1)h/2\pi \ldots h/2\pi$. The smaller values of angular momentum correspond to orbits in which the ellipse is long and narrow, the larger values to near-circular orbits. In the quantum-mechanical theory of the hydrogen atom, we shall no longer be able to picture the motion of the electron in the simple mechanical terms used here, but we shall find a result similar to this. Corresponding to a given energy of the electron, there will generally be a number of different allowed states characterized by different allowed values of the angular momentum.

An entirely new phenomenon predicted by the Wilson–Sommerfeld quantum condition is that of *space quantization*. If we choose a set of coordinate axes, then we must specify three independent coordinates to define the position of the electron in space relative to these axes. Now there is a quantum condition which must be satisfied for each independent coordinate occurring in a problem. For the hydrogen atom, two of these conditions are required to specify the size and shape of the allowed elliptical orbits. The third condition turns out to specify the orientation of the plane of the orbit relative to the chosen coordinate axes. Since the angular momentum of the electron is represented by a vector normal to the plane of the orbit, this result may be interpreted as specifying the angle which the angular momentum vector makes with one of the axes. If the magnitude of the angular momentum is $nh/2\pi$, then the allowed orientations may be shown to be such that the projection of the angular momentum on a given axis can take on the values $nh/2\pi$, $(n-1)h/2\pi$, ... $h/2\pi$, 0, $-h/2\pi$, ..., $-nh/2\pi$. Here the negative values indicate that the projection is antiparallel to the axis. The magnitude of the projection of the angular momentum on the given axis differs by $h/2\pi$ between adjacent allowed orientations, and it is seen that for an orbit of angular momentum $nh/2\pi$, a total of $2n+1$ different orientations are allowed.

It may appear quite unreasonable that our choice of coordinate system could have any effect on the physical properties of a system, but it is necessary to consider how such a coordinate system would be established on an atomic scale. This is illustrated by the experiment of Stern and Gerlach which gave a direct demonstration of space quantization. To discuss this result, however, it is first necessary to introduce the idea of the magnetic moment of an atomic system. In the Bohr model, the electron circulates around the nucleus in one of its allowed orbits. This moving electric charge is equivalent to an electric current, and according to the laws of electromagnetism, would be expected to set up a magnetic field. Now for a current flowing in a plane loop, it can be shown that the magnetic field produced is the same as would be produced by a small bar magnet or magnetic dipole at the centre of the loop with the axis of the magnet normal to the plane of the loop. The dipole moment of the equivalent bar magnet is given in terms of the properties of the circuit by the relation $\mu = iA$ where i is the current flowing in the loop and A the area of the loop. The magnetic properties of the circuit can then be characterized by the single parameter μ. There is also a very simple relationship between the angular momentum of a particle moving in a closed orbit, and the magnetic moment of the equivalent circuit. From the above definition for μ, it can be shown that $\mu = eL/2m$ where L is the angular momentum of the particle of charge e and mass m.

The idea of the *Stern–Gerlach experiment* is the following. Since the magnetic moment of the atom is proportional to the angular momentum, the space quantization of the latter would imply that the magnetic moment also could take on only certain discrete orientations relative to a given axis. If this axis is defined by the direction of an external magnetic field, then the interaction of the magnetic moment with the field should be quantized, and it would be possible to observe the space quantization. In the actual experimental arrangement, a beam of silver atoms evaporated from an oven was passed through a strong, inhomogeneous magnetic field and allowed to deposit on a cold plate. If we suppose the magnetic field B to be

Bibliography p. 33

in the direction of the z axis, and to be increasing in this direction, then there will be a force in the direction of the z axis acting on a dipole, given by $F_z = \mu(dB/dz) \cos\theta$ where θ is the angle between the dipole axis and the direction of the field. Hence in passing through the inhomogeneous field, atoms will be deflected by an amount proportional to $\cos\theta$. Classically, all values of θ are allowed and it would be expected that the original beam would simply be smeared out in the z direction. What was actually observed was that the beam was split into a number of discrete components, indicating the existence of discrete, allowed values of $\cos\theta$. Thus at one step, this very elegant experiment provided direct experimental evidence for the existence of magnetic dipole moments of atoms, and for the space quantization of angular momentum and the associated magnetic moment.

This experiment also illustrates the meaning of a coordinate system on an atomic scale. The direction of the magnetic field provides a natural choice for the direction of one of the coordinate axes, and it is relative to this axis that the orientation of the atom is quantized. We do not observe the orientation directly though, but only the effect of the orientation on the interaction between the atom and the external field. Thus it is only through some interaction between the atom and an external field that the space quantization becomes observable, and the axis of quantization is then defined by the direction of the external field. This result provides a first illustration of a general quantum-mechanical conclusion: the only properties of an atomic system which should enter into the theory are those which can actually be measured in some conceivable experiment. As we shall see later, there is no way, even in principle, by which the orbit of the electron could be observed, and its orientation in space measured. It is possible on the other hand to observe the space quantization of the magnetic moment, but it is necessary to adopt the point of view that it is in the process of making such a measurement that the magnetic moment is forced into one of the possible quantized states.

In spite of its many successes, the Bohr theory was unable to account for many of the features of the spectra of atoms more complex than hydrogen, and it was eventually recognized that some radically new approach was needed to the problems of atomic structure. This was provided by the development of quantum mechanics. The importance of the Bohr theory in the development of quantum mechanics arises from the way in which it clarified our understanding of certain *fundamental properties of atomic systems*. These were (*a*) the existence of discrete, allowed energy states in which not only the energy, but other properties such as angular momentum might also take on discrete values; and (*b*) the connection between the allowed energy states and the radiation emitted and absorbed by the system. In addition, the results of the Bohr theory provide a simple mechanical model of the atom which is often useful in formulating a qualitative physical picture of the mathematical results of quantum mechanics.

3. Basic concepts of quantum mechanics – The De Broglie hypothesis

Just as the laws of Newtonian mechanics can be used to provide a quantitative description of the motion of a macroscopic mechanical system, so the laws of quantum mechanics provide an analogous description of the properties of atomic systems. However, the mathematical techniques employed in the formal solution of quantum mechanical problems are both extensive and rather specialized. For this reason, it will not be possible in this chapter to develop the detailed formalism of quantum mechanics and apply it to atomic problems. Instead, the principal physical concepts involved in the theory will be presented, and applied to obtain a rather qualitative understanding of the structure of atoms.

Fundamental to the whole subject of quantum mechanics is the *concept of the wave nature of matter*. At first sight this appears to be a contradiction in terms, at least in the terms of classical physics. Matter is pictured as composed of particles which are by definition localized in small regions of space. A wave, on the other hand, is pictured as a disturbance of some sort which in general is not localized at all; or if initially localized, it will spread out over increasingly greater regions as it propagates. It has already been noted, however, that light exhibits characteristics of both waves and particles; the former in the phenomena of interference and diffraction, the latter in processes involving the emission or absorption of radiation. It was suggested by L. de Broglie in 1924, that this duality exhibited by light might be a basic property of nature, and that the *"particles"* of atomic physics, such as electrons and atomic nuclei, might under suitable circumstances exhibit wave properties. Pursuing this hypothesis further, he suggested that the frequency of the associated wave should be related to the energy of the particle, W, by the familiar relationship

$$v = W/h$$

It was then possible to show that the wavelength λ of the wave was given in terms of the momentum p of the particle by the relation

$$\lambda = h/p$$

We may note here in passing the order of magnitude of the wavelengths predicted by this equation. For an electron which has been accelerated through a potential difference of ten kilovolts, the wavelength of the

Bibliography p. 33

associated De Broglie wave is about 10^{-9} cm. By comparison, the wavelength of visible light is about $5 \cdot 10^{-5}$ cm.

The characteristic phenomena associated with waves, such as diffraction, are observed most readily when the wave interacts with structures whose size is comparable with the wavelength. With visible light, with a wavelength of about 0.0005 mm, diffraction effects are readily observed if the light passes through slits having a width of a few times this value. Similar effects arising from matter waves were not observed in early experiments with beams of particles simply because the dimensions of the apparatus were always large compared with the wavelength. Following De Broglie's suggestions, however, experiments were performed which clearly demonstrated the matter waves associated with a beam of electrons. In the experiments of G. P. Thomson, and others, a beam of high-energy electrons was passed through a very thin metal foil, and detected on a photographic plate behind the foil. In addition to the image produced by the direct beam, the plate showed a series of rings, just as in the diffraction of a beam of X-rays of a definite wavelength. The quantitative analysis of such diffraction patterns showed that they were produced by waves of a wavelength equal to the De Broglie wavelength of the electrons. This result was very convincing evidence for the existence of the De Broglie waves, but emphasized the problem of understanding how a single entity could possess the apparently irreconcilable properties of wave and particle. It is not possible to discuss in detail the resolution of this problem, but we may note that it comes about by considering what is meant by the physical nature or properties of an atomic system. We do not directly sense these properties as we do in dealing with macroscopic objects, but we infer them from the results of more or less indirect measurements. In studying the properties of electrons for instance, the results of a diffraction experiment may be described in terms of waves; the deflection of a beam of electrons in a magnetic field would be described, however, in terms of the motion of particles. In each case we use the language of the macroscopic world to form a picture or a model of an entity that cannot be observed directly. In any one type of experiment, either the wave-like or particle-like properties may be dominant. Only one or the other will be needed to describe the results of a given experiment, but both are needed to describe all possible experiments. The problem of trying to picture something that is both wave and particle is essentially one of language, arising from our attempts to describe an entity that we cannot directly observe, using concepts defined in terms of our own sense perceptions.

(a) Physical significance of the matter waves

De Broglie's original suggestion of the existence of matter waves immediately raised the question of the physical nature of these waves. How is the propagation of the wave to be related to motion of the material particle? Given the amplitude of the wave, what information does this yield about the particle? One step towards the solution of these problems was provided by De Broglie. He pointed out that the relationship $\lambda = h/p$ leads to a complete formal analogy between classical mechanics on the one hand and geometrical optics on the other. Now geometrical optics is the study of the propagation of light, or of electromagnetic waves in general, under circumstances in which typical wave phenomena such as diffraction are unimportant. It is thus an approximation to the theory of wave propagation, valid in the limit that the wavelength of the waves is small compared with all other dimensions in the problem. This led De Broglie to suggest that the laws of classical mechanics may be an approximation, valid only in case the wavelengths of the particles under consideration were small enough. The correct laws of mechanics would describe the propagation of matter waves, and would reduce to the laws of classical mechanics in case the finite wavelengths of the matter waves could be ignored.

Having this analogy between optics and mechanics, it might be supposed that the relationships between material particles and their associated De Broglie waves would be similar to the relationship between the quantum concept of photons and the classical notion of electromagnetic waves. This is in fact true in a certain sense, and we can approach an understanding of the physical significance of matter waves by considering first one aspect of the relationship between the wave and particle descriptions of electromagnetic radiation.

Energy can be transported by electromagnetic waves, and it is customary to regard the waves themselves as containing a certain energy density. That is to say, the electric and magnetic fields in the wave represent a form of energy, and this energy is transferred from one region to another as the wave propagates. Given a wave in which the electric field has an amplitude E, it can be shown by classical electromagnetic theory that the energy density, or the energy per unit volume associated with the wave is proportional to E^2. We have also noted, however, in discussing the photoelectric effect that we must under some circumstances regard the energy of an electromagnetic wave as being concentrated in discrete photons or quanta, each having a definite energy. From this point of view we would regard the transfer of energy in an electromagnetic wave in terms of the propagation of the individual photons, each one of which would carry its characteristic energy. The energy density associated with the electromagnetic disturbance would then just be proportional to the number of photons per unit volume. We are thus led to this connection between the wave and particle aspects of electromagnetic radiation: The square of the amplitude of the wave is

Bibliography p. 33

proportional to the number of photons per unit volume associated with the wave.

Experimental evidence indicates that photons are indivisible entities, and in an electromagnetic wave of frequency v, only photons of energy equal to hv are found. However, in a wave of small amplitude, the relationship between amplitude and photon density may predict only a fraction of a photon per unit volume. This result is interpreted in terms of probabilities as follows. Suppose the above relationship predicts only 1/10 of a photon will be found in a given volume. If we were to make a suitable measurement in this volume, we would find either no photon at all or one photon. If we were to repeat the measurement a very large number of times, we would find that in approximately 1/10 of the measurements we would observe one photon, and would say that the probability of finding a photon in a given measurement was 1/10. Thus in dealing with very large numbers of photons we conclude that the square of the wave amplitude is proportional to the number of photons present in a given volume; in dealing with small numbers, or with single photons, the square of the amplitude is proportional to the probability of finding a photon in a given volume.

This is just the significance which is attached to the De Broglie wave associated with a material particle. The De Broglie wave will have an amplitude, usually denoted by the symbol ψ. In general this will be a function of both position and time. It is assumed that the probability of finding the material particle at a given point is proportional to the square of the magnitude of ψ at that point.

The problem still remains as to how the quantity ψ, the amplitude of the De Broglie wave, is to be determined. Shortly after the appearance of De Broglie's suggestions, E. Schrödinger showed that ψ should satisfy a certain differential equation which now bears his name. It is not possible here to present Schrödinger's line of reasoning in arriving at his final result. We shall, however, briefly discuss the equation and the way in which the wave amplitude, or as it is more frequently called, the wave function, is determined for a particular system. We shall also see that the quantized properties of the system, such as allowed energy levels, emerge in a very simple fashion from the solution of the Schrödinger equation.

For the simplest possible case of a single particle of mass m, moving in a region in which the force acting on it can be represented by a potential energy function V, the Schrödinger equation takes the form

$$-\frac{h^2}{8\pi^2 m}\left(\frac{\partial^2\psi}{\partial x^2} + \frac{\partial^2\psi}{\partial y^2} + \frac{\partial^2\psi}{\partial z^2}\right) + V\psi = -\frac{h}{2\pi i}\frac{\partial\psi}{\partial t} \qquad (4)$$

This is called the Schrödinger equation including the time. We have already noted that the frequency of the De Broglie wave associated with a particle of energy E is given by $v = E/h$. This means that for a particle having a definite energy, the time dependence of the wave function will have the form

$$f(t) = e^{-\frac{2\pi iEt}{h}}$$

If we then write this time dependence of ψ explicitly *i.e.* we set

$$\psi = u(x,y,z)\ e^{-\frac{2\pi iEt}{h}}$$

and substitute in Eqn. (4) we obtain the equation for $u(x, y, z)$:

$$-\frac{h^2}{8\pi^2 m}\left(\frac{\partial^2 u}{\partial x^2} + \frac{\partial^2 u}{\partial y^2} + \frac{\partial^2 u}{\partial z^2}\right) + Vu = Eu \tag{5}$$

This is called the *time-independent Schrödinger equation*. The wave function for a particle of a definite energy E must always satisfy this equation. Not all possible solutions of this equation can be interpreted as wave functions representing a physical system, however. The wave function must be subject to certain restrictions if we are to interpret the square of its magnitude as proportional to the probability of finding the particle at the point at which the wave function is evaluated. One restriction is that it must be finite at all points. A wave function which was infinite at some point would imply infinite probability (*i.e.* certainty) of finding the particle at that particular point. The second important restriction, for our present purposes, is that the wave function be a single-valued function of position; otherwise it would yield an ambiguous prediction for the probability of finding the particle at certain points.

The effect of these restrictions on the possible solutions may be illustrated with a simple example of a familiar mechanical system. If a stretched string is pulled aside and released, the string will vibrate and under suitable circumstances waves may be observed travelling along the string. If the amplitude of the wave as a function of time and position is represented by $y(x, t)$ then it can be shown that y must satisfy the equation

$$\frac{\partial^2 y}{\partial x^2} = \frac{1}{v^2}\frac{\partial^2 y}{\partial t^2} \tag{6}$$

In this equation v is the velocity of the wave, and x is the position along the string measured from some arbitrary zero position. Now it is easy to show by direct substitution that a solution of this equation is given by

$$y = \sin \frac{2\pi x}{\lambda} \sin \frac{2\pi t}{\tau} \qquad (7)$$

Here λ is the wavelength of the wave, τ the period and $\lambda/\tau = v$. If the string is indefinitely long, this solution is valid for arbitrary values of λ and τ as long as they satisfy the above relation. In an actual physical situation, however, the string would have some finite length L and would be fastened somehow at each end. These requirements immediately place restrictions on the wave amplitude, since if the string is clamped at each end, it cannot move at these points and $y = 0$ at these points. If we choose one end of the string as the point $x = 0$, the other end lies at $x = L$. Now the wave amplitude as written in Eqn. (7) does indeed vanish at $x = 0$, but it vanishes at $x = L$ only if

$$\sin \frac{2\pi L}{\lambda} = 0$$

or alternatively

$$2L/\lambda = n$$

where n is an integer. This illustrates the fact that when the possible solutions of the general differential equation characteristic of wave motion are subject to specific restrictions (usually referred to as boundary conditions for the problem of interest), then only certain solutions are appropriate. These allowed solutions are always characterized by certain numbers called proper values. In the above examples these are the allowed values of the wavelength $\lambda = 2L/n$. The solution corresponding to a given proper value is called a proper function for the problem.

Though for the sake of simplicity this example was taken from the theory of mechanical vibrations, a completely analogous situation arises when we consider solutions of the Schrödinger equation for a given system. In this case the boundary conditions on the wave function are the requirements of finiteness and single-valuedness. Usually solutions satisfying these requirements can be found only for certain values of the energy of the system.

Since any physical system must be characterized by a finite, single-valued wave function, this result means that the energy of the system cannot take any value, as in classical physics, but only one of the values for which a suitable wave function exists. Thus the discrete allowed energy levels appear in quantum mechanics not as the result of some special quantum assumption as in the Bohr theory, but as a consequence of the very general boundary conditions to which the wave function is subject.

(b) The hydrogen atom

Without attempting to present the mathematical details, we can now discuss the application of quantum mechanics to the solution of the problem of the hydrogen atom. Again we consider the hydrogen atom as consisting of a massive nucleus carrying a positive charge $+e$ and an electron bearing a negative charge $-e$. Since the nucleus is so massive, we can to a good approximation consider it to remain at rest, and consider the problem of the motion of the single particle, the electron, about the fixed nucleus. The force acting on the electron is the electrostatic attraction between opposite charges, hence the potential energy will be

$$V = -\frac{e^2}{r}$$

where r is the distance between the electron and the nucleus. The time-independent Schrödinger equation then takes the form:

$$-\frac{h^2}{8\pi^2 m}\left(\frac{\partial^2 u}{\partial x^2} + \frac{\partial^2 u}{\partial y^2} + \frac{\partial^2 u}{\partial z^2}\right) - \frac{e^2 u}{r} = Eu$$

Using standard mathematical procedures, the values of the energy E, for which the solutions of this equation are everywhere finite can be shown to be given by

$$E_n = -\frac{2\pi^2 m e^4}{n^2 h^2}$$

These are then the allowed values of the energy of the electron in the hydrogen atom. It is to be noted that these are identical with the values predicted by the Bohr theory, so that the spectrum of the hydrogen atom is accounted for by the quantum mechanical theory.

In the Bohr theory, the allowed energy levels were found from the requirement that the angular momentum of the electron take on only certain allowed values. The quantization of angular momentum appears also in quantum mechanics, not as a separate assumption, but from the requirement that the wave function be everywhere finite, just as for the determination of the allowed values of the energy. When the electron is in the state of energy E_n, it turns out that the angular momentum can take on any one of the values $\sqrt{l(l+1)}\, h/2\pi$, where l is an integer less than or equal to $n-1$. Thus in the ground state $n = 1$ and the angular momentum must be zero. In the first excited state $n = 2$ and the electron may have angular mo-

Bibliography p. 33

mentum o or $\sqrt{2}h/2\pi$. The quantization of the orientation of the angular momentum relative to some fixed direction arises as a result of the requirement that the wave function be single-valued, and it turns out that the allowed values of the projection of the angular momentum on a fixed direction are given by $m_l h/2\pi$ where m_l is an integer satisfying the relationship

$$l \geq m_l \geq -l$$

Though the angular momentum is quantized in the quantum mechanical theory of the hydrogen atom as in the Bohr theory, we see that the predictions of the two theories are not identical. For one thing the allowed values of angular momentum are no longer simple integral multiples of $h/2\pi$ but have the slightly different form $\sqrt{l(l+1)}\, h/2\pi$. Also the allowed value of the angular momentum in the ground state is zero in the quantum mechanical result, rather than $h/2\pi$ as required in the Bohr theory. It has been found that the quantum mechanical result agrees with experimental measurements. This is another illustration of the fact that the Bohr theory possessed very fundamental shortcomings, in spite of its many successes.

A standard notation is commonly used to indicate the quantum numbers n and l for an electron in an atom. The first is simply written as a number, the second as a lower case letter as shown in Table I. The origin of this notation goes back to early empirical classifications of spectra. The ground state of the hydrogen with $n = 1$ $l = 0$ is called a 1s state. An excited state with, say, $n = 3$ $l = 2$ would be written 3d and so on.

TABLE I

THE STANDARD SPECTROSCOPIC NOTATION FOR INDICATING THE ORBITAL ANGULAR MOMENTUM QUANTUM NUMBER l

l	0	1	2	3	4	5	6	7	8
designation	s	p	d	f	g	h	i	k	m

Beyond $l = 8$, the letters are in alphabetical order except that s and p are omitted. In atomic phenomena, values beyond $l = 6$ rarely are encountered.

In the state of energy E_n, angular momentum $\sqrt{l(l+1)}\, h/2\pi$ and projected angular momentum $m_l h/2\pi$, the wave function is characterized by the three integers n, l and m_l. These are called the quantum numbers specifying that particular state, and are equivalent to a complete specification of the state of the atom. (This neglects electron spin for the moment.) By a complete specification is meant the following: given the quantum numbers n, l and m_l, the wave function of the atom is completely determined, and using the wave function, all observable properties of the atom may be calculated. The details of such calculations will not be carried out here, but we will write down wave functions for a few of the allowed states of the hydrogen atom, in order to carry out a comparison between the models of the atom predicted by the Bohr theory and by quantum mechanics.

If several rather small effects are neglected, the energies of the allowed states of the hydrogen atom depend only on the quantum number n. The state of lowest energy, which is the normal state of the atom, is given by $n = 1$. The only allowed value of the angular momentum quantum number is $l = 0$, and hence $m_l = 0$. The wave function for this state is then

$$\psi_{n,l,m_l} = \psi_{1,0,0} = \frac{1}{\sqrt{\pi}} \left(\frac{1}{a}\right)^{\frac{3}{2}} e^{-r/a} e^{-\frac{2\pi i E_1 t}{h}}$$

where

$$a = \frac{h^2}{4\pi^2 m e^2}$$

is the radius of the first Bohr orbit. The first excited state has $n = 2$. Corresponding to this energy state, however, there are two allowed values of the angular momentum. For $n = 2$, the orbital angular momentum quantum number may take on values $l = 0$, or $l = 1$. Finally for $l = 0$, $m_l = 0$; for $l = 1$, $m_l = 1$, 0 or -1. The physical significance of this result is the following. In the second excited state, the electron may have an orbital angular momentum of zero, in which case its projection on any axis is zero; or it may have angular momentum of $\sqrt{2}h/2\pi$, in which case its projection on an arbitrary axis can take on one of the values $h/2\pi$, 0 or $-h/2\pi$. To a very good approximation, all these allowed angular momentum states for $n = 2$ have the same energy, however. Such a group of states all having the same energy, but differing in some other property, are said to be degenerate. The wave functions for the states with $n = 2$ are as follows, where r, θ and φ are the usual spherical polar coordinates, with origin at the centre of the atom.

For $l = 0$, $m_l = 0$

$$\psi_{2,0,0} = \frac{1}{\sqrt{32\pi}} \left(\frac{1}{a}\right)^{\frac{3}{2}} \left(2 - \frac{r}{a}\right) e^{-\frac{r}{2a}} e^{-\frac{2\pi i E_2 t}{h}}$$

For $l = 1$, $m_l = 0$

$$\psi_{2,1,0} = \frac{1}{\sqrt{32\pi}} \left(\frac{1}{a}\right)^{\frac{3}{2}} \left(\frac{r}{a}\right) e^{-\frac{r}{2a}} e^{-\frac{2\pi i E_2 t}{h}} \cos \theta$$

Bibliography p. 33

For $l = 1$, $m_l = \pm 1$

$$\psi_{2,1,\pm 1} = \frac{1}{\sqrt{64\pi}} \left(\frac{1}{a}\right)^{\frac{3}{2}} \left(\frac{r}{a}\right) e^{-\frac{r}{2a}} e^{-\frac{2\pi i E_2 t}{h}} \sin\theta \, e^{\pm i\varphi}$$

For our present purposes, the significance of these expressions is that they define the probability of finding the electron at a given point in an atom. More precisely, if it is known that the electron is in a state characterized by quantum numbers n, l, m_l, the probability of finding the electron within a small volume element dV centred at the point $(r_1, \theta_1, \varphi_1)$ is given by

$$p(r_1, \theta_1, \varphi_1) \, dV = |\psi_{nlm_l}(r_1, \theta_1, \varphi_1)|^2 \, dV$$

In this expression the numerical value of the wave function is to be evaluated by substituting the actual coordinate values $(r_1, \theta_1, \varphi_1)$ into the appropriate wave function. In general, this will be a complex number, and the vertical bars indicate that it is the square of the magnitude of this number which must be taken to find p. In many problems, the quantity of interest is not the probability of finding the electron within a volume element dV at a particular point, but the probability of finding the electron within a given volume element at a distance r from the centre of the atom. This latter quantity, which is obtained by averaging p over all angles, is shown for the ground state and first excited states of the hydrogen atom in Fig. 5. For the ground state (1s), it is seen that while the electron is most likely to be found near a radius $r = a$, there is a fair chance of its being found anywhere from the centre of the atom out to a radius several times the most likely value. This is in marked contrast to the Bohr theory of the hydrogen atom in which the electron was pictured as moving in a fixed orbit of well-defined radius. Thus according to the Bohr theory a measurement of the radial position of the electron in the ground state of the hydrogen atom would necessarily yield the value $r = a$. For the higher states, the radial density distributions extend to larger radii and may become more complex, but still have the general property that the electron is most likely to be found near a radius equal to the radius of the Bohr orbit corresponding to that energy state.

The Bohr model provides an appealing mechanical picture of the electron moving in a well-defined, classical trajectory, the atom as a whole comprising a tiny solar system, as it were. The quantum-mechanical model says nothing about the motion of the electron in the atom. It only predicts the likelihood that the electron will be found at different points near the atomic nucleus. But since it predicts that the electron has a fair chance of being found throughout a rather large region, it seems to imply that the electron is moving around somehow within this region. A picture that is sometimes used is to say that the electron is "smeared out" throughout the volume of the atom. This may be a useful picture in some circumstances, but may be misleading in the sense that a measurement always reveals a whole electron or none at all. It is not smeared out in any physical way that would allow us to observe a fraction of an electron in some type of measurement.

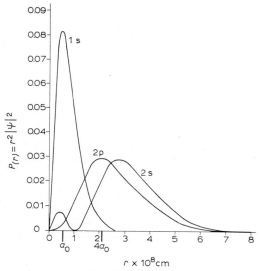

Fig. 5. Radial probability density distributions for the electron in the ground state and first excited states of the hydrogen atom. The ordinate on each curve gives the probability that in that state the electron will be found within a volume of 10^{-24} ml at the indicated distance from the nucleus. The radius of the first Bohr orbit is equal to a_0.

The difficulties of forming a concrete physical picture of the structure of the atom corresponding to quantum-mechanical predictions illustrates the basic change in outlook that was introduced by the development of quantum mechanics. This basic change was the realization that in general, when we make an observation of any system, we disturb the system in an unpredictable manner. This is not the result of any imperfection in our techniques, but a fundamental property of matter and radiation. It is true that in our own world of macroscopic objects, the disturbances associated with the measurement are generally small compared with other errors, and can be neglected entirely. This is no longer true, however, when we attempt to carry out measurements on atomic systems. Consider, for instance, the problem of measuring the position of the electron in a hydrogen atom. To

Bibliography p. 33

measure position to within a distance of a, the radius of the smallest Bohr orbit, it would be necessary to observe the atom using light (actually X-rays) of wavelength λ appreciably less than a. It must be recalled now that the energy of electromagnetic radiation is quantized in units of $h\nu$ or hc/λ. The smallest amount of radiation that could possibly be used to observe the atom would be a single quantum. But for radiation of wavelength $\lambda = a$, the quantum energy is about 25,000 electronvolts or nearly two thousand times the energy needed to remove the electron completely from the atom. Thus the most delicate observation we can make of the position of the electron in the atom is likely to disrupt the atom entirely. It is true that we can in principle make a measurement which will tell where the electron was at the instant of observation, but then we are completely unable to tell what became of the electron after the observation. When we speak of an electron moving in an orbit, as in the Bohr model, it carries the implication that we could somehow observe the successive positions of the electron as it moved around the orbit, tracing out a path in space. This we cannot do on an actual atomic system, and it is for just this reason that the quantum-mechanical theory predicts the probability of obtaining a certain result in a measurement, but does not provide a simple physical model of the motions of the parts of the atom.

Of course, our concepts such as wave or particle have been developed to describe things that can be directly observed, and we are conditioned to thinking only of systems that can be observed, one way or another, without appreciable disturbance. In this circumstance it is not surprising that we encounter difficulties in trying to construct simple mechanical models of the atom. On the other hand, it is true that we can make measurements on single atoms and we describe the measurements and their interpretation in macroscopic terms. It may be that a model will be useful in discussing the measurements, but it should not be surprising if a model used to describe one type of measurement is unsuited to describing a different sort of observation. The important fact is that the mathematical formalism of quantum mechanics provides a prediction of the result of any measurement. Physical models may be useful in visualizing the results of the theory, but the shortcomings of a particular model should not be thought of as indicating any shortcoming in the basic theory.

(c) Complex atoms

Before discussing the theory of complex atoms, it is necessary to consider two additional factors: *electron spin*, and the *Pauli exclusion principle*. The first of these, electron spin, is an intrinsic property of the electron just as are its mass and electrical charge. In order to understand the spectra of complex atoms it was found necessary to assume that the electron possessed an intrinsic angular momentum, quite independent of the orbital angular momentum associated with motion about the atomic nucleus. Classically such an intrinsic angular momentum of a body would be associated with a spin of the body about an axis through its centre of gravity. For example, the earth has an intrinsic angular momentum, or spin, associated with its daily rotation, as contrasted with its orbital angular momentum associated with its motion around the sun. Because of this analogy, the intrinsic angular momentum of the electron is usually referred to as *"spin"* even though we cannot form a satisfactory picture of the electron as a spinning rigid body.

The quantum number specifying this intrinsic angular momentum, usually written s, is found to take on the single value $s = \frac{1}{2}$. That is to say, the magnitude of the electron's intrinsic angular momentum is $\sqrt{s(s+1)}h/2\pi$ $= \sqrt{\frac{3}{4}}h/2\pi$. It will be noted that electron spin differs from orbital angular momentum both in being fixed in magnitude, and in being specified by a half-integral rather than an integral quantum number. The orientation of the spin in space is quantized also, and the projection of the spin on an axis of quantization can take on the two values $\frac{1}{2}h/2\pi$ and $-\frac{1}{2}h/2\pi$, corresponding to spin projection quantum numbers $m_s = +\frac{1}{2}$ and $m_s = -\frac{1}{2}$. These two states are usually referred to as *"spin up"* and *"spin down"* states, according as the projection of the spin is parallel or antiparallel to the quantization axis.

The exclusion principle was also enunciated originally as a result of spectroscopic studies. In its original form it may be stated: no two electrons in an atom may occupy identical quantum states. If we recall that a quantum state may be identified by the group of quantum numbers specifying the allowed values of the various quantized quantities, the principle may be stated; no two electrons in an atom can have identical sets of quantum numbers. The exclusion principle may be treated as an empirical fact, and used as presented, but it arises from more basic considerations, which deserve mention here.

It has been noted that all electrons have identical properties—mass, charge, and spin. Any one electron is identical with any other. Now on a macroscopic scale, when we say two bodies are identical, we mean that they may have the same size, shape, mass, colour and so on. But, we can observe them directly, and if we have decided to distinguish between the two initially, say on the basis of position in space, we can in principle observe them as they move or interact and ever after identify each one on the basis of the original distinction. For example, in the collision of identical billiard balls, we could watch them during the collision and afterwards identify one as being the one initially at rest and the other as the one initially in motion. Now this is not true of electrons. We may originally distinguish between two electrons as being at different points in space. If these two electrons collide, however,

Bibliography p. 33

we cannot observe the collision in detail without disturbing the electrons' motion. As a result, we must conclude that after the collision the electrons are really identical, in the sense that any distinction we may have made between them before the collision is completely lost in the collision. Thus the identity of electrons takes on quite a different meaning in quantum mechanics than in classical physics.

Since electrons are identical in this fundamental sense, the wave function describing a pair of electrons must be written in such a way that it does not imply any physical distinction between the two. To illustrate this point, consider an atom with two electrons, one in quantum state α, one in quantum state β. Suppose the coordinates of one electron are written collectively as r_1, those of the other as r_2. Then it can be shown that an appropriate solution of the Schrödinger equation for the two electrons can be written as

$$\psi = \psi_\alpha(r_1)\,\psi_\beta(r_2)$$

This is not a suitable wave function for the problem, however, since as written it indicates that the electron we have called 1 is in quantum state α and electron 2 is in quantum state β. This implies a distinction between the two electrons which, as we noted above, is impossible to make in principle. Actually a suitable wave function can be constructed by writing

$$\psi = \psi_\alpha(r_1)\,\psi_\beta(r_2) + \psi_\beta(r_1)\,\psi_\alpha(r_2)$$

It may easily be shown that this is still a solution of the Schrödinger equation, but now it is completely symmetric in the coordinates of the two electrons. It does not specify that a particular electron is in given state, but only that one electron is in each of states α and β. This wave function is said to be symmetric in the exchange of the two electrons, since it is completely unchanged if the two electrons are interchanged with one another, and we accordingly write the coordinates of electron 2 in place of those of 1 and vice versa. A second possible wave function for the two electrons could also be constructed by writing

$$\psi = \psi_\alpha(r_1)\,\psi_\beta(r_2) - \psi_\beta(r_1)\,\psi_\alpha(r_2)$$

Again this makes no distinction between the two electrons, but changes sign if the coordinates of the two electrons are interchanged. Such a wave function is said to be antisymmetric in the exchange of the two electrons.

Now the basic principle from which the exclusion principle arises is this: A proper wave function for a system containing identical particles must be either symmetric or antisymmetric in the exchange of the coordinates of any pair of identical particles. For electrons, it is found from experiment, that only the antisymmetric wave function occurs. It is now seen that if we attempt to construct an antisymmetric wave function in which two identical particles are in the same state, α say, the wave function must vanish:

$$\psi = \psi_\alpha(r_1)\,\psi_\alpha(r_2) - \psi_\alpha(r_1)\,\psi_\alpha(r_2) = 0$$

i.e. such a system cannot be formed, hence no two electrons can exist in the same quantum state.

Phenomena arising as a result of the symmetry requirements on the many-electron wave function are generally referred to as exchange effects. The most important of these for problems of atomic structure is the Pauli exclusion principle, which determines the distribution of electrons within the atom. It is not possible to pursue the matter here, but it may be noted that exchange effects of a different nature often play an important role in the bonding of atoms into molecules.

With the theory of the hydrogen atom, plus the exclusion principle we are now in a position to discuss a model for complex atoms which will account for the outstanding properties of the chemical elements. Probably the most striking feature of these properties is the occurrence of groups of elements having similar chemical and physical properties. These regularities were most clearly brought out by Mendeleyev who noted that if the elements were arranged in order of increasing atomic weight, they showed a periodic recurrence of certain properties such as chemical activity and physical form. Initially this periodic classification, as it was called, was purely empirical, but using it, Mendeleyev was able to predict the existence and properties of several elements which were later discovered. Some insight into the significance of these regularities was achieved just on the basis of the Bohr theory. It was not until the advent of quantum mechanics, however, that a quantitative understanding became possible. In this discussion we shall employ a rather rough approximation which accounts qualitatively for the essential features of atomic properties. The theory may be extended to provide a quantitative understanding of many of the details of atomic structure by treating smaller effects as perturbations, but the required calculations become quite complicated.

We will consider the following model for a complex atom: At the centre of the atom is the massive nucleus carrying a positive electrical charge of magnitude Ze. Here e is the magnitude of the electron charge and Z is an integer called the atomic number for that nucleus. In order that the atom as a whole be electrically neutral, a total of Z electrons must surround each nucleus of atomic number Z. Heavy nuclei are of course larger than the proton, the nucleus of the hydrogen atom, but are always much smaller

Bibliography p. 33

than the dimensions of the electron distributions. To determine the allowed states of the electrons in a heavy atom, we make the approximation of neglecting the forces acting between the individual electrons, and consider only the interaction between single electrons and the atomic nucleus, or the atomic core as will be described shortly. The justification for this approximation lies in the fact that the Coulomb force acting between the nucleus and an electron is Z times greater than that between pairs of electrons at the same separation.

As described earlier, the energies of the allowed states of the electron in the hydrogen atom are given by

$$E_n = -\frac{2\pi^2 me^4}{n^2 h^2}$$

Using the same procedures as in the solution of problem of the hydrogen atom, it may be shown that for a single electron in the field of a nucleus of charge $+ Ze$, the allowed energy levels are given by

$$E_n = -\frac{2\pi^2 me^4 Z^2}{n^2 h^2}$$

Also for a given n, the orbital angular momentum quantum number l may take on any integral value between $l = 0$ and $l = n - 1$. Thus the quantum numbers specifying the state of the electron are just those used for the hydrogen atom, while the magnitude of the electron energy in a given state is greater by a factor Z^2 than the energy in the corresponding state of the hydrogen atom.

It is found that the electronic structure of an atom is described quite well by the following model. In the ground state of the atom, the electrons fill the lowest single-electron states, with one electron in each state as required by the exclusion principle, until the atom as a whole is electrically neutral. The most tightly bound electrons, which are also the ones closest to the nucleus, are in the states with $n = 1$. In this state $l = m_l = 0$ while $m_s = \pm \frac{1}{2}$. Thus two electrons are allowed in states with $n = 1$. The two states with $n = 1$ are said to constitute an electron shell, and this shell is filled, or closed, when it contains its full complement of two electrons. This innermost shell is, for historical reasons, referred to as the K shell. It is a general quantum-mechanical result, that the angular momenta of the different electrons in a closed shell will add up in such a way that the net angular momentum for all electrons in the shell is zero. Thus the electrons in a shell may be pictured as forming a spherically symmetric charge distribution surrounding the nucleus. A nucleus enclosed by one or more closed electron shells forms a relatively inert structure called an atomic core. At points outside the closed shells, the atomic core will then appear as a nucleus with a charge equal to the nuclear charge minus the total charge on the electrons in the closed shells. In an atom with more than two electrons, the lowest energy states available to the third and succeeding electrons will be those with $n = 2$. States with $n = 2$ may have $l = 0$ or $l = 1$. For the former, $m_l = 0$ while the latter may have $m_l = 1, 0$ or -1. Finally corresponding to each set of quantum numbers n, l, m_l, the spin projection quantum number may take on either of the values $m_s = \pm \frac{1}{2}$. Hence the total number of electrons that can be accommodated in the shell with $n = 2$ (the L *shell*) will be $2 \times \{(2 \times 0) + 1 + (2 \times 1) + 1)\} = 8$. It may be shown in general that the maximum number of electrons in a shell specified by quantum number n is equal to $2n^2$.

We can illustrate these ideas in somewhat more detail by discussing briefly the structure of some of the simpler atoms, and the relationship between structure and properties. The simplest atom after hydrogen is helium with a nuclear charge of $+ 2e$. In its ground state the helium atom has both electrons in states with $n = 1$, forming a closed shell. It is because of this especially stable electronic structure that helium is chemically inert, forming no compounds at all. The electronic configuration of helium is written $(1s)^2$ indicating 2 electrons in the state $n = 1, l = 0$.

The next simplest atom is lithium with $Z = 3$. The electronic configuration of Li consists of a filled K shell containing two electrons, with the third electron in a state with $n = 2$. Because this third electron is at a mean radius of $4a$ outside an atomic core with net charge $+ e$, it is relatively weakly bound to the atom, and may be easily removed yielding a positive lithium ion. It is for this reason that lithium is chemically very reactive, readily forming ionic compounds.

It will be recalled that in the hydrogen atom, the energy of the electron in a state of given n did not depend on the orbital angular momentum. For heavier atoms, one of the effects of the interactions between electrons is to produce an energy difference between states of different l for a given n. It is easy to see how this comes about by reference to Fig. 5. It is seen there that the radial probability distribution for an electron with $n = 2, l = 0$ is appreciable in the region close to the nucleus. Physically this means that an electron in this state has a good chance of being found inside the atomic core, where the K electrons no longer shield out part of the nuclear charge. The electrons with $n = 2, l = 1$ also penetrate the core to some extent, but are not found as close to the nucleus as electrons with $n = 2, l = 0$. As a result of this decrease in shielding for electrons with $l = 0$, the electron energy will be lower in these states than in states with $l = 1$. Thus the ground

Bibliography p. 33

state of the *lithium* atom, that is the state of lowest energy, will have a configuration $(1s)^2(2s)$ rather than $(1s)^2(2p)$.

The next heaviest element is *beryllium* with atomic number $Z = 4$. This atom has a second electron with $n = 2$, $l = 0$ giving the configuration $(1s)^2(2s)^2$. The two 2s electrons are said to form a closed subshell, but since the energy corresponding to an electron with $n = 2$, $l = 1$ is not much different for one with $n = 2$, $l = 0$, this structure is not particularly stable, and either of the 2s electrons may be involved in forming chemical compounds.

Boron $Z = 5$, *Carbon* $Z = 6$, *Nitrogen* $Z = 7$, *Oxygen* $Z = 8$, *Fluorine* $Z = 9$ and *Neon* $Z = 10$. The electronic structures of these elements are characterized by the addition of electrons to states with $n = 2$, $l = 1$. Boron, carbon, nitrogen and oxygen all have several electrons which are relatively weakly bound, and which can take part in forming chemical compounds. This accounts for the wide variety of compounds formed by these elements. The structure of fluorine is that of a closed shell lacking a single electron. As a result fluorine tends to form the stable closed shell structure by picking up an extra electron to become a negative ion which then enters into the formation of ionic compounds. At neon the L shell is filled, yielding the tightly bound structure characteristic of a rare gas.

Sodium $Z = 11$. With the K and L shells filled with ten electrons, the last one must go into a state with $n = 3$. The electronic structure of sodium may be written $(1s)^2(2s)^2(2p)^6 3s$. This again represents a single s electron outside an atomic core consisting of a nucleus plus closed electron shells. This structure is analogous to that of lithium, with the result that the physical and chemical properties of sodium and lithium are very similar.

The elements from sodium through *argon* form a series similar to those from lithium through neon. It might be expected, however, that the closing of the 3p subshell at argon would not result in a rare gas because the 3d states would be filled next. However, because of the penetration of electrons with $l = 0$ inside the closed shells, it turns out that electrons in states with $n = 4$, $l = 0$ have energies comparable with those having $n = 3$, $l = 2$. Thus argon $(Z = 18)$ with a configuration $(1s)^2(2s)^2(2p)^6(3s)^2(3p)^6$ is an inert gas. The next element, *potassium* has as its outermost electron one with $n = 4$, $l = 0$ and chemical properties similar to those of lithium and sodium.

For heavier elements, the effect of electron–electron interactions becomes increasingly important, with the result that the ordering of energy states derived from the study of the hydrogen atom is no longer appropriate. This is illustrated by the appearance of potassium after argon in the periodic arrangement of the elements. We will not pursue this description of the electronic structure of the elements beyond this point, but simply note that the foregoing ideas provide a statisfactory understanding of the chemical properties of all the elements, and a useful model of the structure of all atoms.

BIBLIOGRAPHY

Further discussion of the topics presented in this chapter will be found in many text books of modern physics and quantum mechanics. The following have been found most useful in assembling the material for this chapter.

[1] A. P. FRENCH, *Principles of Modern Physics*, John Wiley and Sons, New York, 1958.

This volume presents a good discussion of the experimental results leading to the formulation of quantum mechanics, plus an introduction to the theory. Much of the material in the present chapter is discussed in considerable detail.

[2] U. FANO AND L. FANO, *Basic Physics of Atoms and Molecules*, John Wiley and Sons, New York, 1959.

Well over half of this volume is devoted to the development of the concepts and techniques of quantum mechanics. Mathematics is used very extensively but the authors present interesting discussion of the physical significance of the theory. The latter part of the book presents the theory of the hydrogen atom and a brief but lucid discussion of complex atoms, molecular structure and chemical bonding.

[3] L. PAULING AND E. B. WILSON, *Introduction to Quantum Mechanics*, McGraw-Hill, New York, 1935.

This has long been a standard reference for anyone interested in the application of quantum mechanics to problems of atomic and molecular structure. Chapter V presents a detailed solution of the Schrödinger equation for the hydrogen atom.

[4] D. BOHM, *Quantum Theory*, Prentice-Hall, Englewood Cliffs, New Jersey, 1951.

The first part of this volume contains an extensive discussion of the physical meaning of quantum mechanics. The significance of the De Broglie wave, the origin and consequences of the uncertainty principle, and the wave–particle dualism are all considered in detail. A rather extensive mathematical background is assumed.

[5] L. DE BROGLIE, *Matter and Light, The New Physics*, W. W. Norton and Co., New York, 1939.

A series of essays dealing mainly with the conceptual and philosophical problems arising from the development of quantum theory.

Chapter II

Electronic Theory of Organic Molecules

H. H. JAFFÉ

Department of Chemistry, University of Cincinnati, Ohio (U.S.A.)

1. Introduction

Throughout organic chemistry, most compounds occur as individual and distinct molecules. Solids with ionic lattices are relatively rare, except the salts of organic acids and bases, and even in these the structure of the organic ion is of prime interest, rather than the structure of the lattice. In biochemistry, one frequently deals, aside from compounds made up of individual molecules, with structures involving large aggregates of individual molecules held together through a relatively small class of special types of bonds, as in the polypeptides, proteins and large carbohydrates. Chapter III deals with the actual geometric structure, *i.e.* the arrangement, of atoms in the molecule. Chapter III also, and later chapters, deal with the forces and the manner of combining individual molecules into crystals and other large aggregates. The present chapter deals with the forces which hold together the individual atoms within a given molecule and determine its geometry.

Before going on to the detailed treatment of any molecule, however, some preliminary reflections may be useful. The problem of the accurate description of a molecule and its electronic structure is intrinsically one which is readily formulated. It is a result of quantum mechanics that it is not possible to determine, simultaneously, the position and momentum of a given particle. It is usual to choose to define accurately the energy, and hence the momentum, and to be satisfied with a probability distribution of position. This probability distribution is given by the square of a function, the so-called wave function. The wave function is the solution of the Schrödinger equation, the basic equation of quantum mechanics. This function is, generally, a function of the three space coordinates of each of the fundamental particles (*i.e.* nuclei and electrons), and in addition a fourth coordinate for each, the spin coordinate. If the Schrödinger equation could be solved in general for an assembly of any number of particles, it would be possible to arrive at a perfectly adequate description of any molecule, and to provide almost any desired information about the molecule. Thus, the space coordinates for which the energy of the molecule is a minimum would be the most stable geometric arrangement and would be expected to determine the structure of the molecule. The variation of the energy with variation of the nuclear coordinates would give the vibrational force constants.

Unfortunately, however, the Schrödinger equation for a system of more than two or three particles cannot be solved. Consequently, the quantum-mechanical description of molecules requires long series of drastic approximations, which preclude a completely satisfactory solution of the problem of the intimate structure of molecules. Nevertheless, the approximate solutions obtainable have considerably contributed to the understanding of molecules, their structure and behavior, and progress toward more intimate understanding is constantly being made.

2. The hydrogen molecule-ion and the hydrogen molecule in molecular orbital and valence bond theory

The simplest of all molecular structures is the hydrogen molecule-ion, H_2^+, consisting of two hydrogen nuclei and one electron. Although the Schrödinger equation for this molecule can be solved, it is most profitable for us to consider the approximate treatment of this "molecule" by the two main approximation methods which we intend to use for larger molecules. The first of these is the so-called *molecular orbital* (MO) method. Calling the two H atoms A and B, this method says that, as long as the electron is near atom A it will be likely to behave like an electron on an isolated hydrogen atom A, which is described by a wave function ϕ_A. On the other hand, while the electron is near B, it is likely to behave like an electron on the isolated atom B, described by ϕ_B. Consequently, the MO method describes the electron in the molecule as a linear combination of the atomic orbitals, $\psi = \phi_A + \phi_B$, where ψ is the wave function of the molecule*. The phrase "linear combination of atomic orbitals" is commonly abbreviated to LCAO, and such a wave function is called a LCAO MO function.

An alternate way of describing the hydrogen molecule-ion, by the *valence bond* or *resonance theory*, is as follows: we can at any particular moment consider the electron as belonging to either one or the other of the hydrogen atoms, *i.e.* we can describe the molecule at any particular time as consisting of a hydrogen atom and a proton. Two such arrangements are possible.

---

* Actually, this function is to be multiplied by a constant N, the so-called normalizing constant, which, however, does not change the qualitative arguments to be presented, and hence will usually be ignored in this chapter.

$$H_A \cdot H_B^+ \quad \text{or} \quad H_A^+ \cdot H_B$$

In the first of these, the electron might well be described by the function ϕ_A, in the second by ϕ_B. The molecule actually will not be part of the time one, part the other of these extremes, but will be some form of intermediate between them, a so-called *resonance hybrid*. The wave function, however, will again be a linear combination of the wave functions of the two structures, $\psi = \phi_A + \phi_B$, which, *in this case*, is seen to be identical to the MO wave function.

When a second electron is added to these considerations, *i.e.* if we pass from the hydrogen molecule-ion to the hydrogen molecule, the two theories lose their great similarity. MO theory in its lowest approximation treats H_2 very much like H_2^+: each electron is described by a one-electron function $\psi = \phi_A + \phi_B$ of exactly the same form as in H_2^+. The total wave function of the molecule[*] Ψ is the product of the two functions for the two separate electrons,

$$
\begin{aligned}
\Psi &= \psi(1)\psi(2) \\
&= [\phi_A(1) + \phi_B(1)][\phi_A(2) + \phi_B(2)] \\
&= \phi_A(1)\phi_A(2) + \phi_B(1)\phi_B(2) + \phi_A(1)\phi_B(2) + \phi_A(2)\phi_B(1) \quad (1)
\end{aligned}
$$

where the parentheses behind each one electron function specify the electron the coordinates of which the function depends on.

Valence bond theory again starts with a description of the molecule in terms of complete atoms. It describes the hydrogen molecule as composed of two hydrogen atoms, A and B, each bearing its particular electron, say electrons 1 and 2. The complete wave function Ψ for the molecule thus is

$$\Psi_1 = \phi_A(1)\,\phi_B(2)$$

But it is impossible to tag electrons, and hence a conformation where electron 2 is on atom A, and electron 1 on atom B is equivalent to the above:

$$\Psi_2 = \phi_A(2)\,\phi_B(1)$$

In quantum mechanics, when two such equivalent, and physically indistinguishable wave functions exist, neither one alone is a satisfactory

---

[*] Lower case Greek letters will be used for functions describing one electron, capitals for those describing many; ϕ's will be used for atomic, ψ's for molecular functions. The numbers in parentheses following one-electron functions specify the electrons, the behavior of which is specified by the function.

description of the physical situation; instead a linear combination of the two must be used:

$$\Psi_C = \Psi_1 + \Psi_2$$

$$= \phi_A(1)\,\phi_B(2) + \phi_A(2)\,\phi_B(1) \tag{2}$$

This is the lowest approximation of valence bond theory for the description of the hydrogen molecule. Comparison of eqns. (1) and (2) shows that eqn. (1) involves the same terms as eqn. (2), but two additional ones. It now remains to carry the two methods further, to remove some of the approximations made.

In VB theory, the approximation made involved the assumption that the only structures contributing to the hydrogen molecule—we should add, to the normal or ground state of this molecule—are the two structures described by Ψ_1 and Ψ_2, in which each hydrogen atom has near it one of the electrons. In addition to these, however, we should also consider two further structures, in which both electrons are close to a single atom, none to the other; in other words structures in which the molecule appears to be made up of a proton (H^+) and a hydride ion (H^-) : $H^+ H^-$. Again two such structures are possible and equivalent, $H_A^+ H_B^-$ and $H_A^- H_B^+$, and are described by

$$\Psi_I = \phi_A(1)\,\phi_A(2) + \phi_B(1)\,\phi_B(2)$$

Such structures Ψ_I are called *ionic* structures in contrast to the Ψ_C, which are called *covalent* structures. The total wave function is a linear combination of Ψ_I and Ψ_C, where, however, there is no need that the two Ψ enter with the same coefficient:

$$\Psi = \Psi_C + \lambda\Psi_I = \phi_A(1)\,\phi_B(2) + \phi_A(2)\,\phi_B(1) + \lambda\,[\phi_A(1)\,\phi_A(2) + \phi_B(1)\,\phi_B(2)] \tag{3}$$

where λ is some numerical coefficient determining the contribution of the ionic structures. λ, or more commonly λ^2, is often called the ionic character of the H–H bond.

Comparison of eqns. (1) and (3) now shows that the terms of eqn. (1) missing in eqn. (2) now appear in eqn. (3), but multiplied by a numerical coefficient λ (which is generally less than 1). Since these terms arise from ionic structures, as was seen in proceeding from eqn. (2) to eqn. (3), it now appears that MO theory, *i.e.* eqn. (1), has overestimated the ionic terms. This is quite reasonable, since in deriving eqn. (1) no reference was made to the interaction of the two electrons, and their Coulombic repulsion is apt to keep them apart.

Refinement of MO theory to the same point as we have brought VB theory is slightly less straightforward. We have stated above that the wave function ψ of a single electron in an assembly involving two hydrogen nuclei, *i.e.*, the hydrogen molecule-ion or the hydrogen molecule, is a linear combination of the two atomic functions ϕ_A and ϕ_B of the electron near one or the other of the atoms, and have taken $\psi = \phi_A + \phi_B$ as this combination. This was reasonable since it should be intuitively obvious that the two indistinguishable hydrogen atoms should appear in the wave function in a symmetrical manner. This conclusion, however, is not quite true. No experiment has yet been, or can ever be devised which measures the wave function, or any quantity depending on the first power* of the wave function. Expressed quantum mechanically, any property which can be measured, or as one generally says, any observable property, depends on the *square* of the wave function, or some function thereof. Thus, for instance, the density of charge (electrons) at any point in space is given by ψ^2. Consequently, our above intuitive conclusion that the H atoms appear symmetrically applies, not to ψ, but only to its square. Now it is obvious that this restriction on ψ^2 is fulfilled not only by the linear combination $\psi_1 = \phi_A + \phi_B$, but also by the combination $\psi_2 = \phi_A - \phi_B$. Depending on their symmetry properties, ψ_1 is called a symmetric, ψ_2 an antisymmetric function**. Thus we find that we have another wave function (molecular orbital) $\psi_2 = \phi_A - \phi_B$ in the hydrogen molecule-ion or molecule. We will see in the next sections that this is associated with a higher energy than ψ_1 and is usually called *antibonding*, in contrast to ψ_1 which is called *bonding*, and pictorial representation of these orbitals will be presented below.

The hydrogen molecule contains two electrons. In the MO description given above***, $\Psi = \psi_1(1)\,\psi_1(2)$, both electrons were assigned to the lowest MO, ψ_1, giving what is called a configuration. It is obvious that other configurations, $\psi_1(1)\,\psi_2(2)$, $\psi_1(2)\,\psi_2(1)$ and $\psi_2(1)\,\psi_2(2)$ can also be written, but since the energy associated with ψ_2 (the energy of ψ_2) is higher than the energy of ψ_1, the latter configurations have higher energy. The functions $\psi_1(1)\,\psi_1(2)$ and $\psi_2(1)\,\psi_2(2)$ do not imply distinguishing the electrons since they are unchanged when the 1 and 2 in the parentheses are exchanged. The other two configuration functions, $\psi_1(1)\,\psi_2(2)$ and $\psi_1(2)\,\psi_2(1)$, again, by themselves, are unsatisfactory since they imply that we can distinguish electrons 1 and 2, and must be replaced by linear combinations. Again, positive and negative combinations are possible, leading then to the four configurations:

---

* Or any odd power.
** Antisymmetric here denotes that, if the indices A and B are exchanged, the function changes sign, but not absolute value. For a general discussion of symmetry, see Herzberg[1].
*** See footnote p. 36.

$$\Psi_1 = \psi_1(1)\,\psi_1(2)$$
$$\Psi_2 = \psi_1(1)\,\psi_2(2) + \psi_1(2)\,\psi_2(1)$$
$$\Psi_3 = \psi_1(1)\,\psi_2(2) - \psi_1(2)\,\psi_2(1)$$
$$\Psi_4 = \psi_2(1)\,\psi_2(2)$$

(4)

Next, the spin of the electrons must be considered. Electrons behave as if they rotated about an axis, and depending on the direction of rotation, each electron is assigned a spin function, α or β. Two electrons together may have any one of four spin functions

$$\alpha(1)\,\alpha(2)$$
$$\beta(1)\,\beta(2)$$
$$\alpha(1)\,\beta(2) + \alpha(2)\,\beta(1)$$
$$\alpha(1)\,\beta(2) - \alpha(2)\,\beta(1)$$

The first three are readily seen to be unchanged when the two electrons are exchanged, *i.e.* if the labels 1 and 2 are switched, and are therefore called symmetric in exchange of the electrons; the last one, however, when the electrons are exchanged, changes sign and is accordingly called anti-symmetric in exchange of electrons. It may be shown quantum mechanically that the three symmetric functions correspond to the spins of the two electrons being parallel, the antisymmetric one to antiparallel spins. This seems quite obvious for the first two, and the last of these functions, sur-prising, however, for the third, but must be accepted as one of the results of quantum mechanics the proof of which is beyond the present treatment.

These spin functions must now be combined with the four configuration functions of eqns. (4), leading to 16 possibilities. Not all of these, however, are acceptable, due to the Pauli principle. This principle is frequently formulated that no two electrons shall have the same set of 4 quantum numbers, or that no more than two electrons may occupy a single orbital (wave function), and then must have opposite spin. These statements can, however, be shown to be equivalent to the statement that *the wave function of any many-electron system must be antisymmetrical in exchange of any two electrons.* Now, it is readily seen that the product of two symmetric, or two antisymmetric functions is symmetric $[(+\,1)\,(+\,1) = (+\,1), (-\,1)\,(-\,1) = (+\,1)]$, but the product of one symmetric and one antisymmetric one is anti-symmetric $[(+\,1)\,(-\,1) = (-\,1)]$. Consequently, the configurations (orbital functions) Ψ_1, Ψ_2 and Ψ_4, which are symmetric in exchange of electrons must be multiplied by the antisymmetric spin function $[\alpha(1)\,\beta(2) - \alpha(2)\beta(1)]$, and the antisymmetric orbital function Ψ_3 may be multiplied by any of the three symmetric spin functions. Thus we obtain the functions:

$$\Psi_1 = \psi_1(1)\,\psi_1(2)\,[\alpha(1)\,\beta(2) - \alpha(2)\,\beta(1)]$$

$$\Psi_2 = [\psi_1(1)\,\psi_2(2) + \psi_1(2)\,\psi_2(1)]\,[\alpha(1)\,\beta(2) - \alpha(2)\,\beta(1)] \tag{5}$$

$$\Psi_3 = [\psi_1(1)\,\psi_2(2) - \psi_1(2)\,\psi_2(1)]\begin{cases} \alpha(1)\,\alpha(2) \\ [\alpha(1)\,\beta(2) + \alpha(2)\,\beta(1)] \\ \beta(1)\,\beta(2) \end{cases}$$

$$\Psi_4 = \psi_2(1)\,\psi_2(2)\,[\alpha(1)\,\beta(2) - \alpha(2)\,\beta(1)]$$

The three functions Ψ_3 are written together as one, since, in the absence of a magnetic field, they have the same energy; they are called *degenerate*; they jointly define one state of the molecule, which, because it consists of three degenerate functions, is called a *triplet* state. Of the other three functions, each is non-degenerate (or singly degenerate) and is a *singlet* state.

Next, we must consider the symmetry properties of our Ψ. The hydrogen molecule is a highly symmetrical entity. It may be rotated about its length-wise axis by any angle whatsoever, without any observable change occurring. It may be reflected from any plane through this axis, again without any noticeable change. The same is true of all four wave functions Ψ_1 to Ψ_4. Such wave functions in linear systems are referred to by the symbol $\sum^{+}$ (for several electrons) or σ (for one electron). In addition, the hydrogen molecule has a center of inversion, *i.e.*, each point may be reflected at the center of gravity without any observable change. The same is true for the function ψ_1, but not for ψ_2, which changes sign under this operation. Symmetric behavior under the inversion operation is called gerade, denoted by the letter g, usually as a subscript, and antisymmetric as ungerade (u). Since ungerade character simply means that a function changes sign under inversion, gerade that it remains unchanged, it is again obvious that the product of two g or two u functions is g, the product of one each is u. Since Ψ_1 and Ψ_4 are products of two like functions, both are g, and Ψ_2 and Ψ_3, as products of unlike functions (or rather sums of such products) are u. Finally, one prefixes the multiplicity, *i.e.*, the number of degenerate functions due to spin, to the symmetry symbol, *i.e.*, a 1 for a singlet, 3 for a triplet, and obtains as symmetry symbols

$$^{1}\sum_{g}^{+} \text{ for } \Psi_1, \quad ^{1}\sum_{u}^{+} \text{ for } \Psi_2, \quad ^{3}\sum_{u}^{+} \text{ for } \Psi_3 \text{ and } ^{1}\sum_{g}^{+} \text{ for } \Psi_4$$

These symbols are frequently used to represent the wave function.

We are finally ready to complete the molecular orbital treatment of hydrogen. Ψ_2 and Ψ_3, $^1\sum_u^+$ and $^3\sum_u^+$ are complete descriptions of two states, both excited, *i.e.*, of higher energy than the lowest, of the molecule. However, in writing our configuration function as a product of one electron functions we have made an approximation. This approximation may be corrected for by permitting *all configurations* of *equal symmetry and multiplicity* to interact. In other words, the correct function for an observable state is a linear combination of the functions of all configurations of equal symmetry and multiplicity. Ψ_2 and Ψ_3 are the only functions of that symmetry *and* multiplicity considered; this is the reason why they serve as adequate functions for their respective states. Ψ_1 and Ψ_4, however, both are $^1\sum_g^+$, hence of equal symmetry and multiplicity. These functions interact, and this interaction must be allowed for in so-called configuration interaction, to form a linear combination

$$\Psi_1^S = \Psi_1 + \mu\Psi_4$$

and

$$\Psi_4^S = \mu\Psi_1 - \Psi_4$$

where μ is a coefficient obtained by some rather extensive computation which will not be discussed here. Substituting for Ψ_1 and Ψ_4 we obtain

$$\Psi_1^S = \{\phi_A(1)\,\phi_A(2) + \phi_B(1)\,\phi_B(2) + \phi_A(1)\,\phi_B(2) + \phi_A(2)\,\phi_B(1)$$
$$+ \mu[\phi_A(1)\,\phi_A(2) + \phi_B(1)\,\phi_B(2) - \phi_A(1)\,\phi_B(2) - \phi_A(2)\,\phi_B(1)]\}$$
$$[\alpha(1)\,\beta(2) - \alpha(2)\,\beta(1)] \qquad (6)$$

$$= \{(1 + \mu)\,[\phi_A(1)\,\phi_A(2) + \phi_B(1)\,\phi_B(2)]$$
$$+ (1 - \mu)\,[\phi_A(1)\,\phi_B(2) + \phi_A(2)\,\phi_B(1)]\}\,[\alpha(1)\,\beta(2) - \alpha(2)\,\beta(1)]$$

$$\Psi_4^S = \{(1 + \mu)\,[\phi_A(1)\,\phi_A(2) + \phi_B(1)\,\phi_B(2)]$$
$$- (1 - \mu)\,[\phi_A(1)\,\phi_B(2) + \phi_A(2)\,\phi_B(1)]\}\,[\alpha(1)\,\beta(2) - \alpha(2)\,\beta(1)]$$

Similarly, substituting in the expressions for Ψ_2 and Ψ_3 gives

$$\Psi_2^S = \{[\phi_A(1) + \phi_B(1)]\,[\phi_A(2) - \varphi_B(2)]$$
$$+ [\phi_A(1) - \phi_B(1)]\,[\phi_A(2) + \phi_B(2)]\}\,[\alpha(1)\,\beta(2) - \alpha(2)\,\beta(1)]$$

$$= 2\,[\phi_A(1)\,\phi_A(2) - \phi_B(1)\,\phi_B(2)]\,[\alpha(1)\,\beta(2) - \alpha(2)\,\beta(1)]$$

$$\Psi_3^S = [\phi_A(1)\,\phi_B(2) - \phi_A(2)\,\phi_B(1)] \begin{cases} \alpha(1)\,\alpha(2) \\ \alpha(1)\,\beta(2) + \alpha(2)\,\beta(1) \\ \beta(1)\,\alpha(2) \end{cases}$$

We have thus the description of the ground state Ψ_1^S and of three excited states, Ψ_2^S, Ψ_3^S and Ψ_4^S as the final result of MO theory.

In order to compare these with the corresponding results of VB theory, we must still introduce spins in this theory, and construct the excited states. First, examination of Ψ_C and Ψ_I shows that these are symmetric in exchange of electrons, and hence are to be multiplied by the spin function $[\alpha(1)\,\beta(2) - \alpha(2)\,\beta(1)]$, leading to

$$\Psi_1^S = \{\phi_A(1)\,\phi_A(2) + \phi_B(1)\,\phi_B(2) + \lambda[\phi_A(1)\,\phi_B(2) \pm \phi_A(2)\,\phi_B(1)]\}$$
$$[\alpha(1)\,\beta(2) - \alpha(2)\,\beta(1)]$$

Comparison shows that this expression is equal in form with the above MO expression for Ψ_1^S, and indeed identical with it if $(1 - \mu)/(1 + \mu) = \lambda$, which follows from the arithmetic computation, remembering that each function remains to be multiplied by a normalization factor. Thus, we see that the two theories, when carried to their logical conclusion, give identical results.

To obtain the excited states in VB theory, we must remember that, in generating Ψ_C and Ψ_I, we used only a linear combination with a plus sign, and also in forming the combination of Ψ_C and Ψ_I we used only the positive combination. If we now use the negative combination,

$$\Psi_4 = \lambda\Psi_C - \Psi_I$$

and, since this also is symmetric in the electrons, multiply by the anti-symmetric spin function, we obtain

$$\Psi_4^S = \{ \lambda[\phi_A(1)\,\phi_A(2) + \phi_B(1)\,\phi_B(2)]$$
$$- [\phi_A(1)\,\phi_B(2) + \phi_A(2)\,\phi_B(1)]\}\,[\alpha(1)\,\beta(2) - \alpha(2)\,\beta(1)]$$

in agreement with the MO expression. The alternate combination corresponding to Ψ_C, $\phi_A(1)\,\phi_B(2) - \phi_A(2)\,\phi_B(1)$, is antisymmetric with respect to the electrons, and must therefore be multiplied by the three symmetric spin functions to give an expression identical with Ψ_3^S of MO theory. The alternate expression of Ψ_I, $\phi_A(1)\,\phi_A(2) - \phi_B(1)\,\phi_B(2)$, is symmetric in exchange of the electrons, and hence multiplied by the antisymmetric spin function, resulting in an expression identical with that for Ψ_2^S.

Finally, one extension may be considered briefly. So far we only have considered a single function, ϕ, by implication the 1s function, of each hydrogen atom. Further states can, of course, be derived by consideration of higher orbitals of hydrogen, 2s, 2p, etc. Consideration of such states would seriously increase the labor, particularly in configuration interaction. These states are, however, quite high in energy and are consequently generally ignored with safety. As long as the same sets of orbitals are considered in both theories, and as long as no differing assumptions are made, the results will always be identical, provided the calculation is carried to completion.

(a) The physical meaning of the wave function

In the preceding section, we have given a rather complete quantum mechanical treatment of the hydrogen molecule-ion and hydrogen molecule. The treatment, or rather two parallel treatments by molecular orbital and valence bond theory were predominantly concerned with arriving at an approximate, but adequate wave function. We must now return to these wave functions and attempt to interpret them in terms of physical concepts.

One of the basic concepts of quantum mechanics is the Heisenberg uncertainty principle, which states that it is not possible to determine simultaneously the position and momentum of a particle. In the description of molecules we choose to determine accurately the momentum of the electrons, but then, as a consequence of the uncertainty principle, the position cannot be specified. Instead the position is given by a probability distribution, which is given by the square of the wave function. In other words, in order to be able to speak of an electron, or an atom or molecule with several electrons, as having a given momentum, and hence energy, we content ourselves with the statement that the probability that an electron is in a given element of volume $d\tau$ is given by the square of the wave function ψ^2. A graphical representation of the wave function ψ or Ψ thus would permit an easy visualization of the distribution of the electron or electrons.

Unfortunately, such a graphic representation is not too readily given. The wave function Ψ of the two electrons of H_2 is a function of six coordinates, three (the Cartesian coordinates x, y, and z, or the polar coordinates r, θ, and ψ) for each of the two electrons. Showing Ψ as a function of the six coordinates would then be a seven-dimensional problem! As a consequence it has become customary to think largely of each electron separately and molecular orbital theory, which first constructs individual MO's for each electron, is particularly adaptable for this purpose.

Unfortunately, each one electron function, i.e. each MO, ψ, still is a function of three coordinates, and a graph of such a ψ as function of the three coordinates would still involve four dimensions, two too many for convenience. Consequently, many different schemes have appeared to provide qualitative graphical pictures of the wave functions.

The first of these schemes is shown in Fig. 1. Fig. 1a shows separate plots

References p. 112

of ϕ_A and ϕ_B, the 1s atomic wave functions as a function of r, the distance from the nucleus. The nuclei A and B are actually located at the distance they have in a normal hydrogen molecule. Now, the wave function (MO) for an electron in the molecule is $\psi_1 = \phi_A + \phi_B$, and Fig. 1b is simply the sum of the two curves (corrected for the normalizing factor N)*. This graph shows, then, the value of the wave function of the electron anywhere along the molecular axis, *i.e.* along the line joining the two H atoms. A graph along any line parallel to this axis would look similar. A graph of the probability distribution is given in Fig. 1c; this is simply the graph obtained by plotting the square of the function of Fig. 1b, and possibly has more physical significance. However, for many purposes symmetry properties and the sign of the wave function are of prime importance, and hence graphs such as Fig. 1b are frequently more useful.

In the preceding section we have seen that, besides the lowest energy MO $\psi_1 = \phi_A + \phi_B$, another one, $\psi_2 = \phi_A - \phi_B$ is of interest. This orbital is shown in Fig. 1d, obtained by subtracting ϕ_A and ϕ_B as given in Fig. 1a (and multiplying by an appropriate normalization factor**). The associated probability distribution $\psi_2{}^2$ is shown graphically in Fig. 1e.

Although many other systems for representing wave functions have been proposed and used, we will at this point introduce only one additional one. This system actually is an adaptation from the system of representing three dimensions in a two-dimensional graph, which is probably most familiar in terms of the contour map of the geographer, in which he draws a line on the map connecting all points of a given altitude. In a similar manner, it is possible to draw three-dimensional drawings (through the use of perspective) connecting points of equal electron density. In practice, one usually draws not a series of contours for different values of the electron density (although this is sometimes done) but a single one. This single contour is then frequently interpreted as the contour inside of which the electron has a certain, high probability, say 90%, of being found. Roughly, then, one may say that the electron is within this contour. A last simplification is finally made. Many

---

* Actually, more correctly, $\psi_1 = N(\phi_A + \phi_B)$. Since ϕ^2 is the probability of finding the electron in an element of volume $d\tau$, and since the probability of finding the electron someplace must be unity, $\phi^2 d\tau$ summed over all volume elements, *i.e.* integrated over all space must be unity: $\int \phi^2 d\tau = 1$. Similarly, $\int \psi^2 d\tau = 1$. The factor N, called a normalizing factor, is given by

$$\int \psi^2 d\tau = N^2 \int (\phi_A + \phi_B)^2 d\tau = N^2 \left[\int \phi_A{}^2 d\tau + \int \phi_B{}^2 d\tau + 2 \int \phi_A \phi_B d\tau\right] = N^2[2 + 2S] = 1;$$
$$N = 1/\sqrt{2(1 + S)}$$

where $S = \int \phi_A \phi_B d\tau$ is called the *overlap integral*. Although the *normalizing* factor is not generally written explicitly in this chapter, it is always implied, and graphs such as Fig. 1 are drawn so as to take N into account.

** In this case, $N = 1/\sqrt{2(1 - S)}$, as the reader can readily verify.

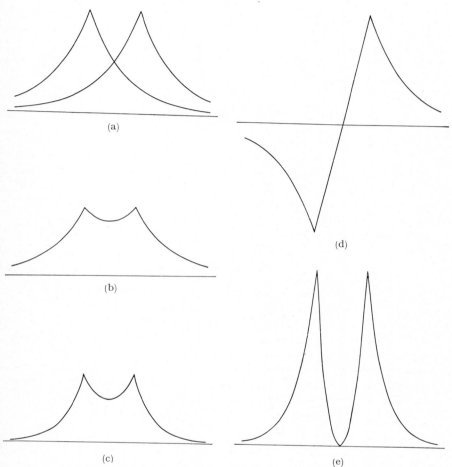

Fig. 1. The wave functions of the hydrogen molecule. (a) ϕ_A and ϕ_B as a function of r. (b) $\psi_1 = N(\phi_A + \phi_B)$. (c) The probability distribution ψ_1^2. (d) $\psi_2 = N(\phi_A - \phi_B)$. (e) ψ_2^2.

wave functions are actually symmetrical about an axis, and the provision of the third dimension by perspective adds little information, and may be omitted.

This system of representing wave functions is illustrated in Fig. 2. Fig. 2a, analogous to Fig. 1a, shows the contours of the two separate atomic functions ϕ_A and ϕ_B, the 1s functions of the hydrogen atoms A and B. Since a wave function can be either positive or negative, the sign of the function within the contour is indicated by an algebraic sign. Actually, of course, each of the

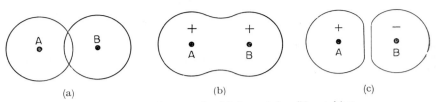

Fig. 2. Contour diagrams for (a) ϕ_A and ϕ_B; (b) ψ_1; (c) ψ_2.

circles of Fig. 2a represents a sphere, but the third dimension is omitted. Addition of the two functions gives the MO ψ_1 shown in Fig. 2b, corresponding to Fig. 1b. Again, a third dimension must be imagined supplied by rotation about the molecular axis. Finally, the orbital ψ_2 is shown in Fig. 2c, corresponding to Fig. 1d. Since the sign of the wave function is frequently of great importance, and to focus on the symmetry properties, signs (+ or −) are commonly inserted within the contours, as shown in Fig. 2c.

(b) The energies

Having in the preceding sections discussed the wave functions of the hydrogen molecule-ion and the hydrogen molecule at length, it now remains to consider the energy of these molecules. Again we must go back to the basic postulates of quantum mechanics. One of the ways of introducing quantum mechanics is to state the Schrödinger equation as a basic postulate. Although there are other possible starting points which might permit the derivation of this equation, some basic postulate is required, which cannot be proven or derived, but which is shown to be useful or correct only by the fact that it leads to consequences which are in agreement with experimental facts.

The Schrödinger equation may, for our purposes, be stated:

$$H\Psi = E\Psi \qquad (7)$$

where H is a mathematical quantity, called the Hamiltonian operator, the exact form of which need not concern us, Ψ is, of course, the wave function, and E is the energy associated with the wave function. H and Ψ are functions of the various coordinates of the particles involved, in our case the electrons, but E is a constant. If Ψ were an *exact* wave function, this equation would be an identity, and it would suffice to evaluate $H\Psi/\Psi$ for any value of the coordinates to obtain E.

Unfortunately, however, it is not possible in molecular problems to find exact wave functions Ψ. When we introduced the linear combination function

$\psi = \phi_A + \phi_B$ for the hydrogen molecule-ion, we stated that the electron, when near A, would behave approximately as an electron on the isolated atom A, and hence we chose the *approximate* wave function ψ. Now, according to a well-known principle of quantum mechanics, the most probable value of E for an approximate function Ψ is found by multiplying eqn. (7) by Ψ, and integrating over all space:

$$\int \Psi H \Psi \, d\tau = \int \Psi E \Psi \, d\tau = E \int \Psi^2 \, d\tau = E \qquad (8)$$

Here, the second equality is obvious because E is a constant, and the third one because Ψ is normalized (*cf.* footnote on p. 44) so that the integral $\int \Psi^2 \, d\tau$ is equal to unity. The problem of evaluating the energy then becomes the problem of evaluating the integral on the left-hand side of eqn. (8). This can, of course, be a formidable problem when one inspects the form of the complete wave function as shown in eqn. (6).

For the qualitative treatment and discussion intended here, this problem will not be undertaken. Instead, we will return to an earlier step in the treatment, and discuss separately each electron and associate with it an energy quantity, which is the energy that would be required to remove the electron to infinity. The procedure to obtain this energy is analogous to that outlined, but the many electron function Ψ in eqn. (8) is replaced by the one electron function ψ, and the energy is generally referred to by ε. Using $\psi_1 = (\phi_A + \phi_B)/\sqrt{2(1 + S)}$ of the hydrogen molecule, we obtain:

$$\varepsilon = \frac{1}{2(1 + S)} \int (\phi_A + \phi_B) \, H \, (\phi_A + \phi_B) \, d\tau$$

$$= \frac{1}{2(1 + S)} [\int \phi_A H \phi_A \, d\tau + \int \phi_B H \phi_B \, d\tau + 2 \int \phi_A H \phi_B \, d\tau] \qquad (9)$$

The first two integrals in eqn. (9) are identical in value, and are usually called *Coulomb integrals* and abbreviated by α (or α_H). They are, of course, themselves integrals of the form of the left-hand side of eqn. (8) and hence just represent the energy of an electron on a hydrogen atom (*i.e.* the energy required to remove the electron from a hydrogen atom). The last integral in eqn. (9) is called a *resonance integral* and referred to by the symbol β. It may be evaluated theoretically, but for many purposes empirical estimates are used. With these definitions or abbreviations, eqn. (9) becomes

$$\varepsilon_1 = (\alpha + \beta)/(1 + S)$$

$$= \alpha + (\beta - \alpha S)/(1 + S) \qquad (10)$$

The energy for the other wave function of H_2, $\psi_2 = (\phi_A - \phi_B)/\sqrt{2(1 - S)}$ is similarly derived, and found to be

$$\varepsilon_2 = \alpha - (\beta - \alpha S)/(1 - S) \tag{11}$$

If it is remembered that α is the energy of the isolated hydrogen atom, then it is obvious that the energy of a "normal" hydrogen molecule, with two electrons in ψ_1 is lower than that of the isolated atoms by $2(\beta - \alpha S)/(1 + S)$. This quantity is often called the binding energy, and should equal the energy required to dissociate the molecule into two atoms. It is a negative quantity, thus corresponding to a lowering of the energy, because β is an inherently negative quantity. A diagram of the energies is shown in Fig. 3a, where the outside lines represent the energies of the two isolated hydrogen atoms, α, and the two lines in the center represent the energy of the two MO's of the molecule. The two electrons, which in the ground state occupy the lowest energy level, are indicated by crosses. The zero-point of the energy scale, which is actually arbitrary, is usually chosen as the energy of an isolated electron, and would be high above the top of the paper.

One further approximation is frequently made, and considerably simplifies the work. The *overlap integral* $S = \int \phi_A \phi_B \, d\tau$ is a quantity which is *always* smaller than 1, usually for chemical bonds of the order of $\frac{1}{4}$ to $\frac{1}{2}$. Although this quantity is far from negligible with respect to 1, for many semi-quantitative purposes, it is neglected. Eqns. (10) and (11) then reduce to

$$\varepsilon_1 = \alpha + \beta, \quad \varepsilon_2 = \alpha - \beta \tag{10', 11'}$$

With this assumption, then, the binding energy is just 2β. It should be noted in particular that the two energy levels now are symmetrically spaced with respect to the free atom, a relation which is almost universal in MO theory, and which is illustrated in Fig. 3b, where the energy values obtained with the assumption $S = 0$ are plotted.

Two further quantities appear directly from the energy level diagrams, Fig. 3a or 3b. The first of these is the ionization potential (IP) *i.e.* the energy required to completely remove one of the electrons from the molecule. Numerically, this quantity is equal to $\alpha + (\beta - \alpha S)/(1 + S)$ or $\alpha + \beta$; graphically, it is the distance between the highest occupied energy level (in this case only the lowest one is occupied) and the zero of the energy scale. The other quantity immediately apparent is the energy $(h\nu)$ required to excite an electron to a higher energy level, *i.e.* the energy absorbed if a molecule is excited by visible or ultraviolet light. Numerically, this is equal to

$$(\beta - \alpha S)/(1 + S) + (\beta - \alpha S)/(1 - S) = 2(\beta - \alpha S)/(1 - S^2)$$

or, if S is neglected, just 2β. Graphically, it is the distance between the two energy levels.

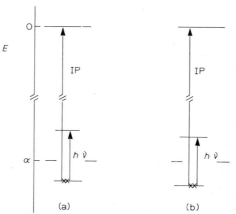

Fig. 3. The energy level diagram of H_2 (a) from eqns. (10) and (11); (b) from eqns. (10') and (11'), *i.e.* with neglect of S.

Finally, Fig. 3 helps to explain and introduce a notation very common in chemistry today. An electron in the orbital ψ_1 helps to hold the molecule together; for this reason the orbital is often called a *bonding* orbital. The bonding character is immediately apparent because ψ_1 lies below the level of either of the isolated atom orbitals from which it is formed. Part of the reason for this bonding character can be seen from Fig. 1. Comparison of Figs. 1a and 1b shows that the wave function, and hence the electron density in the molecule is particularly high in the region between the atoms, where the electrostatic attraction of the nuclei for the electrons is particularly high, and consequently the electrons are more tightly bound than in the isolated atoms. Looking back to Fig. 3, we see that an electron in ψ_2 is less tightly bound than on either of the separated atoms. Such an electron not only does nothing to hold the molecule together, but, on the contrary, adds to the energy and decreases the stability of the molecule. For this reason, orbitals such as ψ_2 are called *antibonding*. The reason is again apparent from Fig. 1, where Fig. 1d shows that, on the average, the electron is further distant from the nuclei than in the isolated atoms, and consequently the Coulomb attraction is less.

3. Other diatomic molecules

In the preceding sections we have treated the hydrogen molecule in detail, and we are now ready to extend these treatments to larger, more complex molecules. However, we have seen that the two treatments of H_2 turned

References p. 112

out quite complex, and the treatment of larger molecules to the same degree of approximation is beyond the scope of the present chapter. Consequently, we will content ourselves with quite crude approximations, realizing that we cannot expect more than qualitative or at best semiquantitative information from them.

For these approximations, we have available to us two methods, the MO and the VB method. We shall spend most of our effort on the former, only giving VB description of a few molecules to show the comparison between the two.

Before proceeding further, it will be profitable to reiterate the description of H_2 at the level of approximation we shall use from here on. From the two atomic orbitals of the hydrogen atoms, ϕ_A and ϕ_B, we constructed two molecular orbitals $\psi_1 = \phi_A + \phi_B$ and $\psi_2 = \phi_A - \phi_B$. According to the symmetry classification discussed above, ψ_1 may be described as σ_g and ψ_2 as σ_u; to indicate that the latter is antibonding, an asterisk is commonly added, and it is denoted by σ_u^*. In MO theory then, the description of the ground state of H_2 was $\Psi_1 = \sigma_g^2$, $i.e.$ both electrons occupying the lowest MO, ψ_1, with approximate energy $\alpha + \beta$. Other states were available, such as Ψ_2 (and Ψ_3) $= \sigma_g \sigma_u^*$; it may be interesting to note here that, in the approximation we now use, the states of different multiplicity belonging to the same configuration cannot be distinguished. And finally the state $\Psi_4 = \sigma_u^{*2}$.

In VB theory, we constructed two equivalent covalent structures, one with electron 1 on atom A and electron 2 on atom B, and the other one with the electrons reversed, and called this structure Ψ_C. In addition we had two ionic structures H^+H^- and H^-H^+, which we called Ψ_I, and the wave function was a linear combination of the two, $\Psi = \Psi_C + \lambda\Psi_I$.

(a) Dilithium, Li_2

The next stable molecule is Li_2. In this molecule, each Li atom contributes three electrons; according to the Aufbau principle, two of these are assigned to 1s orbitals of each atom, one to a 2s orbital. In forming the appropriate molecular orbitals, the two 1s orbitals interact to form two MO's $\sigma_g(1s)$ and $\sigma_u^*(1s)$, perfectly analogous to the MO's in H_2,* and the 2s orbitals interact to form another pair of MO's, $\sigma_g(2s)$ and $\sigma_u^*(2s)$, which are again analogous to $\sigma_g(1s)$ and $\sigma_u^*(1s)$, except that they are formed from the 2s orbitals of the atoms. The energies (assuming neglect of overlap integrals) are given by

$$\varepsilon_1 = \alpha(1s) + \beta_1, \varepsilon_2 = \alpha(1s) - \beta_1, \varepsilon_3 = \alpha(2s) + \beta_2, \varepsilon_4 = \alpha(2s) - \beta_2$$

The energy levels are shown schematically in Fig. 4. In the ground state of

---

* The 1s in parenthesis is added since several σ_g and σ_u^* orbitals exist, and indicates the atomic orbitals from which the MO is formed.

the molecule six electrons are assigned in pairs to $\sigma_g(1s)$, $\sigma_u^*(1s)$ and $\sigma_g(2s)$, while $\sigma_u^*(2s)$ remains vacant. The total energy of the molecule is then

$$2[\alpha(1s) + \beta_1] + 2[\alpha(1s) - \beta_1] + 2[\alpha(2s) + \beta_2] = 4\alpha(1s) + 2\alpha(2s) + 2\beta_2$$

and since, in the same approximation, the energy of each Li atom is $2\alpha(1s) + \alpha(2s)$, the binding energy is just $2\beta_2$, *i.e.* just twice the resonance integral for interaction of the 2s electrons only. This result is obtained because the bonding contribution of the two 1s electrons in $\sigma_g(1s)$ is just balanced by the an-

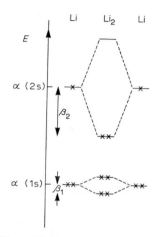

Fig. 4. The energy levels of Li$_2$.

tibonding contribution of the two 1s electrons in $\sigma_u^*(1s)$. This result is general whenever one deals with closed shells, and consequently these are frequently ignored, or at least treated as if they were non-interacting. The two 1s electrons, in other words the K shell electrons of Li atom A, are simply abbreviated K_A, etc., and the electronic structure of Li$_2$ is written $K_A K_B \sigma_g^2(2s)$.

Actually the cancellation described is only an approximation. The energy of $\sigma_g(1s)$ is, to a better approximation, given by

$$\alpha(1s) + [\beta_1 - S_1\alpha(1s)] / (1 + S_1)$$

and that of $\sigma_u^*(1s)$ is

$$\alpha(1s) - [\beta_1 - S_1\alpha(1s)] / (1 - S_1)$$

Twice the sum of these quantities is

$$2\alpha(1s) - 2S_1[\beta_1 - S_1\alpha(1s)] / (1 - S_1^2)$$

The last term actually increases the energy slightly, *i.e.* is a repulsive term, and is often referred to as *inner shell* or closed-shell *repulsion*. In this case, however, S_1, the overlap integral for the overlap of the two 1s electrons is quite small, and hence the inner shell repulsion is probably quite negligible.

Excited states of Li_2 are readily formed by assigning one or both electrons to $\sigma_u^*(2s)$ instead of $\sigma_g(2s)$. States in which electrons from the K shell are promoted to $\sigma_u^*(2s)$ are probably of no interest because their energy would be very high. More likely to be of interest are states in which one electron is promoted from $\sigma_g(2s)$ to a bonding MO formed from 2p orbitals of the Li atoms.

The Li_2 molecule in terms of VB theory greatly resembles the H_2 molecule. The structures Ψ_C, of course, involve six electrons each, but the K shells may also substantially be ignored. The structures Li^+Li^- etc. are perfectly analogous to the corresponding structures in H_2. Additional ionic structures, such as $Li^{++}Li^{--}$, may be written, but they are energetically so unfavorable that they may safely be neglected because they involve promotion of a 1s electron from one atom to a 2p orbital of the other. Just as in MO theory, excited structures with Li atoms involving 2p electrons may be written.

(b) The nitrogen, oxygen and fluorine molecules

The formation of the molecular orbitals of the N_2 molecule from the nitrogen atoms in terms of energy levels is shown in Fig. 5. Attention should first be focused on Fig. 5a. The problem is to combine the seven electrons (two 1s, two 2s, and three 2p) of each nitrogen atom into molecular orbitals and place the fourteen electrons of the N_2 molecule in MO's of lowest energy in accordance with the Aufbau and Pauli principles. As in the Li_2 molecule, the four electrons of the 1s orbitals are placed in $\sigma_g(1s)$ and $\sigma_u^*(1s)$ and these MO's are of little concern since they are neither involved in chemical properties nor in the commonly observed spectroscopic states. Next to be considered is the 2s orbital of each atom whose combination (assuming no hybridization as in Fig. 5a) results in the two MO's, $\sigma_g(2s)$ and $\sigma_u^*(2s)$ into each of which two electrons are placed, thus accounting for four more of the electrons and leaving six electrons to be accommodated. The wave functions of the MO's from the 2s orbitals may be written:

$$\psi_1 = 2s_A + 2s_B = \sigma_g(2s)$$

$$\psi_2 = 2s_A - 2s_B = \sigma_u^*(2s)$$

The contours of ψ_1 and ψ_2 are shown in Figs. 6a and 6b. The next MO to be filled is the one which is formed from the single 2p orbital of each atom which has cylindrical symmetry around the bond axis (which can arbitrarily

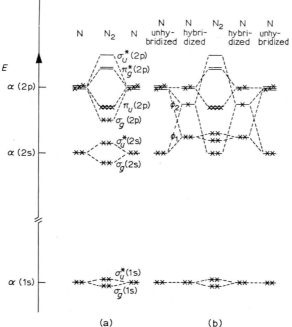

Fig. 5. The energy levels of N_2 (a) without and (b) with hybridization.

be chosen as the z axis). This MO is called $\sigma_g(2p)$ since it has cylindrical symmetry around the bond axis. The wave function may be written

$$\psi_3 = 2p_A\sigma + 2p_B\sigma = \sigma_g(2p)$$

The contour of ψ_3 is shown in Fig. 6c. The atomic p orbital used for the formation of this MO is one of three degenerate (equal energy) p atomic orbitals in the isolated atom. In the field of another atom, the degeneracy of the three p orbitals splits; the p orbital pointing in the direction of the other atom (pσ) is raised slightly more than the other two (pπ) which remain degenerate. The pσ level is higher because under the influence of the second atom, this electron is more effectively repelled than those in the other two p atomic orbitals*. However, when the atoms are within bonding distance, the pσ electrons overlap effectively in the bonding MO, leading to a lower energy MO, ψ_3, than the MO's formed from the other p electrons. With the filling of $\sigma_g(2p)$, only four electrons remain to be placed. The next two MO's

---

* This may be considered as the simplest example of what is often called a ligand field (or a crystal field) effect.

are degenerate. These MO's result from the combination of pπ electrons[*] in the two atoms and since the pπ atomic orbitals occur as degenerate pairs (*i.e.*, $2p_y$ and $2p_x$ have the same energy) the molecular π orbitals also occur as degenerate pairs. The wave functions of the π MO's are identical and can be written:

$$\psi_{4,5} = 2p_A\pi + 2p_B\pi = \pi_u(2p)$$

The contour of one of these wave functions is shown in Fig. 6d. Examination of this figure shows that ψ_4 (and ψ_5), the bonding molecular orbitals, are ungerade, since reflection at the center of symmetry changes the sign; this is true in general of the lowest bonding π orbital. The bond axis lies in the nodal plane of the orbitals which can be thought of as "sausages" lying above and below, and in front of and in back of, the bond axis.

The combination of the two degenerate pπ orbitals of each atom leads to four MO's. The bonding MO's, ψ_4 and ψ_5, called $\pi_u(2p)$ have been described. The corresponding antibonding MO's from this combination are also degenerate and are called $\pi_g^*(2p)$. The wave functions of these orbitals are $\psi_{6,7} = 2p_A\pi - 2p_B\pi = \pi_g^*(2p)$ and the contour of ψ_6 is shown in Fig. 6e. The gerade character of this antibonding MO is obvious. In the ground state $\psi_{6,7}$ are not occupied since the fourteen electrons have already been accommodated in MO's of lower energy. The antibonding MO resulting from the combination of the pσ electrons is denoted as $\sigma_u^*(2p)$ and $\psi_8 = 2p_A\sigma - 2p_B\sigma = \sigma_u^*(2p)$. The contour of this wave function is shown in Fig. 6f. The electronic structure of N_2 (if hybridization is neglected) is thus denoted by $K_AK_B\sigma_g^2(2s)\,\sigma_u^{*2}(2s)\sigma_g^2(2p)\,\pi_u^4(2p)$.

In considering the atomic orbital of each atom and their combination into molecular orbitals, only the equivalent atomic orbitals of the two nitrogen atoms were combined. The 2s and 2p electrons do not have the same symmetry properties with respect to the symmetry operations applicable to each separated nitrogen atom. However, with respect to the more restricted number of symmetry elements of the less symmetrical N_2 molecule, 2s and 2pσ have the same symmetry properties. Now, the symmetry properties determine what orbitals can combine, and consequently it is possible to *hybridize* or mix the 2s and 2pσ orbitals and to replace them by two *hybrid orbitals* given by some linear combinations of the two:

$$\phi_1 = \lambda 2s + 2p\sigma \text{ and } \phi_2 = 2s - \lambda 2p\sigma$$

---

[*] The matter of the symmetry classifications in a linear molecule is unfortunately quite complicated, and cannot be discussed adequately here. The distinction of σ and π classifications may crudely be made on the basis that any σ orbital has perfect cylindrical symmetry about the molecular axis, while an orbital is said to have π symmetry or π character if one, and just one plane including the bond axis exists in which ψ is zero; such a plane is called a nodal plane. Orbitals having two such nodal planes are called δ orbitals, but only occur with d and f orbitals.

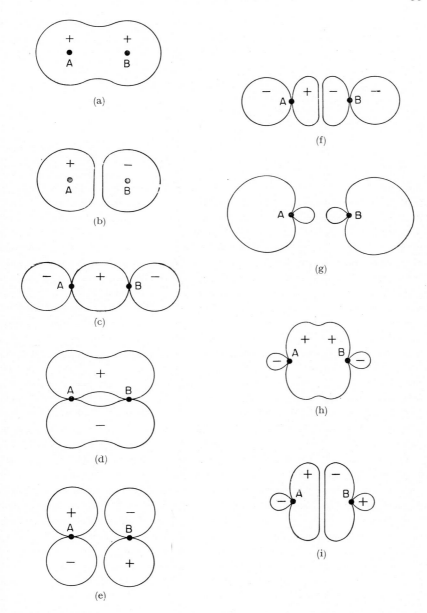

Fig. 6. The MO's of N_2 (a) $\psi_1 = \sigma_g(2s)$; (b) $\psi_2 = \sigma_u^*(2s)$; (c) $\psi_3 = \sigma_g(2p)$; (d) ψ_4 and $\psi_5 = \pi_u(2p)$; (e) ψ_6 and $\psi_7 = \pi_g^*(2p)$; (f) $\psi_8 = \sigma_u^*(2p)$; (g) $\psi_1 = \sigma_g(\varphi_1)$ (h) $\psi_3 = \sigma_g(\varphi_2)$; (i) $\psi_8 = \sigma_u^*(\varphi_2)$.

where λ is a weighting factor. This weighting factor would be unnecessary if the hybrid orbitals were made of equal parts of s and p, but one orbital has more s than p character, the other less. The new molecular orbitals are now:

$$\psi_1 = \phi_{1A} + \phi_{1B} = \sigma_g(\phi_1)$$

$$\psi_2 = \phi_{1A} - \phi_{1B} = \sigma_u^*(\phi_1)$$

$$\psi_3 = \phi_{2A} + \phi_{2B} = \sigma_g(\phi_2)$$

$$\psi_8 = \phi_{2A} - \phi_{2B} = \sigma_u^*(\phi_2)$$

and are shown schematically in Figs. 6g–6i. The relative energies of the new MO's are shown schematically in Fig. 5b. The energetics of the hybridization process are of interest. If the 2s and 2pσ orbitals were each doubly occupied, hybridization to ϕ_1 and ϕ_2 would involve no appreciable change in energy. However, 2s is doubly occupied, but 2pσ has only a single electron. Hybridization to a doubly occupied ϕ_1 and a singly occupied ϕ_2 involves promotion of a fraction of an electron (given by λ) from a 2s to a 2p atomic orbital. This promotion from one atomic orbital to another is energetically expensive. The energy expended, however, is more than compensated by two factors: (1) increased binding energy due to $\sigma_g(\phi_2)$ for which the overlap integral and the resonance integral are much larger than for $\sigma_g(2p)$, *i.e.*, the hybridized orbitals overlap much better than unhybridized orbitals, or in the words of Mulliken "a little hybridization goes a long way"; and (2) greatly reduced repulsion of ϕ_1 electrons. The reduced repulsion arises out of the fact that S and β for the ϕ_1 orbitals are much smaller than for the unhybridized 2s orbitals which means that the excess of antibonding by $\sigma_u^*(\phi_1)$ over bonding by $\sigma_g(\phi_1)$ (where the approximation $S = 0$ is not made) is much smaller than the same excess for $\sigma_u^*(2s)$ over $\sigma_g(2s)$.

The orbitals ϕ_{2A} and ϕ_{2B} overlap to form the strong σ bond. The orbitals ϕ_{1A} and ϕ_{1B} barely overlap; they have their small negative lobes between the two atoms and the large positive lobes directed away from the bond. These two orbitals which correspond to ψ_1 and ψ_2 in the unhybridized case have almost the same energy. They are non-bonding orbitals and contain the lone-pair electrons. The electronic structure of N_2 then is $K_A K_B \sigma_g^2(\phi_1)$ $\sigma_u^{*2}(\phi_1) \sigma_g^2(\phi_2) \pi_u^4(2p)$ or again abbreviated $K_A K_B \phi_{1A}^2 \phi_{1B}^2 \sigma_g^2(\phi_2) \pi_u^4(2p)$. In the N_2 molecule there is thus one doubly occupied bonding σ orbital and two doubly occupied bonding π orbitals, each representing a bond and giving the well-known triply-bonded electronic structure $:N \equiv N:$ The electron distribution of the four π electrons in the two π orbitals represents a distribution of charge cylindrically symmetrical about the $N-N$ axis.

The energy diagrams of Fig. 5 were derived only by consideration of the interaction of the atomic orbitals of two nuclei for which we needed to consider the K and L shells, and without any reference to the number of electrons they would eventually have to accommodate. They can, therefore, be used immediately to derive the electronic structure of O_2 and F_2. In O_2, two more electrons must be added. According to the Aufbau principle they should go into ψ_6 and $\psi_7[\pi_g^*(2p)]$, and since these are degenerate, Hund's rule indicates that one should be assigned to each of these, with parallel spins. Accordingly, the electronic structure of O_2 is $K_A K_B \phi_{1A}^2 \phi_{1B}^2 \sigma_g^2(\phi_2)$ $\pi_u^4(2p)\pi_g^{*2}(2p)$, and since the last two electrons have equal spin, the ground state of O_2 should be a triplet, as it actually is. The two electrons in $\pi_g^*(2p)$ are antibonding. There are thus 6 electrons in bonding and two electrons in antibonding orbitals leaving a net of 4 bonding electrons, *i.e.* a "double bond."

Addition of two more electrons leads to the structure $K_A K_B \phi_{1A}^2 \phi_{1B}^2 \sigma_g^2(\phi_2)$ $\pi_u^4(2p) \pi_g^{*4}(2p)$ of F_2. Here the bonding character of π_u^4 is essentially balanced by the antibonding character of π_g^{*4}, except for closed shell repulsion, and these orbitals may formally be replaced by $2p\pi_A^4 2p\pi_B^4$, leading to the single bond in $F_2[\sigma_g^2(\phi_2)]$ and to the 3 lone pairs in each $F(\phi_{1z}^2 p\pi^4)$ and the familiar structure $:\overset{\cdot\cdot}{\underset{\cdot\cdot}{F}}:\overset{\cdot\cdot}{\underset{\cdot\cdot}{F}}:$

In VB theory, of the three molecules N_2, O_2 and F_2, the latter is most readily described, and hence will be treated first. In the free fluorine atoms, we have seven valence electrons each, and the odd electron is a 2p electron, the others being necessarily paired. A number of different atomic functions Φ_A can be written such as $1s^2 2s^2 2p_x 2p_y^2 2p_z^2$, $1s^2 2s^2 2p_x^2 2p_y 2p_z^2$ and $1s^2 2s^2 2p_x^2$ $2p_y^2 2p_z$. For compound formation with another F atom described by a like wave function (assuming the bond axis to be the z axis), only the last of these functions is of interest and is multiplied by a like function Φ_B for atom B. Of all the possible exchanges of electrons, only exchange of the two $2p_z$ electrons of the two atoms is of real interest, and hence we obtain again a covalent wave function Ψ_C, which differs only from that for H_2 in that there is a common factor involving the atomic functions of all the non-bonding electrons. Two ionic structures, F^+F^- and F^-F^+, jointly given as Ψ_I, can also be written, and when combined with Ψ_C give a description which is quite analogous to that of H_2 and Li_2, and which is, in general, characteristic of a homonuclear single bond, *i.e.* a single bond between like atoms.

In the MO treatment of N_2, and hence of O_2 and F_2, we introduced hybridization by allowing the 2s and $2p_z$ atomic orbitals of each atom to mix. We can, of course, do the same thing in the VB method, and the pertinent atomic function of F_2 becomes $\Phi_A = 1s^2 \phi_1^2 2p_x^2 2p_y^2 \phi_2$, and just as in the MO method, the two ϕ_2 electrons form the chemical bond.

The VB descriptions of N_2 and O_2 are considerably more difficult. Take N_2 first: the atomic structure of N is given by $1s^2 2s^2 2p^3$. Calling Φ the atomic wave function obtained by multiplying together two 1s orbitals, two 2s orbitals (with opposite spins in each pair) and one each $2p_x$, $2p_y$ and $2p_z$ orbitals, and multiplying together such Φ functions of the two atoms, Φ_A and Φ_B, one may obtain, after permitting exchanges, a whole series of functions. Whenever the spins of the two $2p_x$, the two $2p_y$, and the two $2p_z$ electrons of the two atoms are paired, the linear combination of these products together corresponds to a triple bonded structure $| N \equiv N |$ where each dash represents a pair of electrons with antiparallel spins. Other structures, in which only some of the corresponding electrons of the two atoms are paired belong to high-energy structures which may be represented by $| \dot{N} = \dot{N} |$, $| \dot{N} - \dot{N} |$, $\langle N - N \rangle$, where a dot represents a lone electron; such structures are generally ignored because of their high energy.

Thus, while we can again write a single structure Ψ_C ($| N \equiv N |$), instead of being a linear combination of two functions, it is a linear combination of quite a large number. When going on to ionic structures, the situation is even worse. Ionic structures may be formed by transferring any one of the three 2p electrons of atom A to any one of the three singly occupied 2p orbitals of B and *vice versa*; this, thus, represents, without electron exchanges, a total of 18 wave functions. Six of these represent the structures $N^+ = N^-$ and $N^- = N^+$, the others involve higher energy structures with fewer covalent bonds. Although considerably higher in energy, structures such as $N^{++} - N^=$, in which two electrons are transferred from one atom to the other also may have to be considered, and accordingly the VB description of this molecule becomes quite complicated.

The situation is even worse in O_2. The VB method in general is dependent on pairing appropriate electrons which are unpaired in the free atoms, and consequently almost universally leads to a ground state without unpaired electrons (a singlet ground state), in agreement with the chemical experience that the ground states of almost all molecules are singlets. Oxygen is one of the notable exceptions, having a triplet ground state. This fact was readily explained by MO theory, but does not follow directly from VB theory. In order to explain this fact, Pauling[2] has introduced the concept of the three electron bond. Since such bonds occur only in a relatively restricted number of compounds, the structure of which is usually quite readily explained by MO theory, we will not discuss three electron bonds further.

(c) Molecules, LiH and CO

Heteronuclear diatomic molecules are a little more difficult to handle. Here, the symmetry requirements are much less, and do not so readily determine the molecular orbitals. In LiH, *e.g.*, the bonding molecular orbital, ψ_b, will be a combination of the 1s orbital of H and the 2s orbital of Li (although some hybridization with 1s and $2p\sigma$ orbitals should really be considered). However, hydrogen is more electronegative than lithium, and hence the electron density near H should exceed that near Li. Thus the bonding orbital becomes[*] $\psi_b = N_b(\lambda_b 1s_H + 2s_{Li}) = \sigma$ and ψ_a the antibonding orbital becomes $\sigma^* = N_a(1s_H - \lambda_a 2s_{Li})$ where λ_a and λ_b are two constants, both larger than 1, the values of which are so far unknown, and N_a and N_b are the usual normalization factors.

In the evaluation of λ_a and λ_b, use is made of the variational principle. This principle states that the energy value obtained from the true wave function is lower than that obtained from any approximate wave function, provided the complete Hamiltonian operator is used in the evaluation of the energy. Consequently, it is only necessary to find the value of λ_b for which ε_b is a minimum, and this value of ε_b is the best energy value obtainable with a wave function of the form given. It is then generally assumed, although not necessarily true, that the function so obtained is the best wave function of that form. The application of standard methods of calculus gives two equations:

$$(\alpha_H - \varepsilon)N\lambda + (\beta - \varepsilon S)N = 0$$

$$(\beta - \varepsilon S)N\lambda + (\alpha_{Li} - \varepsilon)N = 0$$

These equations are called the secular equations, and have solutions for λ and ε only when the determinant of the coefficients, the so-called secular determinant, vanishes:

$$\begin{vmatrix} (\alpha_H - \varepsilon) & (\beta - \varepsilon S) \\ (\beta - \varepsilon S) & (\alpha_{Li} - \varepsilon) \end{vmatrix} = 0$$

Expansion of this determinant gives

$$(\alpha_H - \varepsilon)(\alpha_{Li} - \varepsilon) - (\beta - \varepsilon S)^2 = 0$$

$$\varepsilon^2(1 - S^2) - \varepsilon(\alpha_H + \alpha_{Li} - 2\beta S) + \alpha_H \alpha_{Li} - \beta^2 = 0$$

$$\varepsilon = \frac{1}{2(1 - S^2)}\{\alpha_H + \alpha_{Li} - 2\beta S \pm [(\alpha_H + \alpha_{Li} - 2\beta S)^2 -$$
$$4(1 - S^2)(\alpha_H \alpha_{Li} - \beta^2)]^{\frac{1}{2}}\}$$

Using the common approximation $S = 0$,

$$\varepsilon = \frac{1}{2}\{\alpha_H + \alpha_{Li} \pm \sqrt{(\alpha_H + \alpha_{Li})^2 - 4(\alpha_H \alpha_{Li} - \beta^2)}$$

$$= \frac{1}{2}\{\alpha_H + \alpha_{Li} \pm \sqrt{(\alpha_H - \alpha_{Li})^2 + 4\beta^2}\}$$

---

[*] Since the molecule has no center of symmetry, no g,u classification is possible.

When $\alpha_H - \alpha_{Li}$ is small compared to 2β, which is one condition of effective interaction of orbitals, this becomes approximately

$$\varepsilon \approx \tfrac{1}{2}\{\alpha_H + \alpha_{Li} \pm (2\beta + \alpha_H - \alpha_{Li})\}$$

and hence

$$\varepsilon_b \approx \alpha_H + \beta \text{ and } \varepsilon_a \approx \alpha_{Li} - \beta$$

It is seen that this method gives two values of the energy One of these corresponds to ψ_b, the other to an orbital orthogonal to ψ_b and hence identifiable with ψ_a. Substitution of these values of ε, one at a time, into the secular equations, then permits solution for λ_b and λ_a, and finally the N is found by normalization.

The value of λ so obtained estimates the distribution of the charge between the two atoms involved in the bond, and hence permits evaluation of the dipole moment. Alternately, λ is often estimated from experimental dipole moments. The energies of ψ_b and ψ_a are schematically shown in Fig. 7. It should particularly be noted that, in the approximation used, the bonding orbital is stabilized by the resonance integral, β with respect to the atomic orbital of the hydrogen atom, while the antibonding orbital ψ_a is destabilized by an equal amount with respect to the atomic orbital of lithium.

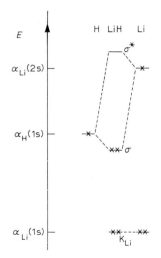

Fig. 7. The energy levels of LiH.

In the VB treatment of LiH, the same problem occurs in a different manner. The covalent structure, Ψ_C can immediately be written down in the usual manner, as a linear combination of the product of $\Phi_H = $ 1s(H) and $\Phi_{Li} = $ 1s^2(Li)2s(Li) with the appropriate exchange. Two ionic structures are readily written: H$^+$Li$^-$ and H$^-$Li$^+$. The wave function for the first is simply $\Psi_{I1} = $ 1s^2(Li)2s^2(Li), the wave function for the second, $\Psi_{I2} = $ 1s^2(H)1s^2(Li). But in the homonuclear molecule, the two atoms A and B were alike, hence A$^+$B$^-$ and A$^-$B$^+$ were equivalent, and entered with the same coefficient into the final wave function. In the present case, the two structures H$^+$Li$^-$ and H$^-$Li$^+$ are different, and hence enter with different coefficients. The wave function then becomes

$$\Psi = \Psi_C + \lambda_1 \Psi_{I1} + \lambda_2 \Psi_{I2}$$

Frequently, as a further approximation, only the ionic structure of lowest energy is considered, and sometimes all of them are neglected.

We have so far neglected to discuss the evaluation of the weighting factors λ connecting covalent and ionic (or several covalent) structures. Whenever we write such weighting factors we imply that they may be evaluated using the variational principle, just as outlined above for the MO treatment of LiH. Unfortunately, however, the evaluation is not very simple. The diagonal terms of the secular equation involve the energies associated with the various structures. Although these can often be evaluated mathematically, they can frequently be estimated roughly by use of chemical reasoning and intuition. In the present case, *e.g.*, the energy of H$^+$Li$^-$ may be derived by adding to the energies of Li and H the electron affinity of Li and subtracting the ionization potential of H; the energy of H$^-$Li$^+$ is similarly obtained by adding to the energies of Li and H the electron affinity of H and subtracting the ionization potential of Li. The off-diagonal elements, however, produce considerably more difficulty, since they are rather complex integrals involving all the electrons in the molecule. This fact alone makes even rough calculations by the valence bond method unattractive.

The last diatomic molecule to be considered in this discussion will be CO. Following the procedure used in N$_2$ the 2s and 2p$_z$ orbitals are hybridized into ϕ_1 and ϕ_2; but since ϕ_{1A} and ϕ_{1B} refer to C and O atoms, there is no need that both involve the same mixture of 2s and 2p character, and they undoubtedly do not. Just as in LiH, the molecular orbitals are formed from unequal amounts of the atomic orbitals of the two atoms.

In the case of carbon monoxide, since the atomic orbitals of the two atoms which form the sigma bond need not be equivalent as they must be in N$_2$, their relative energies must also be considered. It is well-known that two atomic orbitals, other things being equal, form the strongest bond the closer their energies. Inspection of the energy level diagram, Fig. 8b, shows that this criterion of similar energies in CO can only be met if ϕ_1 of carbon interacts with ϕ_2 of oxygen to form the sigma bond (the comparable energy level diagram of N_2 is shown in Fig. 8a) and have the form:

$$\sigma = \phi_{1C} + \lambda_\sigma \phi_{2O}$$

$$\sigma^* = \lambda_\sigma \phi_{1C} - \phi_{2O}$$

As a result, the lone pair of the carbon atom in $:C = O:$ will be in a ϕ_{2C} orbital and have largely p_z character and the lone pair of the oxygen atom will be in ϕ_{1O}, and have largely s character.

The bonding and antibonding π orbitals in CO resemble those in N_2, except for one major difference. Just as in the LiH σ orbitals, the contribu-

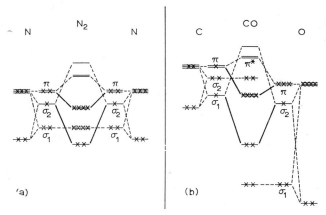

Fig. 8. The energy level diagrams of (a) N_2 and (b) CO.

tions of the Li and H orbitals were different and determined by a constant λ evaluated through solution of a secular equation, so, in the π orbitals of CO (as well as in the bonding and antibonding σ orbitals), such unequal mixing occurs. Thus the π orbitals of CO take the form

$$\pi = 2p\pi_C + \lambda_\pi 2p\pi_O$$

$$\pi^* = \lambda_\pi 2p\pi_C - 2p\pi_O$$

Since the energy of $2p\pi_O$ is lower than that of $2p\pi_C$, $\lambda_\pi > 1$, and the bonding π orbital is concentrated more on O (polarized toward O) and the antibonding orbital more on C. The π and π^* levels are shown in Fig. 8b.

The energy level diagram in Fig. 8b is of value in interpreting the chemical properties of CO, and their relation to those of N_2. The ionization potential of the carbon lone pair in ϕ_{2C} is quite low, making it a relatively basic lone pair. This relatively high energy level of the lone pair and the fact that it is largely p in character and thus strongly directional must be responsible for the many reactions in which carbon monoxide acts as a nucleophile. The ionization potential of the oxygen lone pair is relatively high and these electrons are thus unavailable chemically; further, the orbital has predominantly s character, and is accordingly not strongly directional. The lone pair electrons on the nitrogen atoms in N_2 are similar to those of the oxygen atom in CO. These facts explain why the reactivity of carbon monoxide resides on the carbon atom and is so much greater than that of nitrogen.

The energy level diagram of CO further serves to explain the reactivity of carbon monoxide toward nucleophilic reagents (*e.g.* OR⁻), as well as the unusual ability of carbon monoxide to accept back-donation from filled d orbitals in transition metal carbonyls. The lowest unoccupied orbital is a π^* orbital. Inspection of the MO diagram shows that this orbital receives a predominant contribution from the carbon pπ orbital and a much lesser contribution from the corresponding oxygen orbital. Accordingly nucleophilic attack occurs exclusively on carbon, and overlap of the π^* orbital with a π or d π orbital of a metal is favorable. The relatively low energy of the orbital contributes to its acceptor ability.

A VB treatment of CO is considerably more difficult. Just as in N_2, the number of structures that can be written is large, but now among the ionic structures we must further distinguish in each pair between the two possible polarizations. On the basis of chemical and physical evidence it appears that four main structures make an appreciable contribution to the ground state: two covalent structures both represented by $|C=O\rangle$ and two ionic structures, $|C^+ - \overline{O}|^-$ and $|C^-\equiv O|^+$.

4. Polyatomic molecules: methane, ethane and water

In the saturated molecule methane, CH_4, the carbon atom is attached to four groups and uses sp³ hybrid orbitals. Each of these orbitals has cylindrical symmetry around the bond axis and hence is a σ bond. Each bond is made by the overlap of the sp³ orbital of carbon with the 1s orbital of hydrogen. The formation of one such bond is shown in Fig. 9. Four such s–sp³ bonds are present in methane and form a tetrahedron with carbon at the center. There exists, of course, an antibonding σ^* orbital for each bond, but these are unoccupied and, because they lie at quite high energy levels, these are rarely of interest.

The problem of finding a molecular orbital description for polyatomic molecules is considerably more difficult than for diatomics. But by making full use of symmetry properties, the problem can be solved readily. In the treatment of methane, *e.g.*, the atomic orbitals of the hydrogen atoms are combined linearly with those of the central carbon atom to give functions of the form

$$\psi = c_1\phi_C + c_2 1s_A + c_3 1s_B + c_4 1s_C + c_5 1s_D$$

where $1s_A$, $1s_B$, $1s_C$ and $1s_D$ are the atomic orbitals of the hydrogen atoms A, B, C, D, and ϕ_C are atomic orbitals of carbon. But to insure that the charge distribution, ψ^2, represent the molecular symmetry, c_2, c_3, c_4 and c_5 must obey certain relations, $c_2 = \pm c_3 = \pm c_4 = \pm c_5$. Table I gives the various possible relations of the c_2 to c_5 and lists the corresponding atomic

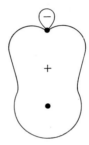

Fig. 9. One of the C—H bonding σ MO's of methane.

orbitals of the carbon atom having the same symmetry as the combination of hydrogen orbital (the so-called group orbital) with the c's given. Having performed this classification, it is readily possible to write down the various bonding molecular orbitals:

$$\psi_1(a_1) = 2s_C + \lambda_a \,(1s_A + 1s_B + 1s_C + 1s_D)$$
$$\psi_2(t) \;= 2p_x + \lambda_t \,(1s_A + 1s_B - 1s_C - 1s_D)$$
$$\psi_3(t) \;= 2p_y + \lambda_t \,(1s_A - 1s_B + 1s_C - 1s_D)$$
$$\psi_4(t) \;= 2p_z + \lambda_t \,(1s_A - 1s_B - 1s_C - 1s_D)$$

and the four antibonding orbitals in which $\psi_5(t) = \lambda_t 2p_x - (1s_A + 1s_B - 1s_C - 1s_D)$, etc. $\psi_2 - \psi_4$, and $\psi_5 - \psi_7$ are degenerate. The electronic structure of methane then is $\psi_1^2 \psi_2^2 \psi_3^2 \psi_4^2$. This description, unfortunately, is of little help to the chemist. It can, however, be readily transformed into one which represents chemical thinking. Assuming $\lambda_a = \lambda_t$ and adding $\psi_1 + \psi_2 + \psi_3 + \psi_4$, one obtains

$$\psi_A = 2s_C + 2p_x + 2p_y + 2p_z + 4\lambda 1s_A$$

TABLE I

RELATION OF THE RELATIVE SIGNS OF THE CONSTANTS c_2–c_5 AND THE
ASSOCIATED CARBON ORBITALS IN METHANE

Φ_c	c_2	c_3	c_4	c_5
s	+	+	+	+
p_x	+	+	−	−
p_y	+	−	−	+
p_z	+	−	−	+

Similarly, adding any two and subtracting the other two, one obtains

$$\psi_B = 2s_C + 2p_x + 2p_y - 2p_z + 4\lambda_{1S_B}$$

$$\psi_C = 2s_C - 2p_x + 2p_y - 2p_z + 4\lambda_{1S_C}$$

$$\psi_D = 2s_C - 2p_x - 2p_y + 2p_z + 4\lambda_{1S_D}$$

But the combinations $2s_C \pm 2p_x \pm 2p_1 \pm 2p_z$ are just the four hybrid sp^3 orbitals of carbons, and thus the molecular orbitals have the form

$$\psi_b = sp_C^3 + \lambda_{1S_H}$$

and there is just one such orbital for each $C-H$ bond. Such orbitals are called *localized* molecular orbitals, as distinguished from the *non-localized* molecular orbitals ψ_1 to ψ_4 above. The four orbitals ψ_b are bonding and a typical one is illustrated in Fig. 9. Application of the same operations to the four antibonding molecular orbitals ψ_5 to ψ_8 leads to the localized anti-bonding orbitals $\psi_a = \lambda sp_C^3 - 1_{S_H}$.

Now the assumption $\lambda_a = \lambda_t$ is not quite correct because α's for the 2s and 2p orbitals of carbon are not identical, because S and β for the inter-action of the 2s and 2p orbitals of carbon with hydrogen orbitals are not the same, and because the 1s orbitals of the hydrogen atoms overlap slightly and hence their interactions make some contribution to the secular equations. But the same operations can still be applied, leading to orbitals

$$\psi_b = sp_C^3 + (\lambda_a + 3\lambda_t) \, 1_{S_A} + (\lambda_a - \lambda_t) \, (1_{S_B} + 1_{S_C} + 1_{S_D})$$

where $\lambda_a + 3\lambda_t \gg \lambda_a - \lambda_t$. Again four such bonding orbitals and four corresponding antibonding orbitals are formed; following Lennard–Jones, they are called *equivalent* orbitals, since they are equivalent to each other except that they involve the hydrogen orbitals in different order. Since

References p. 112

$\lambda_a + 3\lambda_t \gg \lambda_a - \lambda_t$ the equivalent orbitals are very nearly, though not completely, localized in the various bonds.

A description of ethane in terms of non-localized molecular orbitals could be given in a manner similar to that for methane, but it will be sufficient from here on to discuss σ bonds in terms of localized molecular orbitals. In this approximation, the four sp³ hybrid orbitals of each carbon atom, pointing to the corners of a tetrahedron, overlap, respectively, another sp³ orbital of the other carbon atom, and the 1s orbitals of three hydrogen atoms. Thus the electronic structure and σ-bond skeleton is made up of six molecular orbitals of the form $\psi = 2p_C^3 + \lambda 1s_H$ and one molecular orbital $\psi = sp_{CA}^3 + sp_{CB}^3$.

The VB treatment of a polyatomic molecule, such as methane, is actually somewhat simpler, provided one is willing to accept a large number of simplifications and approximations. This is particularly true for compounds which can be described by a single covalent structure, such as the molecules with only single bonds or with single bonds and only isolated (non-conjugated) multiple bonds. The VB method for such molecules consists essentially of writing down the atomic wave functions for all atoms involved, hybridized when necessary, and then permitting exchange only of those pairs of electrons involved in forming any one bond. This is, of course, to some extent an *a posteriori* argument, since one first decides on the bonds present, but is not unreasonable for typical simple molecules in which the chemist has no problem of writing the bonds. Contributions from ionic structures are considered included. In this way, a single structure with its bonds represents a wave function (which, if written completely, would be almost hopelessly complicated) and describes the molecule. Such a structure would be

$$
\begin{array}{c}
\text{H} \\
| \\
\text{H--C--H} \\
| \\
\text{H}
\end{array}
$$

for methane, implying a C — H bond, *i.e.* a wave function as discussed for diatomic molecules for each of the four C — H bonds. This description is quite similar, mathematically, to the MO description given above in terms of localized bonds.

As a further example of the treatment of polyatomic molecules, we shall briefly discuss water. In MO theory, in its simplest form, the MO's must be of the type

$$\psi = c_1\phi_O + c_2 1s_A + c_3 1s_B$$

where ϕ_O represents a 2p atomic orbital of the oxygen atom, and $1s_A$ and

$1s_B$ represent the $1s$ orbitals of the two hydrogen atoms. Again, just as in methane, the equivalence of the two hydrogen atoms requires $c_2 = \pm c_3$. The combined symmetry of the two H atoms for $c_2 = c_3$ is the same as that of $2p_z$ of oxygen*, and for $c_2 = -c_3$ as that of $2p_x$ of oxygen. Hence the MO's are

$$\psi_1 = 2p_z(o) + \lambda_1(1s_A + 1s_B)$$

$$\psi_2 = 2p_x(o) + \lambda_2(1s_A - 1s_B)$$

Two atomic orbitals of oxygen, $2s$ and $2p_y$ remain unused and accommodate two electrons each, the so-called lone pairs. The other four electrons occupy ψ_1 and ψ_2. Addition and subtraction of ψ_1 and ψ_2 leads to two localized (if one assumes $\lambda_1 = \lambda_2$) or equivalent (if $\lambda_1 \neq \lambda_2$) orbitals; the oxygen contribution to the localized or equivalent orbitals is $2p_z \pm 2p_x$, which just represent two oxygen p orbitals, with direction of maximum intensity in two directions at right angles to each other. If one assumes, as one generally does, that the direction of a bond is along the axis along which the orbital has a maximum value, this picture predicts an HOH angle of 90°, instead of the known angle of about 104°. This discrepancy is overcome by allowing for hybridization of the $2s$ and $2p_z$ orbitals of oxygen. Both orbitals behave equally under all symmetry operations of the molecule, and hence may mix to form $\phi_1 = 2s - \lambda_0 2p_z$ and $\phi_2 = \lambda_0 2s + 2p_z$. Use of ϕ_2 in ψ_1 leads to a wider HOH angle, depending on the value assigned to λ_0 between 90 and 120°, and occupation of ϕ_1 by one of the lone pairs. Another considerable difference arises from the changed description. In the first description, both lone pairs of electrons are in orbitals having a center of gravity at the O atom, and hence the considerable dipole moment of water must arise from the polarity of the OH bonds only; i.e. from the deviations of λ_1 and λ_2 from unity. A quite considerable polarity must be postulated to explain the dipole moment. If, however, one lone pair of electrons is assigned to ϕ_1, this pair also makes a contribution to the dipole moment. The center of gravity of ϕ_1 lies a considerable distance from the O atom and hence the electron pair occupying this orbital gives rise to a considerable dipole moment, which is often called the lone pair dipole. Thus we may write the electronic structure of water as $\phi_1^2 \psi_1^2 \psi_2^2 2p_y^2$.

5. Comparison of MO and VB theories

At this point it may be profitable to contrast molecular orbital and valence bond theories. The first of these considers the molecule as a whole. It starts by constructing one-electron wave functions extending over the entire

---

* We chose the symmetry axis of the molecule as the z axis, and the plane of the molecule as the xz plane.

molecule. For approximate and qualitative purposes, it stops there. For more extensive calculations, it then generates the many-electron function of the molecule by multiplying together the appropriate one-electron functions, together with spin functions, allowing for equivalence of electrons, and, finally, taking care of configuration interaction.

Complete valence bond theory consists of substantially the same steps, but in a different order, and hence, unless both are carried to completion, may lead to different answers. First, the many-electron atomic wave functions are written down, and multiplied together to give molecular wave functions called structures. Then allowance is made for indistinguishability of the electrons (exchange) and finally the overall wave function is a weighted sum of all structure functions. The simplifications usually made in VB theory do not represent a truncation in the number of these steps undertaken, but rather a restriction in the number of structures considered.

Theoretically neither theory can be said to be superior when not carried through completely. MO theory tends to overemphasize ionic structures, VB theory to underemphasize them. For this reason, when both theories in crude approximation give the same result, one may be quite confident of its validity; when they diverge one may assume that the truth lies somewhere in between, but one cannot say where.

Concerning their utility, both methods have advantages and disadvantages. The molecular orbital method is particularly well-suited to any consideration relating to the property of single electrons, since it treats every electron separately. Thus a discussion of molecular spectra and of ionization potentials is easiest done in terms of MO theory. Also approximate calculations are fairly simple in this theory. On the other hand, it is not always easy to get a qualitative physical interpretation of the results of MO theory.

Valence bond theory lends itself particularly well to the description of compounds with only single bonds, or isolated double bonds, and compounds in which all electrons are paired. Excited states are difficult to obtain. It has the tremendous advantage of being largely non-mathematical and dealing with chemical structures, which are readily visualized by the practising chemist. This at the same time can be a disadvantage because the real nature of the interaction of the structures may be obscured by their apparent connection with the physical concepts of the chemist. For any approximate quantitative work, VB theory requires a knowledge of the energy of each structure, a requirement which may be met on the basis of general chemical knowledge and intuition, but may easily lead to abuse and unwarranted speculation.

6. The geometry of molecules

Since much information is available on the geometry of molecules in their ground states (*cf.* Chapter III) it is tempting to inquire to what extent the theoretical description is capable of predicting these geometric features. Ideally, one would like to perform calculation for the total energy of molecules without any empirical information, and minimize the energy with respect to the various geometrical parameters (bond distances and angles) to obtain theoretical values for these parameters, which could then be compared with experimentally determined values. Unfortunately, such calculations are prohibitively complicated: it is almost never possible to derive an analytical expression for the energy in terms of these parameters, and the only procedure generally available is to make calculations for a variety of values and then construct an energy surface. However, even this procedure is usually prohibitive except for diatomic molecules, largely because the number of parameters is extremely large, even for relatively simple molecules. Thus a triatomic non-linear molecule involves three such parameters (two bond lengths and one angle) and methane involves nine.

Fortunately, however, certain qualitative predictions about major geometric features can readily be deduced from theory, and generally agree with experimental fact.

Thus the knowledge that the electronic structure of oxygen and sulfur in the ground state is s^2p^4 immediately suggests that two bonds formed by these atoms in such compounds as R_2O and R_2S should be formed by p electrons in orbitals at right angles, and hence not be linear, but nearly at right angles. This argument is found to be correct for sulfur; in oxygen, hybridization and repulsion of the bonded groups opens the angle to about 105°, or 15° above a right angle. In mercury, with electronic structure s^2, which, for formation of 2 bonds requires that one electron be promoted to give the configuration sp, the same type of argument predicts a linear structure with sp hybridization in agreement with the experimental findings.

The angle between the two HOO planes in HOOH is another example of simple qualitative theoretical arguments that give information about ground state geometry. Each single bond in this molecule may be considered as being formed from pure p orbitals of the oxygen atoms*. Then the two lone pairs of each oxygen atom must be assigned to an s and a p orbital. Owing to the spherical symmetry around the oxygen nuclei of the s orbitals, the s electrons do not affect the geometry of the molecule. If the molecule had a planar structure, the p orbitals holding the four electrons, or two lone pairs would be able to interact, leading to a bonding and an anti-bonding molecular orbital. These would be occupied by two electrons each. It is, however, a result of the quantum-mechanical treatment that, when two atomic orbitals combine to form a bonding and an anti-bonding molec-

---

* Correctly, allowance for hybridization should be made, but the overall argument would not be affected thereby.

ular orbital, the stabilization by the bonding orbital is always less than the destabilization by the anti-bonding one*. Thus the total energy of the planar structure must be higher than that of a structure in which the lone pair p electrons do not interact, a condition which is realized in a structure in which the two HOO planes are at right angles. Consequently, it may be predicted from theory that H_2O_2 should have a structure with these planes at an angle close to 90°. Experiment indicates the actual angle to be 94° in solid H_2O_2.

Another example of the prediction of the geometry of a molecule based on a consideration of the orbitals involved is the case of allene, $CH_2=C=CH_2$. The middle carbon of this molecule uses sp-hybrid orbitals, and hence the three carbon atoms must lie in a straight line. The remaining two $p\pi$ orbitals on the middle carbon atom are, of course, at right angles to each other and may arbitrarily be designated the p_y and p_z orbitals. These orbitals will overlap the p_y and p_z orbitals of carbons 1 and 3, respectively, which have similar symmetry. In order to form the two π bonds at right angles to each other, the terminal CH_2 groups must be forced into positions at right angles to each other. The alternate possibility of a completely planar structure in which one MO overlaps the three carbon atoms and two electrons remain in an atomic orbital would obviously lead to a structure of higher energy.

These three examples illustrate how qualitative theory may be applied in making important prediction about the geometry of ground states of atoms. Many further cases have been treated, *e.g.*, in a long series of papers by Walsh, and by many other authors.

7. Unsaturated compounds

In the preceding section we have discussed the MO and VB treatment of saturated compounds. We have found that an adequate treatment by either theory, even with many approximations, is highly complicated and tedious. By using the localized orbitals of MO theory, or by using the crude structures, already implicitly containing ionic character, we found that molecules for which we can readily write down structures with specific bonds could be adequately described. All the bonds so treated were formed from orbitals of the atoms which were cylindrically symmetrical around the bond axis, and all such bonds are called σ bonds in a crude analogy with the symmetry classification of diatomic (or more generally linear) systems.

In the compounds which chemists call unsaturated and conjugated we

---

* This statement does not hold for the lowest approximation, the LCAO method with neglect of overlap integrals, in which the two quantities are identical. Inclusion of overlap, however, leads to factors in the first of them $1/\sqrt{(1+S)}$, $1/\sqrt{(1-S)}$ in the second, and thus to the stated inequality.

encounter, besides σ bonds, bonds made up of orbitals having a nodal plane which includes the bond axis; in a crude analogy with the symmetry classification of linear systems, chemists have become accustomed to call such orbitals π orbitals, and the bonds they form π bonds. The electrons occupying π orbitals, the π electrons, are generally less tightly bound than σ electrons, and consequently are responsible for much of the physical and chemical behavior of the molecules. The σ bonds determine, to a large extent, the geometry of the molecule, but the π electrons determine most spectroscopic properties, chemical reactivity, ionization potential, etc. For this reason it is profitable to consider π electrons in some detail; the σ electrons are used to obtain gross information about geometry, but are, thereafter, neglected.

The simplest unsaturated molecule is ethylene. Each carbon atom is attached to three other atoms, and hence carbon utilizes three σ orbitals; these are sp^2 hybrid orbitals*, and are directed at about 120° from each other. Each carbon atom forms three σ bonds, and these are in a plane. The σ bonds thus define a skeleton of six atoms in two planes, one about each carbon atom, with bond angles in the neighborhood of 120°.

In formation of this σ bond skeleton, one p orbital of each carbon atom remains unused, and each of these p orbitals has π character with respect to the carbon atom to which it belongs. The interaction of these π orbitals leads to formation of the second bond of the double bond, the π bond. This bond formation is completely analogous to the formation of the bond in H_2 (except that the orbitals involved are 2pπ orbitals) or to formation of one of the two π orbitals in N_2. The development up to this point is identical in MO or VB theory. The bonding MO π_u of ethylene has the exact form of the MO ψ_4 (or ψ_5) of N_2 (cf. Fig. 6d, p. 55), and the corresponding antibonding MO π_g the form of ψ_6 (or ψ_7) (cf. Fig. 6e, p. 55). The energetics are also qualitatively similar as in H_2, and Fig. 3a or 3b (p. 49) might equally well be used to represent the energy level diagram of the π electrons of ethylene, if the atomic orbitals were labelled 2pπ, and the MO's (from the bottom up) π_u and π_g*. The energy scale, of course, would be different since β for the interaction of the two 2pπ orbitals of carbon is considerably smaller than it is for its 1s orbitals of hydrogen.

The formation of the π orbital further affects the geometry. The σ bond skeleton defined *two* planes, one about each carbon atom. But the overlap, and hence β, between the two carbon atoms is largest if these two planes coincide, and hence the π electrons constrain the molecule to planarity.

---

* It is usually assumed that all three σ bonding orbitals are equal mixtures of s and p orbitals. This is probably not so. The HCH angle in ethylene is about 116°, suggesting that the orbitals forming the bonds with hydrogen have more p character than the orbital forming the bond with the other carbon atom.

References p. 112

Also, the distance between two carbon atoms having four σ bonds each is 1.54 Å, and it has been estimated that with just a σ bond between two sp^2 hybridized carbon atoms, the distance would be 1.48 Å. In ethylene, the distance is 1.34 Å, and this shortening by 0.14 Å is ascribed to additional shortening by the π electrons, *i.e.* due to the π bond.

The π orbitals do not overlap as effectively as σ orbitals, and hence the energy contributed by the π electrons is smaller; a carbon–carbon single bond has an energy of about 80 kcal/mole, a double bond, about 140 kcal/ mole. This difference accounts for the greater chemical reactivity of double bonds, since the π bond is more readily broken.

Another treatment, which at first sight appears considerably at variance with the above one, has occasionally been given. Except for details of hybridization, which are not necessarily completely defined in either treatment, however, the two are equivalent. The new treatment assumes each carbon atom substantially (although not necessarily exactly) tetrahedrally hybridized. The CH bonds are formed from two of the tetrahedral hybrid orbitals of each carbon atom, and the other two tetrahedral hybrids interact with the corresponding ones of the other carbon atom. In other words, if a single bond is described as a pair of tetrahedra (one on each C atom) sharing one apex, a double bond is visualized as the two tetrahedra sharing an edge. It can, however, be readily shown that simple linear transformation (*i.e.* addition and subtraction) of the localized $C-C$ σ-bonding and π-bonding MO's leads to two localized MO's having just the geometry described by sharing of one edge of two tetrahedra. Such localized orbitals have sometimes been called bent bonds. In VB theory, also, the two descriptions are analogous, depending only on the particular set of atomic orbitals used in the description of the structures. Thus, unless one wants to be dogmatic about the hybridization, the two treatments are equivalent; and it now appears clear that the hybridization must lie somewhere between the extremes suggested by the two models since the CH bonds appear to be formed from carbon orbitals somewhere between sp^2 and sp^3[*].

In acetylene, each carbon atom is bonded to two other atoms, and hence may be assumed to use sp hybridized orbitals, and consequently the molecule should be linear. Two p orbitals, both having π character, remain unused on each carbon atom, and form two π bonds. These are completely analogous to the two π bonds (described by ψ_4 and ψ_5) in nitrogen, and do not require any further description. The second π bond in this compound leads to an additional shortening of the $C-C$ bond by a further 0.14 Å to 1.20 Å.

In acetylene, also, an alternate model with substantially localized bonds is possible, and best visualized by the sharing of faces of the two tetrahedra

---

[*] *cf.* footnote p. 71.

of the carbon atoms. Again, the two models suggest rather different hybridization (one sp, the other sp³); the actual hybridization is difficult to determine, but probably lies again somewhere between these extremes.

Detailed VB descriptions of ethylene and acetylene lead, of course, to the complications similar to those encountered with O_2 and N_2. If, in a very simplified manner, the σ bonds are neglected, one obtains for ethylene again a description greatly resembling that of H_2, with a two-term covalent structure and a two term ionic structure in resonance.

8. Conjugated and aromatic molecules

These MO and VB descriptions for ethylene and acetylene can be immediately generalized to any other *isolated* double or triple bond; the only difference is that one or more of the CH single (σ) bonds are replaced by CC bonds. The situation becomes, however, considerably more complicated when several double (or triple) bonds are adjacent to one another. Thus, *e.g.*, in butadiene

$$\overset{1}{CH_2}=\overset{2}{CH}—\overset{3}{CH}=\overset{4}{CH_2}$$

the overlap of the $2p\pi$ orbitals of atoms 1 and 2 and of atoms 3 and 4 forms the double bonds shown in the structure. But overlap of the $2p\pi$ orbitals of atoms 2 and 3 is about as efficient, and consequently leads to considerable interaction between the two bonds shown as double in the structure. The phenomenon is, of course, general for any pair or group of multiple (double or triple) bonds adjacent to one another.

Molecules in which this situation is encountered are called conjugated and are of tremendous importance, and much of the application of quantum mechanics to chemistry has been concerned with this class of compounds. The simplest example is butadiene, which we shall now treat in some detail.

(a) Butadiene

Each carbon atom in butadiene is attached to three other groups and hence approximately sp² hybrid orbitals of carbon are used. The σ orbitals are formed into localized molecular orbitals and then into a σ bond skeleton which determines the geometry of the molecule but which is of little further chemical interest. There remain four electrons, one from each carbon atom, each of which is in a $p\pi$ orbital. The four $p\pi$ orbitals combine to form four molecular orbitals which are delocalized over all four carbon atoms.

The wave function of each π electron is the weighted sum of the four $2p\pi$ orbitals of the four carbon atoms. $\psi = c_1\phi_1 + c_2\phi_2 + c_3\phi_3 + c_4\phi_4$. Here, however, symmetry alone is insufficient to determine the c's, and recourse must be had to the secular equations. These are readily set up:

$$c_1 (\alpha_1 - \varepsilon) + c_2 H_{12} + c_3 H_{13} + c_4 H_{14} = 0$$

$$c_1 H_{12} + c_2 (\alpha_2 - \varepsilon) + c_3 H_{23} + c_4 H_{24} = 0$$

$$c_1 H_{13} + c_2 H_{23} + c_3 (\alpha_3 - \varepsilon) + c_4 H_{24} = 0$$

$$c_1 H_{14} + c_2 H_{24} + c_3 H_{34} + c_4 (\alpha_4 - \varepsilon) = 0$$

This already assumes neglect of overlap integrals. Now, since all atoms are carbon atoms, $\alpha_1 = \alpha_2 = \alpha_3 = \alpha_4$, and by symmetry $c_1 = \pm c_4$, $c_2 = \pm c_3$. Also, it is customary to neglect H_{AB} if A and B are not neighboring atoms and to assume the other H_{AB} equal, implying equal bond lengths. Making these substitutions one obtains for $c_1 = + c_4$, $c_2 = + c_3$, *i.e.* for the symmetric wave functions

$$c_1 (\alpha - \varepsilon) + c_2 \beta = 0$$

$$c_1 \beta + c_2 (\alpha - \varepsilon + \beta) = 0$$

and hence the determinant

$$\begin{vmatrix} \alpha - \varepsilon & \beta \\ \beta & \alpha - \varepsilon + \beta \end{vmatrix} = 0$$

which can be expanded into the quadratic equation

$$(\alpha - \varepsilon)(\alpha - \varepsilon + \beta) - \beta^2 = 0$$

$$\varepsilon^2 - (2\alpha + \beta)\varepsilon + \alpha^2 + \alpha\beta - \beta^2 = 0$$

This equation in turn leads to the solutions:

$$\varepsilon = \tfrac{1}{2} \left[(2\alpha + \beta) \pm \sqrt{(2\alpha + \beta)^2 - 4(\alpha^2 + \alpha\beta - \beta^2)} \right]$$

$$= \alpha - \tfrac{1}{2}\beta(1 \pm \sqrt{5})$$

Substituting these values back into eqn. (12) gives

for ψ_1
$$- \tfrac{1}{2}(1 + \sqrt{5}) \beta c_1 + \beta c_2 = 0$$
$$c_1/c_2 = \tfrac{1}{2}(1 + \sqrt{5})$$

for ψ_3
$$- \tfrac{1}{2}(1 - \sqrt{5}) \beta c_1 + \beta c_2 = 0$$
$$c_1/c_2 = \tfrac{1}{2}(1 - \sqrt{5})$$

Similarly, for the antisymmetric functions,

$$c_1 = -c_4; \quad c_2 = -c_3$$

$$c_1(\alpha - \varepsilon) + c_2\beta = 0$$

$$c_1\beta + c_2(\alpha - \varepsilon - \beta) = 0$$

$$(\alpha - \beta)(\alpha - \varepsilon - \beta) - \beta^2 = 0$$

$$\varepsilon^2 - (2\alpha - \beta)\varepsilon + \alpha^2 - \alpha\beta - \beta^2 = 0$$

$$\varepsilon = \tfrac{1}{2}\left[2\alpha - \beta + \sqrt{(2\alpha - \beta)^2 - 4(\alpha^2 - \alpha\beta + \beta^2)}\right]$$

$$\varepsilon = \alpha - \tfrac{1}{2}\beta(1 \pm \sqrt{5})$$

for ψ_2 $c_1/c_2 = \tfrac{1}{2}(1 - \sqrt{5})$

for ψ_4 $c_1/c_2 = -\tfrac{1}{2}(1 + \sqrt{5})$

Finally, normalization is achieved by assigning absolute values to the c's such that

$$c_1^2 + c_2^2 + c_3^2 + c_4^2 = 1$$

and the molecular orbitals and their energies are given by:

$$\psi_1 = 0.373(\phi_1 + \phi_4) + 0.602(\phi_2 + \phi_3); \; \varepsilon_1 = \alpha + 1.618\,\beta$$

$$\psi_2 = 0.602(\phi_1 - \phi_4) + 0.373(\phi_2 - \phi_3); \; \varepsilon_2 = \alpha + 0.618\,\beta$$

$$\psi_3 = 0.602(\phi_1 + \phi_4) - 0.373(\phi_2 + \phi_3); \; \varepsilon_3 = \alpha - 0.618\,\beta$$

$$\psi_4 = 0.373(\phi_1 - \phi_4) - 0.602(\phi_2 - \phi_3); \; \varepsilon_4 = \alpha - 1.618\,\beta$$

In deriving the expression for the wave functions of each of these orbitals it is important to note that carbon atoms 1 and 4, and 2 and 3 in butadiene are equivalent. The four MO's are thus combinations in which the functions associated with carbons 1 and 4 are either added or subtracted and this sum (or difference) is added to or subtracted from the sum (or difference) of the c_2, c_3 combination. The four wave functions, neglecting all numerical coefficients, are then of the form:

$$\psi_1 = (\phi_1 + \phi_4) + (\phi_2 + \phi_3) = (\phi_1 + \phi_2 + \phi_3 + \phi_4)$$

$$\psi_2 = (\phi_1 - \phi_4) + (\phi_2 - \phi_3) = (\phi_1 + \phi_2) - (\phi_3 + \phi_4)$$

$$\psi_3 = (\phi_1 + \phi_4) - (\phi_2 + \phi_3) = \phi_1 - (\phi_2 + \phi_3) + \phi_4$$

$$\psi_4 = (\phi_1 - \phi_4) - (\phi_2 - \phi_3) = (\phi_1) - (\phi_2) + (\phi_3) - (\phi_4)$$

References p. 112

The π MO's are shown schematically in Fig. 10. It is apparent from this figure that ψ_1 and ψ_3 are gerade (g) and ψ_2 and ψ_4 ungerade (u). Also, ψ_1 does not change sign, or has no nodes between any two atoms; hence the

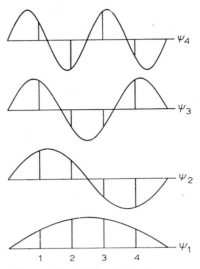

Fig. 10. The MO's of butadiene.

charge density is relatively high between each pair of atoms, and an electron occupying this orbital tends to hold all the nuclei together. Accordingly, ψ_1 is a bonding orbital and makes a bonding contribution for each pair of neighboring atoms. ψ_2 similarly has no nodal planes between the two pairs of outside atoms (1 and 2, 3 and 4), and hence is bonding with respect to these; however, ψ_2 has a nodal plane between the two middle atoms, and hence is antibonding with respect to them. Since, ψ_2 makes two bonding contributions and one antibonding contribution, it has an overall bonding character, although much less so than ψ_1. Since both ψ_1 and ψ_2 are doubly occupied in the ground state, and both contribute bonding to the 1–2 and 3–4 bonds, these bonds are considerably shorter and stronger than a single bond; such bonds are represented as double bonds in the principal resonance structures, and are called essential double bonds. The bonding contribution to the 2–3 bond of two electrons in ψ_1 is, however, largely cancelled by the antibonding contribution of the two electrons in ψ_2 and hence the 2–3 bond is only very slightly shorter and slightly stronger than a single sp^2–sp^2 bond; such bonds are represented as single bonds in the principal resonance structure, and are called *essential single bonds*. Fig. 10 shows that ψ_3 has nodal planes between atoms 1 and 2, and between 3 and 4, and hence makes two antibonding and one bonding contribution and is weakly antibonding, whereas ψ_4 makes three antibonding contributions, and is accordingly strongly antibonding. The bonding character of ψ_1 and ψ_2 can alternately be obtained from the energy of the atomic orbitals given above. Since α is the energy of the free atomic orbitals, and β is a negative quantity, ψ_1 and ψ_2 have energies lower than the atomic orbitals from which they are formed, but this lowering is greater for ψ_1 than ψ_2. The same argument shows ψ_3 and ψ_4 to be antibonding, ψ_3 less so than ψ_4. The energy level diagram for the butadiene system is shown in Fig. 11. It should be noted that the molecular orbitals occur in pairs having energies equally spaced on either side of the energy of the free atomic orbitals (if the overlap integral S is

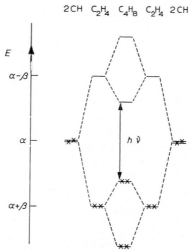

Fig. 11. The energy levels of butadiene.

neglected). This situation is general for all acyclic hydrocarbon molecules, and all cyclic ones not having an odd-membered ring, $i.e.$ all so-called *alternant hydrocarbons*, and is part of the Coulson–Rushbrooke theorem.

The electronic structure of the ground state of butadiene is then given (setting π_u for ψ_1, π_g for ψ_2, π_u^* for ψ_3 and π_g^* for ψ_4) as $\pi_u^2 \pi_g^2$ and for excited states one can write $\pi_u^2 \pi_g \pi_u^*$, $\pi_u^2 \pi_g \pi_g^*$, $\pi_u \pi_g^2 \pi_u^*$, etc.

The total energy $\mathscr{E}$ of the π electrons is of considerable interest. It is defined as the sum of the energies of all the π electrons, and may be simply written as

$$\mathscr{E} = \sum_j n_j \varepsilon_j$$
$$= 2(\alpha + 1.618\beta) + 2(\alpha + 0.618\beta) = 4\alpha + 4.472\beta$$

References p. 112

where n_j is the *occupation number* (2, 0, or occasionally 1) indicating the number of electrons occupying the MO ψ_j which has associated with it the energy ε_j. This total energy is used in the calculation of resonance energies, which will be discussed below in connection with the VB (resonance) treatment, and with certain reactivity calculations. It also may be used, other things being equal, to compare energies of closely related isomers or conformations.

The MO method described here permits the definition of several parameters which aid in the description of the molecule, and particularly of its reactivity. The first of these is the charge density, q. By definition, the square of a wave function at a point, represents the density of electrons at that point. Then, if one integrates the square of the wave function in the neighborhood of an atom, the integral will represent approximately the charge density at that atom. Integrating the square of a LCAO MO of the form $\psi = c_1\phi_1 + c_2\phi_2 + c_3\phi_3 + c_4\phi_4$ near electron 1 gives

$$\int_1 \psi^2 \, d\tau = \int_1 (c_1\phi_1 + c_2\phi_2 + c_3\phi_3 + c_4\phi_4)^2 \, d\tau$$

The integrand can be expanded into 16 terms, four of which are of the form $c_i\phi_i^2$, and 12 of the form $c_ic_j\phi_i\phi_j$. Since in the entire treatment it is assumed that the overlap integral $S_{ij} = \int \phi_i\phi_j \, d\tau$ is negligible, the latter 12 terms may be neglected. Of the first four, only one, $c_1^2\phi_1^2$, makes an appreciable contribution, since the other ϕ_1, ϕ_2, ϕ_3 and ϕ_4 are quite small near atom 1. Also, since ϕ_1 is small except near atom 1, the integral around atom 1, $\int_1 \phi_1^2 \, d\tau$ may be replaced by the integral over all space, $\int \phi_1^2 \, d\tau$, which is equal to unity since ϕ's are assumed to be normalized. Consequently

$$\int_1 \psi^2 \, d\tau \approx c_1^2$$

This is the contribution of one electron in the MO ψ to the density of charge at atom 1. To obtain the total charge near this atom, one must then sum over all electrons:

$$q_r = \sum_j n_j c_{jr}^2$$

where q_r is the density at the r th atom, n_j is the occupation number defined above, and c_{jr} is the coefficient with which the AO ϕ_r enters into the MO ψ_j. Evaluating the q's for butadiene one finds

$$q_1 = 2(0.373)^2 + 2(0.602)^2 = 1$$
$$q_2 = 2(0.602)^2 + 2(0.373)^2 = 1$$

and similarly, but obviously because of symmetry, $q_3 = q_4 = 1$. This result is contained in the Coulson–Rushbrooke theorem, and is perfectly general for any alternant hydrocarbon, *i.e.* any compound in which there is no ring with an odd number of atoms, in which each atom contributes just one π electron, and in which all Coulomb integrals α are equal.

The charge densities q can be used in a number of ways. They permit calculation of the contribution the π electrons make to a dipole moment, and the equality of all q in alternant hydrocarbons is consistent with the finding that such compounds have no dipole moment, or only a very small one.

When unequal, the q also give some indication concerning the position at which a reagent is likely to attack a molecule. Thus an electrophilic reagent is likely to attack at a position of high charge density, a nucleophile at a position of low q. This simple picture has been widely used to interpret reactivity, particularly aromatic substitution.

A second commonly used parameter is the π bond order p. This is defined in a manner quite similar to q:

$$p_{rs} = 1 + \sum_{j} n_j c_{jr} c_{js}$$

where p_{rs} is the order of the bond between r and s, and the additive term of unity reflects the σ bond. For butadiene

$$p_{12} = 1 + 2 \times 0.373 \times 0.602 + 2 \times 0.602 \times 0.373 = 1.889$$

$$p_{23} = 1 + 2 \times (0.602)^2 - 2 \times (0.373)^2 \qquad\qquad = 1.446$$

and $p_{34} = 1.889$. As expected, and derived qualitatively above, the 1–2 bond has a higher bond order than the 2–3 bond. A pure double bond, as in ethylene, has a bond order of 2. Bond orders are defined only for pairs of atoms connected by a σ bond; thus a bond order p_{13} has no meaning.

The bond order is the ideal index to correlate the degree of double bond character. Thus, bond lengths and force constants obtained from infrared or Raman spectra, are well correlated with bond orders. Also, typical double bond reactivity is directly correlated with p.

A third parameter readily obtained from the simple MO treatment is the free valence F. If it is assumed that each carbon atom has a possible maximum valence, *i.e.* a maximum number of bonds it can form, the free valence is defined as this maximum minus the number of bonds actually formed, which in turn is expressed as the sum of all the bond orders of bonds originating at the atom:

$$F_r = F_{max} - \sum_{s} p_{rs}$$

where the summation extends over all atoms bonded to atom r; p_{rs} is 1 for single bonds; F_{max} for carbon atoms (excluding those forming triple bonds) is 4.732[*]. Thus, for butadiene,

$$F_1 = 4.732 - 2 \times 1 + 1.889 = 0.843$$
$$F_2 = 4.732 - 1 + 1.889 + 1.446 = 0.397$$

with F_3 and F_4 again given by symmetry. The free valence has particular usefulness in compounds in which all positions have equal charge density, or in consideration of free radical reactions, in which positions of largest F generally show the greatest reactivity.

The three quantities p, q and F are related to properties of the *stable* molecule, hence are called static properties, and when used as indices of chemical reactivity they ignore the dynamic aspects of reaction process. To arrive at a more adequate picture, let us consider the reaction between butadiene and X^- to give an unstable intermediate, either

$$CH_2 = CH — CH — CH_2X^- \text{ (I)} \quad \text{or} \quad CH_2 = CH — CHX — CH_2^- \text{ (II)}$$

Consideration of the charge density would indicate that both intermediates are equally likely, but the free valence would certainly favor the former. Let us, however, look at the transition states for their formation. These transition states must represent a situation somewhere between the initial molecule and the intermediate. Since the latter is quite unstable and accordingly has a relatively high energy, the transition state will considerably resemble this intermediate, and as an approximation, we shall assume the two to be identical. Now, intermediates I and II have the same number and types of σ bonds, and hence the energy due to the σ bonds may well be considered the same in both. The energy of the π electrons, however, is not. In I, atoms 1, 2 and 3 (if X is attached to 4) bear π-orbitals, atom 4, being attached to four groups by single bonds, has no π orbital. Treatment of the π orbitals, via the secular equation, just as for butadiene, gives, as the reader may verify

$$\psi_1 = \tfrac{1}{2}(\phi_1 + \phi_3) + \sqrt{\tfrac{1}{2}}\phi_2 \qquad \varepsilon_1 = \alpha + \sqrt{2}\beta$$
$$\psi_2 = \tfrac{1}{2}(\phi_1 - \phi_3) \qquad \varepsilon_2 = \alpha$$
$$\psi_3 = \tfrac{1}{2}(\phi_1 + \phi_3) - \sqrt{\tfrac{1}{2}}\phi_2 \qquad \varepsilon_3 = \alpha - \sqrt{2}\beta$$

---

[*] Although the numerical value chosen for F_{max} is unimportant because the value of F lies only in permitting the observation of inequalities, *i.e.* in which compound, or for which position it is largest, the numerical value of 4.732 can be shown to be the largest value F can possibly attain.

In II, however, atom 3 is the one bearing four groups, and atoms 1, 2 and 4 have π orbitals; but atoms 2 and 4 are not adjacent, and hence do not interact. Thus atoms 1 and 2 involve an isolated double bond, with $\psi = (\phi_1 \pm \phi_2)/\sqrt{2}$, $\varepsilon = \alpha + \beta$, and the orbital on atom 4 is an isolated $2p\pi$ orbital with energy α. In the case under consideration, X^- bears a negative charge, *i.e.* comes in with two electrons, so that the 4π electrons of butadiene now must be distributed over the remaining three atoms.

The energies $\mathscr{E}_I$ and $\mathscr{E}_{II}$ of intermediates I and II are hence given by

$$\mathscr{E}_I = 2 \times (\alpha + \sqrt{2}\,\beta) + 2\alpha = 4\,\alpha + 2\,\sqrt{2}\,\beta$$

$$\mathscr{E}_{II} = 2 \times (\alpha + \beta) + 2\alpha = 4\alpha + 2\beta$$

The comparison is made easiest by defining a new quantity, the *localization energy L*, which is the π electron energy $\mathscr{E}$ of butadiene minus the π electron energy of the "transition state", *i.e.* by our approximation of I or II, respectively,

$$L_I = 4\alpha + 4.472\beta - 4\alpha - 2.828\beta = 1.644\beta$$

$$L_{II} = 4\alpha + 4.472\beta - 4\alpha - 2\beta = 2.472\beta$$

Consequently, the energy required to form the intermediate II (or the transition state leading to II) is greater than the corresponding quantity for I by almost 0.8 β. Since β is of the order of 20 kcal/mole, this amounts to a difference of some 16 kcal/mole. Thus, the prediction by the present dynamic method is in agreement with that made from the free valence. This agreement is very common, but by no means universal.

The method just outlined, the so-called *dynamic* or *localization method*, is equally applicable to electrophilic or radical substitution. In the case just treated, the attacking reagent X^- came in with its pair of electrons, hence was seeking out a nucleus, and is called nucleophilic. If the attacking reagent is X^+, its new bond with C is formed using a pair of the π electrons, leaving only two π electrons available. Then the localization energies are

$$L_I = 4\alpha + 4.472\beta - 2\alpha - 2.828\beta = 2\alpha + 1.644\beta$$

$$L_{II} = 4\alpha + 4.472\beta - 2\alpha - 2\beta = 2\alpha + 2.472\beta$$

Surprisingly the difference in localization energies is the same as before. This happens, because in both I and II the last two π electrons occupy orbitals of energy α, *i.e.* orbitals which have the same energy as free $2p\pi$ orbitals; these are commonly called non-bonding orbitals. This situation is general in the case of alternant hydrocarbons.

References p. 112

In a radical reaction $X \cdot$ carries a single electron, which pairs with one of the π electrons, to form a new σ bond, leaving three π electrons in I and II, and the difference in localization energy again is the same.

The picture of localization energies can be extended to double bond reactions. Consider the addition of some reagent X_2 to butadiene. Three adducts are conceivable:

$$XCH_2\!\!-\!\!CH\!=\!CH\!\!-\!\!CH_2X \quad XCH_2\!\!-\!\!CHX\!\!-\!\!CH\!=\!CH_2 \quad \text{and} \quad XCH_2\!\!-\!\!CH\!\!-\!\!CHX\!\!-\!\!CH_2$$

$$\text{(III)} \qquad\qquad\qquad \text{(IV)} \qquad\qquad\qquad\qquad \text{(V)}$$

Every chemist knows that addition to give V does not occur, but we will consider this case also. Localization energies are readily calculated for the three processes. In III and IV, the remaining π-electrons form an isolated double bond, hence the localization energies are the same,

$$L_{\text{III,IV}} = 4\alpha + 4.472\beta - 2\alpha - 2\beta = 2\alpha + 2.472\beta$$

In V, however, the π electrons on atoms 2 and 4 are isolated from one another, and hence each have energy α:

$$L_{\text{V}} = 4\alpha + 4.472\beta - 2\alpha = 2\alpha + 4.472\beta$$

It is immediately obvious that 1,3-addition is energetically extremely unfavorable (by 2β, $i.e.$ about 40 kcal/mole). The localization energy for 1,2- and 1,4-addition is the same, and any difference in reactivity must depend on effects neglected in this approximate treatment. However, in larger conjugated systems, such accidental equality is not likely to occur. More complex cases will be discussed below.

Application of the VB method to conjugated systems similarly involves long series of approximations. Just as in MO theory, the σ bond skeleton is considered to determine the gross geometry, but is otherwise neglected, and attention is focused entirely on the π electrons.

A complete valence bond treatment of the four π electrons of butadiene would then require the various possible atomic wave functions, and multiplying these together. One such function might be

$$\boldsymbol{\Psi} = \phi_1(1)\alpha(1)\phi_2(2)\beta(2)\phi_3(3)\alpha(3)\phi_4(4)\beta(4)$$

By allowing now for exchange between electrons 1 and 2, and electrons 3 and 4 one obtains a rather complicated wave function which may be said to represent a structure with double bonds between atoms 1 and 2, and between atoms 3 and 4. Similarly, terms arising from other exchanges and other assignment of electrons give rise to other structures. In the approximate application of the VB theory to conjugated systems one generally avoids writing down all these wave functions explicitly. Instead of writing the wave function of the complete molecule as a linear combination of the wave functions of these structures, we say that the molecule is a resonance hybrid of the various structures. In this form, VB theory is reduced to what is commonly called resonance theory. Since we have thus eliminated essentially all mathematics, we must, however, introduce a few restrictions. These arise out of the fact that the weighting factors in the linear combination of the wave functions of structures depend on the secular equations. Two structures represented by wave functions Ψ_I and Ψ_{II} interact only, *i.e.* can both contribute to the wave function of the same state (in this case, the ground state) of a molecule only, if the corresponding off-diagonal element in the secular determinant, $\int \Psi_I H \Psi_{II} \, d\tau$, is different from zero. However, this integral is zero unless:

(1) All nuclei in structures I and II have the same, or nearly the same relative positions.

(2) Both structures have the same number of unpaired electrons.

If these two conditions are not fulfilled, resonance between the two structures is impossible. In addition, however, resonance is the less important (1) the smaller the integral $\int \Psi_I H \Psi_{II} \, d\tau$, and (2) the more different the energies of I and II. The second of these two conditions is widely used and leads to the common neglect of all structures felt to be of high energy. The first of these conditions is, however, rarely considered because the integrals of interest are not readily estimated.

Let us return to butadiene, and write down the possible structures. The most important one is undoubtedly VI

$$CH_2 = CH - CH = CH_2 \qquad \overline{CH_2 - CH = CH - CH_2}$$
$$\text{(VI)} \qquad\qquad \text{(VII)}$$

which involves two double bonds. Another purely covalent structure is VII; this has obviously a considerably higher energy than VI, since it has one less double bond. The two structures have the same number of unpaired electrons (zero), but the relative positions of the nuclei are not identical: in VI the central bond is single and may be expected to be 1.54 Å (or according to very recent estimates, 1.48 Å long), in VII it is double, and should be 1.34 Å long. The outer bonds in VI are double, and should be 1.34 Å, in VII single and between 1.48 and 1.54 Å long. The angles, however, are expected to be the same in both compounds. The differences in relative positions in the two structures due to the different lengths are within the range allowed for resonance interaction.

In addition to these covalent structures, certain ionic ones can be written:

$$\overset{+}{H_2C=CH-CH-\overset{-}{C}H_2} \qquad \overset{+}{CH_2-CH=CH-\overset{-}{C}H_2}$$

$$\overset{+}{H_2C=CH-\overset{-}{C}H-CH_2} \qquad \overset{-}{CH_2-CH=CH-\overset{+}{C}H_2}$$

(VIII) (IX)

$$\overset{+}{CH_2-CH-\overset{-}{C}H-CH_2}$$

(X)

The structure of type VIII—there are four such structures,—have higher energy than VII, since energy is required to separate the positive and negative charge. The structures IX (2 structures), have even higher energy, since the charges are separated even further, requiring a further Coulombic energy. Structures X (4 structures) have one bond less than VII–IX, two less than VI, and hence are of sufficiently high energy to be completely negligible. In addition, 6 structures with 4 charges may be written. These also are of very high energy and may be neglected.

Thus butadiene may be considered as a resonance hybrid involving a predominant contribution from VI, a smaller one from VII, even smaller ones from each of the four structures VIII, and the two structures IX. Since, however, there are four structures VIII, it is not easy to say whether their joint contribution will outweigh that of VII or not. This, in general, is an important problem in resonance theory. The more complicated the molecule, the larger the number of structures, particularly higher energy structures, and, although each one of these may make only a very small contribution, their joint contribution frequently is quite important.

Just as MO theory, resonance theory permits the derivation of certain quantities which can be used to characterize the molecule, its properties and reactivity. The first of these to be considered is the resonance energy. On the basis of the concept of bond energies, their constancy and additivity, it is possible to calculate an energy (*i.e.* a ΔH of formation) of any one structure, and particularly of the most stable structure. Thus, structure VI of butadiene has six CH bonds, two $C=C$ double bonds and one C—C single bond. Using 98.75 kcal/mole for the CH bond energy, 83.6 kcal/mole for the C—C single bond energy, and 152.4 kcal/mole for the $C=C$ double bond, we obtain $\Delta H = -[6 \times 98.75 + 2 \times 152.4 + 83.6] = 980.9 -$ kcal/mole. The experimental heat of formation is -984 kcal/mole. Thus, the (negative) heat of formation of the actual compound exceeds that of the most stable structure by 3 kcal/mole. This quantity is called the *resonance energy*.

The discussion in the preceding paragraph serves to emphasize an important point: the actual molecule—the resonance hybrid—is a unique entity; it is *not* a mixture of the structures, *not* a dynamic equilibrium between them. If it were the latter, its energy would be intermediate between the energies of the structures, not lower than any of them, as it actually is.

Resonance theory also permits an evaluation of a charge density, a quantity analogous to q in MO theory. The covalent structures obviously make equal contributions to the charge density but each ionic structure makes contributions different from unity to the charge density of different atoms. Thus the resultant charge density at any atom may be calculated by multiplying the charge at an atom in a given structure by the weight of that structure in the resonance hybrid, and summing over all hybrids. As long as all equivalent structures, such as all four structures VIII, or both structures IX, are considered to have the same weight, as they were above, the resultant charge densities are all equal, as they were in MO theory.

The calculation of the bond order takes a similar path. In each structure (covalent or ionic) each bond is either single or double; long bonds, such as the dashed 1–4 bond in structure VII are neglected. By multiplying the bond number (1 for single, 2 for double and 3 for triple) of a given bond in each structure by the weight of the structure and summing over all structures a quantity is obtained which is called the bond order. If we assume structure VII to make a 10% contribution, structure VI a 90% contribution to the resonance hybrid, we obtain bond orders of 1.1 and 1.9, respectively, for the central and terminal bonds in butadiene.

The free valence (F) of MO theory also has an analogue in resonance theory, which is again readily obtained once we know the contributions of each structure. Two definitions are possible. The first is identical to the MO definition, *i.e.* F_r at atom r is the maximum value (F_{max}) less the sum of the bond orders of all bonds terminating at atom r. An alternate method assumes that electrons paired in long bonds, like the 1–4 bond in structure VII, are essentially free to form other bonds. Hence, the free valence at an atom is the sum of the weights of the structures in which long bonds terminate at atom r.

(b) Benzene

In the MO treatment of benzene, some new principles arise, which make it impracticable to utilize the symmetry properties of the molecule to a full extent, at least in a first treatment. Consequently we shall start by writing down the secular equations:

References p. 112

$$c_{j1}(\alpha - \varepsilon)\,c_{j2}\beta + c_{j6}\beta = 0$$

$$c_{j1}\beta + c_{j2}(\alpha - \varepsilon) + c_{j3}\beta = 0$$

$$c_{j2}\beta + c_{j3}(\alpha - \varepsilon) + c_{j4}\beta = 0 \qquad (13)$$

$$c_{j3}\beta + c_{j4}(\alpha - \varepsilon) + c_{j5}\beta = 0$$

$$c_{j4}\beta + c_{j5}(\alpha - \varepsilon) + c_{j6}\beta = 0$$

$$c_{j1}\beta + c_{j5}\beta + c_{j6}(\alpha - \varepsilon) = 0$$

where we have already introduced the assumptions of neglecting all overlap integrals and all resonance integrals between non-adjacent atoms. The associated secular determinant is:

$$
\begin{vmatrix}
\alpha - \varepsilon & \beta & 0 & 0 & 0 & \beta \\
\beta & \alpha - \varepsilon & \beta & 0 & 0 & 0 \\
0 & \beta & \alpha - \varepsilon & \beta & 0 & 0 \\
0 & 0 & \beta & \alpha - \varepsilon & \beta & 0 \\
0 & 0 & 0 & \beta & \alpha - \varepsilon & \beta \\
\beta & 0 & 0 & 0 & \beta & \alpha - \varepsilon
\end{vmatrix} = 0 \qquad (14)
$$

This 6 × 6 determinant may be factored into a 2 × 2 and a 4 × 4 determinant by the simple expedient of carrying out, in order, the following additions and subtractions of rows and columns*: (1) subtract the 2nd row from the 6th row; (2) add the 6th column to the 2nd column; (3) add the 5th column to the 3rd column; (4) subtract the 3rd row from the fifth row. In this way the determinant, eqn. (14), becomes

$$
\begin{vmatrix}
\alpha - \varepsilon & 2\beta & 0 & 0 & 0 & \beta \\
\beta & \alpha - \varepsilon & \beta & 0 & 0 & 0 \\
0 & \beta & \alpha - \varepsilon & \beta & 0 & 0 \\
0 & 0 & 2\beta & \alpha - \varepsilon & \beta & 0 \\
0 & 0 & 0 & 0 & \alpha - \varepsilon & \beta \\
0 & 0 & 0 & 0 & \beta & \alpha - \varepsilon
\end{vmatrix} =
$$

---

* Any book on matrices and determinants will justify this procedure, and show that the resulting 6 × 6 determinant is the product of a 2 × 2 and a 4 × 4 determinant.

$$\begin{vmatrix} \alpha - \varepsilon & 2\beta & 0 & 0 \\ \beta & \alpha - \varepsilon & \beta & 0 \\ 0 & \beta & \alpha - \varepsilon & \beta \\ 0 & 0 & 2 & \alpha - \varepsilon \end{vmatrix} \times \begin{vmatrix} \alpha - \varepsilon & \beta \\ \beta & \alpha - \varepsilon \end{vmatrix} = 0 \qquad (15)$$

The first of the determinants in eqn. (15) vanishes when $\varepsilon = \pm 2\beta$ or $\pm \beta$, the second when $\varepsilon = \pm \beta$. Substitution of these values into the secular eqns. (13) gives the coefficients c_{jr}. The normalization constants N_j for the wave functions, which now are of the form

$$\psi_j = N_j \sum_{r=1}^{6} c_{jr}\phi_r$$

are obtained from the normalization condition, which, for the case of neglect of overlap integrals S reduce to $\sum_r c_{jr}^2 = 1$. The c_{jr} and N_j are listed in Table II. The resulting MO's are represented graphically in Fig. 12.

TABLE II

THE MO'S IN BENZENE

j	ε_j	N_j	c_{j1}	c_{j2}	c_{j3}	c_{j4}	c_{j5}	c_{j6}
1	$\alpha + 2\beta$	$6^{-\frac{1}{2}}$	1	1	1	1	1	1
2	$\alpha + \beta$	$12^{-\frac{1}{2}}$	2	1	−1	−2	−1	1
3	$\alpha + \beta$	$4^{-\frac{1}{2}}$	0	1	1	0	−1	−1
4	$\alpha - \beta$	$12^{-\frac{1}{2}}$	2	−1	−1	2	−1	−1
5	$\alpha - \beta$	$4^{-\frac{1}{2}}$	0	1	−1	0	1	−1
6	$\alpha - 2\beta$	$6^{-\frac{1}{2}}$	1	−1	1	−1	1	−1

The first thing to note about these MO's is that they do not appear to reflect the symmetry of the molecule. It is well known that benzene is planar and that the six carbon atoms are arranged as a regular hexagon, and are all equivalent to each other. In spite of this, the coefficients in ψ_2, ψ_3, ψ_4 and ψ_5 are not identical for all atoms. This fact is related to the high symmetry of the molecule. At the same time, inspection of Table II shows that ψ_2 and ψ_3 have the same energy ($\alpha + \beta$), and hence are called degenerate, and that ψ_4 and ψ_5 are degenerate with energy $\alpha - \beta$. This situation is general for molecules with high symmetry. Whenever a molecule has a rotational axis higher than two fold, *i.e.* if rotation of the whole molecule by an angle of less than 180° (120° for 3 fold, 90° for 4 fold, 60° for 6 fold axes etc.) moves the molecule into a conformation indistinguishable from the original molecule, energy levels occur in degenerate pairs. When there are several rotational symmetry axes higher than two-fold, energy levels occur in degenerate groups of three as may have been noted in methane, which has four 3 fold axes. When energy levels occur in degenerate pairs (or groups of three) it is not possible to treat each member of a pair as unique. Any nor-

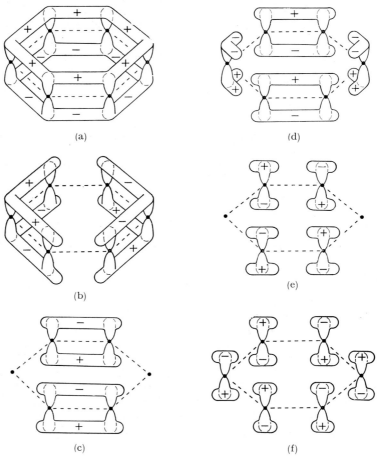

Fig. 12. The MO's of benzene.

malized linear combination of a pair is also a satisfactory wave function, and the symmetry properties of the molecule need not be reflected by each wave function, but only by the product of the pair (or group of three). It is readily verified that the charge distribution resulting from ψ_2 and ψ_3, and from ψ_4 and ψ_5 are reflecting the symmetry of the molecule, *i.e.* represent an equal charge on each atom. An infinite number of other pairs would be possible, but the forms given in Table II are particularly convenient in the treatment of substituted benzenes, and are consequently almost universally used.

It is now a simple matter to verify that all $q_r = 1$, that all $p_{rs} = {}^2/_3$, and that all $F_r = 4.732 - 4.333 = 0.399$. In agreement with expectation, the q and F values are identical for all atoms, the p values for all bonds. Also, the q values are all unity as predicted by the Coulson–Rushbrooke theorem.

The energy level scheme arising from this treatment is shown in Fig. 13. The symmetry of this scheme about the energy α is immediately apparent. A complication for many purposes, particularly for use for spectroscopic predictions, is the fact that both the highest occupied and the lowest unoccupied energy levels are doubly degenerate. Thus one can visualize four

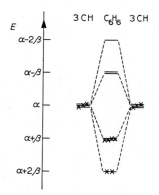

Fig. 13. The energy levels of benzene.

excitation processes, $\psi_2 \to \psi_4$, $\psi_2 \to \psi_5$, $\psi_3 \to \psi_4$, $\psi_3 \to \psi_5$, which, according to this treatment, should all have the same energy. The treatment has, however, completely neglected the mutual repulsion of electrons. If this repulsion is taken account of, it can be shown that these four processes correspond to three different energies (two of the four remaining degenerate), and they give rise to the three absorption bands of benzene near 260, 200 and 180 mμ.

Localization energies for localization of a single atom in benzene can also readily be calculated, and are, of course, equal for the six atoms. This quantity is of little interest in itself, but may be of considerable interest in connection with corresponding values for substituted benzenes or polycyclic

References p. 112

aromatics. Localization energies for 1,3- and 1,4-addition are also readily calculated. It is probably unnecessary to make the calculations—unless one wants to make comparisons with other molecules—since the qualitative results are readily apparent: 1,2-addition leads to a butadiene system, 1,4-addition to two isolated double bonds, and 1,3-addition to an allyl radical and an isolated π orbital. Consequently, 1,2-addition should be more favorable than 1,4-addition by the resonance energy of butadiene, about 3 kcal/mole, a relatively small quantity, but both more favorable than 1,3-addition by the energy of one double bond, about 2β or 40 kcal/mole.

In the valence bond treatment of benzene, two equivalent structures XI, the so-called Kekulé structures make the most important contribution, and three further covalent structures, the Dewar structures (XII) having considerably higher energy, make a significant contribution, estimated at about 22%. In addition, a very large number of ionic structures can be written; among these the 12 structures like XIII have lowest energy, since they involve relatively small charge separation and leave a butadiene system.

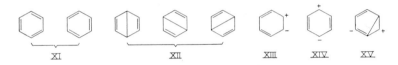

XI   XII   XIII   XIV   XV

Next higher in energy are the six structures like XIV, which involve a greater charge separation, and leave only two isolated double bonds. Twenty four structures of type XV have considerably higher energy and are negligible, even in spite of their large number. Similarly, a very large number of structures with two or three pairs of formal charges are negligible because of their very high energies.

For most practical purposes, only structures XI and XII are considered, and in some approximations, structures XI alone are used. Charge distribution by the VB method is equal on all atoms, independent of the number of structures used. The bond order, using only structures XI, is 1.5 for all bonds; using structures XI and XII with relative weights of 78 and 22% it is about 1.46. Using structures XI alone, the free valence F is zero, a useless result, but using structures XI and XII, F is about 0.07, still quite small. The resonance energy of benzene, calculated from various thermochemical data, is of the order of 36–40 kcal/mole. Theoretically, by MO theory, the π electron energy of benzene is $\mathscr{E} = \sum_j n_j \varepsilon_j = 6\alpha + 8\beta$, that of a Kekulé structure $6\alpha + 6\beta$, and consequently the resonance energy is 2β. Identification of these experimental and theoretical values leads to ~ 20 kcal/mole, the empirical value of β commonly used.

The above experiences with butadiene and benzene indicate that such quantities as bond orders, free valences etc. are not the same in the two theories. This is due largely to the fact that they are not defined in the same manner; even if they were equally defined, however, they would not agree because in the VB method we generally greatly underestimate ionic structures, in the MO method overestimate them. However, in spite of these differences, the trends observed in the MO quantities when various compounds are compared almost invariably parallel the trends of the corresponding VB quantities, so that either may be used consistently.

(c) Hyperconjugation

We cannot leave the discussion of hydrocarbons without, at least, a passing reference to a phenomenon called hyperconjugation. This represents a theoretical interpretation of the Baker–Nathan effect, which is the observation that, in some conjugated systems, the order of electron donation by alkyl groups is H < *tert.*-butyl < *iso*-propyl < ethyl < methyl, opposite to the order observed in aliphatic systems, H < methyl < ethyl < *iso*-propyl < *tert.*-butyl. The normal order, *i.e.* the order in aliphatic systems is that expected on the basis of inductive effects, or, in other words, on the basis of the ionic contributions to the various bonds. The reversed order, observed in some conjugated and aromatic systems is explained on the basis of a delocalization of some of the electrons in the alkyl group. In resonance notation this has frequently been expressed by consideration of resonance between the following structures:

$$H_3C-\langle \bigcirc \rangle \quad \longleftrightarrow \quad H^+H_2C-\langle \bigcirc \rangle-$$

Three such ionic structures, all equivalent, are considered. The MO description of this phenomenon, which is preferable since it is less misleading and less likely to lead to misinterpretation, considers the three hydrogen atoms jointly, as a *pseudo atom*. Combination of the AO's of the three hydrogen atoms leads to three orbitals, often called group orbitals (GO) of the form

$$\chi_1 = (\phi_1 + \phi_2 + \phi_3)/\sqrt{3}$$

$$\chi_2 = (\phi_1 - \phi_2)/\sqrt{2}$$

$$\chi_3 = (\phi_1 + \phi_2 - 2\phi_3)/\sqrt{6}$$

The first of these has no node, and although without cylindrical symmetry, is quite similar to a σ orbital, and joins the H_3 group to the carbon atom by a strong, almost σ, bond. χ_2 and χ_3 have a node each, and hence closely resemble π orbitals. Appropriate orientation of the CH_3 group permits the node of one of these orbitals to coincide with the node of the π orbitals of the conjugated system, and hence the H_3 pseudo atom acts like one of the atoms of a conjugated system, having a π orbital and one π electron. If the orientation of the CH_3 group is not such that the node of χ_2 or χ_3 coincides with the node of the π electron system of the conjugated radical, it is always possible to form a linear combination of χ_2 and χ_3 such that the coincidence is achieved. Hence MO theory considers the methyl group as $H_3 \equiv C-$, quite analogous to $N \equiv C-$. A resonance description of this concept would be resonance between structures

$$H_3 \!\equiv\! C\!-\!\langle\,\bigcirc\,\rangle \quad \longleftrightarrow \quad H_3^+ \!=\! C\!\!=\!\!\langle\,\bigcirc\,\rangle \;-$$

Resonance of this type, expressed either in terms of the formalism of resonance or of MO theory, was quite readily capable of accounting for the Baker–Nathan effect. In recent years, however, some doubt has been cast on this concept, and alternate explanations for this effect have been proposed. Although the theoretical treatment of hyperconjugation is undoubtedly sound, it is not certain whether it leads to any observable effects.

(d) Substituted conjugated systems

In the preceding section we have dealt at some length with some basic conjugated systems. One of the major concerns of the branch of molecular quantum mechanics dealing with the π electrons of conjugated systems, is the comparison between closely related compounds, and particularly the effect of the introduction of new groups, usually thought of as substituents, into the molecule. There is, of course, no great problem involved in dealing directly with such substituted molecules. It is quite apparent that the secular equation for a MO treatment of a substituted molecule can readily be set up, or alternately, that resonance structures for it can be written. However, some new problems often do arise. In the most common cases, the substituent groups contain atoms other than carbon, often called *heteroatoms*, or carbon atoms in a different state of hybridization or appreciably different environment, which will also behave differently from a typical carbon atom in the conjugated molecule, and may best be dealt with as if they were heteroatoms. Also, the new bonds usually are essential single bonds, and may require special consideration.

In VB theory, these problems are generally handled by use of chemical intuition, or by some qualitative arguments based on electronegativity considerations. The main point that distinguishes a molecule involving heteroatoms from a hydrocarbon is that, due to electronegativity differences, certain ionic structures involving displacement of electrons toward a more electronegative atom, are energetically favored and consequently become relatively important, whereas the opposite type of ionic structure, involving a displacement of charge from the more electronegative toward the less electronegative atom, is less important because it has a higher energy. Although this type of qualitative argument is immediately apparent, a more quantitative treatment is extremely difficult because the energy quantities are hard to evaluate.

In MO theory, heteroatoms require special Coulomb integrals, α_H. Since these integrals are largely a measure of the energy of an isolated $p\pi$ electron on the atom, they are likely to be related to the energy required to remove a π electron from the isolated atom, *i.e.* the ionization potential, or alternately a quantity closely related to this, the electronegativity. Inherently, it would appear possible to calculate the α_H theoretically, but probably due to the many approximations involved in MO theory, theoretically calculated integrals have not proved particularly successful. The most common procedure is to use semi-empirical values, obtained by varying α_H until the calculated value of the property of interest becomes identical with the observed value for a reference compound, and then to use the value so obtained in calculations on related compounds. Many physical and chemical properties have been calculated by such procedures, *e.g.* dipole moments, absorption spectra and a number of indices of chemical reactivity. Unfortunately, however, there does not appear to exist a generally acceptable set of Coulomb integrals even for the most common heteroatoms; in most cases, although sets of calculations are internally consistent, there is not very good correspondence between sets.

It may be worth mentioning also that the Coulomb integral, just as the electronegativity, cannot be taken as a fundamental property of a given atom. Thus α-values and electronegativities vary with the hybridization, as *e.g.* for sp^3, sp^2 and sp carbon atoms, and with the type of bonding, *e.g.* α_0 is different for an oxygen atom in a carbonyl group and a hydroxy group. It would be desirable to be able to give a table of α values of general utility, but values reported in the literature for any one atom, even in identical or nearly identical compounds, vary so widely that no such table can be given.

The presence of a heteroatom further influences the carbon atom to which it is bonded. The extent to which such an effect is operative, however, is not clear. The effect is frequently taken account of by varying the Coulomb integral of the carbon atom to which the heteroatom is attached by an increment, which is usually taken proportional to α_H for the heteroatoms, but the proportionality factor is open to serious questions: values as small as $^1/_{10}$ or $^1/_{12}$ have often been used successfully, while values as large as $^1/_3$ have also found quite wide acceptance. In many cases, such effects are not restricted to the carbon atom directly attached to the heteroatom, but are often permitted to be propagated along a chain of atoms, with an appropriate attenuation factor (usually about $^1/_3$ for each bond).

The problem of the resonance integral between a carbon atom and a heteroatom, β for the $C-X$ bond is similarly complicated, although theoretically somewhat simpler. Since the energy of an isolated π bond is equal to 2β (twice the resonance integral) β_{CX} has often been taken as one half the difference between single and double bond energy. This method is, of course, applicable only when both single and double bond energies are available, as for the C—O or C—N bond. Alternately, it has been shown that β is proportional to S, and use of this relation is often made. On the other hand, again, β_{CX} is often treated as a semi-empirical parameter, and adjusted to give agreement between calculation and experiment.

Once Coulomb and resonance integrals for the various atoms in a molecule are thus decided upon, the MO calculations are, of course, straightforward, although time consuming. They can be, and often have been, carried out to obtain energy levels, charge distributions, bond orders, free valences, localization energies and the like. These in turn have been used to calculate measures of the wavelength and intensity of spectroscopic transitions, dipole moments, bond lengths, chemical reactivities, activation energies, and have even been correlated with such complicated molecular properties as carcinogenic activity.

A number of shortcut procedures have been developed to avoid the necessity of a complete MO treatment of all the molecules, and to reduce the labor involved. Since the simple MO theory in itself is highly approximate in nature, there seems little objection to make further drastic approximations. Most of these methods are based in one way or another on *perturbation theory*, a very powerful approximation method commonly used in quantum mechanics. A full discussion of this method is beyond the scope of this chapter and can be found in any book on quantum mechanics, but a brief outline of its principles seems indicated.

Perturbation theory in general starts with an idealized, simplified model, and treats the actual situation as a perturbation of this model. The advantage of this procedure is that the treatment of the idealized model is very commonly considerably easier than the treatment of the actual case. The difference between the ideal and actual case, is generally expressed as a change in the numerical value of some mathematical quantity, some parameter. The change in the property of interest is expressed as a power series in the changes of the parameter, and only the first non-zero term of this expansion is used. When the first term of the expansion is not zero, one has what is called a *first order* perturbation, and use of the second term is called *second order* perturbation. Higher orders are almost never considered. The use of only the first non-vanishing term assumes that the perturbation is small, so that successive powers of the change in the perturbed parameter are rapidly decreasing quantities, and further that the coefficients of these powers, when not zero, are of similar order of magnitude. Consequently, perturbation theory is strictly applicable only to small perturbations. In the highly approximate field of π electron quantum mechanics, however, even relatively large perturbations are handled in this manner, and produce results which, although undoubtedly quite crude, seem to give the correct trends.

Two particular such perturbation methods have been widely used. The first, due to Coulson and Longuet–Higgins, uses as reference molecule one in which all atoms are considered equivalent (*i.e.* to be carbon atoms with equal Coulomb integrals) and all bonds are considered alike, *i.e.* to have equal resonance integrals. The change in Coulomb integrals α_r of the atoms r from the standard value of all the atoms, and the change of resonance integrals β_{rs} of the bonds rs from the standard value are then considered the perturbation parameters. The change in total π electrons energy becomes

$$\delta \mathscr{E} = \sum_r q_r \delta \alpha_r + \sum_{rs} p_{rs} \delta \beta_{rs}$$

so that knowledge of the charge densities q_r and bond orders p_{rs} of the reference molecule permits calculation of the π electron energy of the perturbed molecule. Similarly, changes in charge density (δq_r) and bond order, (δp_{rs}) are given by

$$\delta q_r = \sum_s \pi_{r,s} \delta \alpha_s + \sum_{st} \pi_{r,st} \delta \beta_{st}$$

$$\delta p_{rs} = \sum_t \pi_{rs,t} \delta \alpha_t + \sum_{tu} \pi_{rs,tu} \delta \beta_{tu}$$

Here $\pi_{r,s}$ is the mutual polarizability of atoms r and s, $\pi_{r,st}$ a bond-atom and $\pi_{rs,tu}$ a bond–bond polarizability. These polarizabilities can be calculated relatively readily, and have been tabulated for many important molecules.

This method of calculation is simple and convenient for a number of reasons:

(1) A single reference molecule serves as the unperturbed parent for a reasonable array of molecules; thus, benzene can serve as reference molecule for calculations of pyridine, the three diazines (pyrazine, pyrimidine and pyridazine), the triazines and tetrazines. Similarly, naphthalene serves as reference compound for quinoline, isoquinoline, and all the di- and poly-azanaphthalenes.

References p. 112

(2) The basic MO calculations for benzene and naphthalene are, because of the high symmetry of these molecules, considerably simpler than for the aza derivatives; as an example, in the treatment of naphthalene, the secular equation, a 10 × 10 determinant, can be factored into two 3 × 3 and two 2 × 2 determinants thus reducing the problem from the solution of a tenth order equation to that of solving two cubics and two quadratics; no such factoring is possible for quinoline and isoquinoline, which have no elements of symmetry other than the molecular plane.

(3) No calculations are needed for the q in benzene and naphthalene, which are, according to the Coulson–Rushbrook theorem, all equal to unity. Since, in an aza derivative, the β's are probably not significantly different from their values in the parent compound, results for the total π electron energy can be written down without any extensive calculation as soon as values for the $\delta\alpha$ are chosen. Further, in an alternant hydrocarbon, all $\pi_{r,st}$ and $\pi_{rs,t}$ vanish, and this fact makes all q independent of the β's, and all p independent of the α's.

(4) All derivatives of benzene carrying one substituent with a pair of π electrons, *i.e.* fluoro-, chloro-, bromo-, iodobenzene, phenol, anisole, aniline and its N-methyl derivatives, thiophenol etc. are treated as perturbations of a single parent, the benzyl anion. Here, unfortunately, we do not deal with an alternant hydrocarbon, but, owing to the extra electron, with what has been called an alternant hydrocarbon ion, and the q are not equal to unity, nor do the $\pi_{r,st}$ and $\pi_{rs,t}$ vanish. However, some results can be obtained without detailed computation even here.

The benzyl radical, the same molecule with one less electron, is an alternant hydrocarbon with an odd number of electrons and atoms, a so-called *odd alternant hydrocarbon*. According to the Coulson–Rushbrook theorem, in any alternant hydrocarbon, energy levels occur in pairs, with energy equal in magnitude but opposite in sign. However, in an odd molecule, there is an odd number of levels, so that one of them cannot be paired. This level must have zero energy, *i.e.* its energy is the same as that of an isolated carbon π orbital, and hence is a non-bonding orbital. In the benzyl radical this level is singly occupied, in the anion it is doubly occupied. It can be shown that this orbital, and orbitals like it in any odd alternant, has special properties. To consider this orbital in a little more detail, let us inspect the molecule, and let us divide its atoms into two sets, one starred and one unstarred, so that no two atoms of one set are adjacent:

By convention, the starred set is chosen to have the larger number of atoms.

It is just this ability to choose two sets which distinguishes alternant from non-alternant molecules, and the reader should convince himself that this separation into two sets is possible for any molecule which does *not* have a ring with an odd number of atoms. In general each MO ψ_j is given by

$$\psi_j = \sum_r c_{jr}\phi_r$$

For the present purpose, let us split this sum into two sums, one over each set of atoms, and call the unstarred atoms r, the starred ones r^*. Then

$$\psi_j = \sum_r c_{jr}\phi_r + \sum_{r*} c_{jr*}\phi_{r*}$$

Now, the non-bonding level, which we shall designate as ψ_0, has the special property that all c_{0r} (but not c_{0r*}) are zero. This property is directly related to its non-bonding character: as discussed above, an orbital makes an anti-bonding contribution to the total energy whenever it changes sign between adjacent atoms, a bonding contribution if it fails to change sign. Whenever an orbital vanishes *at* an atom, it makes no contribution (bonding or anti-bonding) in the bonds adjacent to this atom. For ψ_0, this situation holds for all bonds, so that ψ_0 makes no bonding or anti-bonding contributions at all, and is nonbonding.

The c_{0r*} also can be obtained readily: It has been shown that the sum of the c_{0r*} of all the atoms bonded to any atom r must vanish. Then, if use is made of symmetry, and c_{0_1} is arbitrarily set equal to $2a$, the values shown in the diagram follow:

The absolute value of a is obtained readily since $\sum_{r*} c_{0r*}^2 = 1$; $(2a)^2 + a^2 + a^2 + a^2 = 1$, $a = 1/\sqrt{7}$. Thus, the orbital ψ_0 becomes $\psi_0 = [2\phi_1 - \phi_3 + \phi_5 - \phi_7]/\sqrt{7}$. The benzyl radical, as an alternant hydrocarbon, has all q equal and equal to unity. The q in the benzyl anion then are readily obtained by adding to these values of unity the c_{0r*}^2 values which represent the contribution of the last electron added, giving $q_1 = 1.572, q_3 = q_5 = q_7 = 1.143$, $q_2 = q_4 = q_6 = 1.000$.

The Coulson–Longuet–Higgins perturbation method thus permits ready calculations to be made for a whole family of compounds on the basis of solution of the secular equation for a single one, and this generally a relatively simple one. This method is particularly well-suited for evaluation of empirical parameters because these parameters, the $\delta\alpha_r$ and $\delta\beta_{rs}$ of the above equations, occur in simple linear equations, and analytical solutions are readily obtained.

An alternate perturbation method is due to Dewar. This perturbation method divides the whole conjugated system into individual parts, and uses the MO description of the individual parts. Thus, the monosubstituted benzene discussed above, C_6H_5X, may be considered as a compound RS, with $R = C_6H_5$ and $S = X$. The MO's of R are, of course, the same as those of benzene, and hence readily obtainable. S in this case is a single atom, involving only one AO of π symmetry, but this is only a special case. Considering the molecule as two separate parts is equivalent to assuming that the resonance integral β_{rs} for the bond r–s which connects R and S is zero. This resonance integral is the perturbation parameter, which is varied. The method has the tremendous advantage that it permits many generalizations to be made, which cannot be discussed here, and that it involves a MO treatment only for the individual parts of the molecule, which generally is quite simple. At the same time, the method suffers from the disadvantage that the perturbation from $\beta_{rs} = 0$ to a realistic value is far from a small perturbation, and that the results are consequently open to a good deal of question.

Many other modifications and alternate treatments of conjugated molecules could be listed; only a few of these will be mentioned briefly. The highest occupied orbital is of primary concern when discussing spectra and ionization potentials, since these processes generally involve excitation of removal of an electron in this orbital. A group of Japanese workers lead by Fukui has postulated that, in reactivity phenomena also, the least tightly bound electrons, *i.e.* the electrons in the highest occupied orbital, are of the greatest importance. These electrons have been called *frontier electrons*, and in the work of this group the contribution of these electrons to charge density, bond order, localization energy etc. take the place of the complete quantities which are sums over all π electrons. The method has the advantage of relative ease of computation; *e.g.* it was shown above that the zero energy non-bonding orbital of odd alternant system, which is the frontier orbital, can be obtained with almost no labor. The results obtained by frontier electron theory usually parallel those of a more complete MO theory.

Another, rather drastically different method, the free electron method, has found rather wide use, and has in some applications met with phenomenal success. The methods used in previous sections all were based on an expression of the molecular wave functions in terms of atomic functions in one form or another. The method to be discussed now makes no reference whatever to individual atomic functions; it is related, however, to MO theory in that the molecular wave function is expressed as a product (or rather a determinant of products) of one electron functions.

The free electron method (FEM) is essentially applicable only to sets of electrons with very analogous properties. In practice, its usefulness has been almost completely restricted to π electron systems in conjugated organic compounds. In such systems, chemists have long considered the electrons as being especially *mobile,* and little restricted to specific nuclei. The FEM makes use of this property by assuming that there is a region in which the electron is free to move without restriction, and that this region extends over the entire π electron system. In other words it assumes that there is a region in space in which the potential energy of the electron is finite (and constant), and that, outside this region it is infinite. With this assumption the problem of the behavior of the electrons becomes simply the well-known problem of the particle or electron in a box.

A little further discussion of this box, or better this potential well, is indicated. Logically the potential well should be a three-dimensional one. However, from the molecular point of view the only freedom of motion of the electrons of interest is the motion along the conjugated system. Motion away from it is probably not, or at best little, affected by conjugation, and hence is ignored. With this restriction, the problem becomes one-dimensional, with the dimension being the "electron path" along the conjugated system. The next problem to be considered is the form of the potential energy function along this path. It stands to reason that the potential energy should be lowest near the nuclei and higher between; further, that some distance *beyond* the end nuclei the potential energy should rise steeply, but not discontinuously; that it should rise to a high value (approximately equal to the ionization potential), but not to infinity. In most applications of the FEM, this potential energy function is approximated by one in which the periodic potential is replaced by a constant one and the steep rise to a high value is replaced by a discontinuous rise to infinity. A rather arbitrary decision has to be made as to the point at which this rise to infinity occurs. Apparently the most satisfactory convention is to place this wall of the energy well one bond distance beyond the end atoms of the conjugated system.

In the region within the one-dimensional box, it is therefore assumed that the potential energy is constant and equal to zero. The wave equation is:

$$\frac{h^2}{8\pi^2 m} \frac{d^2\psi}{dx^2} = E\psi \qquad (0 \leqslant x \leqslant a)$$

the solution for which is

$$\psi_n = \sqrt{2/a} \, \sin\left[\frac{\pi n}{a}\right] x \qquad (0 \leqslant x \leqslant a)$$

where a is the length of the potential well or box, x is the distance along the well and the quantum number n is a positive whole number $1, 2, \ldots$. To each ψ_n there is corresponding an energy:

$$E_n = \frac{n^2 h^2}{8ma^2}$$

where n and a have the above defined meaning, h is Planck's constant, and m is the mass of the electron. In a conjugated hydrocarbon containing k double bonds there are $2k$ pπ electrons. In the ground state of the molecule each of the k lowest molecular orbitals is doubly occupied. The model is particularly applicable to long conjugated systems, and has been eminently successful in the hands of H. Kuhn, one of its originators, in predicting the electronic spectra of polymethine dyes of the general structure:

$$R_2N—(CH=CH)_x—CH=\overset{+}{N}R_2$$

The method can also be applied to cyclic compounds where the "box" actually is a closed path around the periphery, and in such systems it has been used by Platt to define a scheme for correlating spectra of cyclic and polycyclic hydrocarbons.

The FEM is of particular simplicity since it involves the treatment of molecules in terms of some very well known and easily carried out quantum-mechanical problems: the treatment of an electron in a one-dimensional box, for linear systems, and the rigid rotator, for cyclic ones. Considerable refinements of the simplest model have been proposed, but the complexities arising from these seem to be more serious than the results warrant.

(e) Small ring compounds

Throughout much of this chapter, MO and VB (or resonance) theories have been carried along side by side. There is a large class of compounds, however, in which resonance theory either fails to give reasonable answers, at least without special definitions, or becomes so hopelessly complicated that it is virtually useless. These are compounds which involve structures consisting of small (three- and to some extent four-membered) rings, *i.e.* compounds in which the orbitals of more than two atoms overlap simultaneously in a single region of space. Such compounds include cyclopropane, ethylene oxide and the boron hydrides, the complexes of certain transition metals with olefins and aromatics, the complexes of olefins with bromonium ion, and finally the compounds of transition metals with cyclopentadiene and aromatic rings. In contrast to resonance theory, MO theory encounters little difficulty in the treatment of these compounds.

As examples of the problems involved it may be of interest to consider a series of molecules involving three membered rings. At one extreme end of this series lies cyclopropane, which most chemists will consider as involving three single $C-C$ bonds. The fact that the total bonding energy is less than expected for three single $C-C$ bonds is recognized either in terms of *ring strain*, or by considering the bonds as *bent bonds*, and hence somewhat different from *normal* single bonds. At the other extreme end of the series one might consider the intermediate known to be involved in the bromination of olefins, the ethylene bromonium ion, which, if it is to be represented by resonance theory, is commonly represented as a hybrid of the structures

$$H_2C^+{-}CH_2 \longleftrightarrow CH_2{-}CH_2^+ \longleftrightarrow CH_2{=}CH_2$$
$$\quad\diagup \qquad\qquad \diagdown \qquad\qquad$$
$$\quad Br \qquad\qquad\quad Br \qquad\qquad Br^+$$

In MO theory, this ion is quite readily expressed, starting with the MO's of ethylene and the AO's of the bromonium ion. An sp^2 hybrid AO of Br^+ is considered as pointing along the symmetry axis of the complex ion, and has the same symmetry as, and overlaps with the bonding π orbital of ethylene. From these two orbitals a single, fairly strongly bonding MO is formed which gives the complex ion reasonable stability and, at the same time, transfers some of the positive charge to the ethylene part of the complex. In addition, one of the doubly occupied p orbitals of the Br^+ ion has the same symmetry, and hence interacts with the vacant anti-bonding orbital of the ethylene and, although possibly not very important in this case, gives a little additional stability. Since this orbital is formed from orbitals occupied in Br^+ and vacant in C_2H_4, the formation of such an MO involves transfer of charge in the opposite direction as the main bonding orbital, and this is often referred to as *back-donation*. The two MO's are shown graphically in Fig. 14.

In the case of the ethylene–transition metal complex the situation is quite similar: two MO's are formed, the first quite analogous to the one shown in Fig. 14a, except that the metal AO is a hybrid made up of d, s and p orbitals; the other MO is even more favorable to bonding since, as shown in Fig. 14c, the metal AO is a $d\pi$ orbital, with lobes pointing toward the ethylene, or a $d\pi$–$p\pi$ hybrid with even better directional characteristics. Also, the lower electronegativity of the metal atom makes back-donation even more important. The picture used in both of these cases, which involves inter-action between the Br^+ or metal AO with the bonding π MO of ethylene, and no interaction with the bonding σ MO, is somewhat of an oversimplification; however, any interaction with the ethylene σ MO would imply some distortion of the ethylene and the evidence indicates that little, if any, distortion occurs.

References p. 112

The MO treatment of ethylene oxide, the next member of the series, is again quite analogous; the MO's have the same form as in the ethylene bromonium ion, except that back-donation is tremendously more important, and that interaction with the σ-bonding ethylene orbital also is important, which is demonstrated by the fact that the hydrogen atoms are bent back

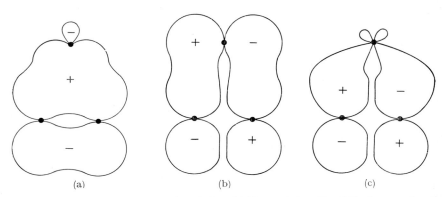

(a)   (b)   (c)

Fig. 14. The MO's in a three-membered ring. (a) The main bonding MO of approximate σ symmetry; (b) the back-donation MO in $C_2H_4Br^+$, involving the $C_2H_4\pi^*$ orbital and a p orbital of Br; (c) A similar orbital in an ethylene–metal complex, involving a dp hybrid of M.

from the position they occupy in ethylene. In all three compounds it is possible to perform a linear transformation, analogous to the one discussed in connection with methane, which leads to localized or equivalent orbitals. However, only when back-donation is of roughly equal importance as the forward donation involved in the orbital shown in Fig. 14a, is this linear transformation really attractive, and then leads, in the case of ethylene oxide, to a structure which might be written as

$$H_2C\text{------}CH_2$$
$$\diagdown O \diagup$$

Only, here the AO's forming the bonds do not point in the direction of the atom forming the opposite end of the bond. The localized orbitals are bent rather than linear as are the usual σ bonding localized orbitals, and consequently bonds such as occur in ethylene oxide have been described as bent bonds.

Cyclopropane, the other extreme member of the series of compounds under discussion, represents a somewhat different situation because of its higher symmetry, and consequently is not readily described as a distorted ethylene. If the six $C-H$ bonds are treated as localized orbitals, each carbon atom has an hybrid orbital (h), made up as some mixture of s and p orbitals, pointing in the direction of the center of the ring, and a p orbital (p) in the plane of the ring. Three bonding MO's result which have roughly the form:

$$\psi_1 = (h_1 + h_2 + h_3)$$
$$\psi_2 = (p_1 - p_2)$$
$$\psi_3 = (p_1 + p_2 - 2p_3)$$

The first (ψ_1) has the lowest energy, and contributes the major portion of the bonding energy of the ring. The other two (ψ_2 and ψ_3) are degenerate, and contribute relatively little to the total binding energy. They have π character with respect to the extracyclic bonds, and therefore, and also due to their relatively high energy, are responsible for the conjugation properties of the cyclopropyl ring. A linear transformation applied to ψ_1, ψ_2 and ψ_3 again leads to three localized bent bonds, giving the familiar picture of the compound with three C—C single bonds.

The treatment of four-membered rings, such as cyclobutane, diborane, $(AlCl_3)_2$, $[Al(CH_3)_3]_2$, $[BeCl_2]_n$, etc. is quite similar to the treatment of three-membered rings, and will not be discussed here. In many other compounds, such as the higher boron hydrides, P_4, and B_4Cl_4, which involve three-dimensional molecules bordered by three-membered rings, simple MO descriptions also permit ready description of the electronic structure. Finally, the rather recently discovered, so-called sandwich compounds, ferrocene, dibenzene chromium and their analogs, can be described by similar MO methods, whereas the VB or resonance theory for such compounds is almost hopelessly complicated.

9. The role of d electrons

Most of the emphasis up to this point has been on organic molecules, and on other molecules of first row elements, and hence we have been concerned almost exclusively with s and p electrons. It remains to discuss briefly the role of d orbitals and d electrons in the structure of molecules. These are of importance in two areas; in the first place, elements of the second row, and the elements of the B subgroups of the lower rows of the periodic systems have d orbitals of the same major quantum number as the valence electrons which are important in chemical bonds. In the second place, the transition metals, with a partially filled d shell in the next to the last electron shell use these d orbitals in bonding. The problems involved in the use of these electrons and orbitals will now be discussed.

Chemical compounds of first row elements generally follow closely the Lewis octet rule, *i.e.* in formation of covalent chemical compounds these elements share enough electrons with other elements to complete an octet. Many compounds of second row elements also appear to obey this rule, but others obviously violate it. Thus the central phosphorus and sulfur atoms of PCl_5 and SF_6 obviously, since they appear to be covalent compounds, must share a total of 10 and 12 electrons, respectively. In terms of orbitals, these electrons can obviously not be accommodated by the 3s and 3p shell, but must, in addition, involve the use of at least one or two 3d orbitals, respectively. PCl_5 in the gas phase has a trigonal bipyramidal structure, SF_6 is octahedral, so that the hybridizations presumably are sp^3d and sp^3d^2. That the availability of relatively low lying d orbitals is involved is strongly suggested by the fact that first row elements do not appear to form any compounds involving more than four ligands around a central atom. No really new problems arise out of this use of d orbitals.

The 3d orbitals of the second row elements may, however, also be involved in other phenomena. Historically, sulfur in sulfuric acid used to be considered hexavalent, phosphorus in phosphoric acid, pentavalent, as shown by the formulas current some 50 years ago:

$$
\begin{array}{cc}
\overset{\displaystyle OH}{\underset{\displaystyle OH}{|}} & \overset{\displaystyle OH}{\underset{\displaystyle OH}{|}} \\
O=S=O & HO-P=O \\
\end{array}
$$

$$\text{(XVI)} \qquad\qquad \text{(XVII)}$$

Under the influence of the Lewis octet rule, these formulas were abandoned because they violated this rule, and formulas involving only four bonds became customary:

$$
\begin{array}{ccc}
\overset{\displaystyle OH}{\underset{\displaystyle OH}{|}} & & \overset{\displaystyle OH}{\underset{\displaystyle OH}{|}} \\
O \leftarrow S \rightarrow O & \text{or} & ^-O-S^{++}-O^- \\
\end{array}
$$

$$\text{(XVIII)}$$

and

$$
\begin{array}{ccc}
\overset{\displaystyle OH}{\underset{\displaystyle OH}{|}} & & \overset{\displaystyle OH}{\underset{\displaystyle OH}{|}} \\
HO-P \rightarrow O & \text{or} & HO-P^+-O^- \\
\end{array}
$$

$$\text{(XIX)}$$

These formulas also did not prove completely satisfactory, since soon evidence accumulated that the bonds drawn in these structures as coordinate covalent bonds $X \rightarrow O$ or $X^+ \rightarrow O^-$ had properties different from those predicted for such bonds. Thus, the bond lengths for such bonds appeared too short, the force constants too large, the bond energies too high, and the dipole moments of the compounds were too small. As a consequence it has been suggested that these bonds must have a partial double bond character. This character may be described in terms of VB theory as resonance between structures XVII and XIX for phosphoric acid, or of structures XVI, XVIII and two structures like XX for sulfuric acid. Alternately, in terms of MO

$$\begin{array}{ccc} \text{OH} & & \text{OH} \\ | & & | \\ {}^{-}\text{O}-\text{S}^{+}{=}\text{O} & \quad \text{or} \quad & \text{O}{\leftarrow}\text{S}{=}\text{O} \\ | & & | \\ \text{OH} & & \text{OH} \end{array}$$

(XX)

theory, this phenomenon may be described as due to the formation of π type MO's involving an AO ($p\pi_O$) of π symmetry of the oxygen atom and a d orbital ($d\pi_X$) of the central atom X (S or P). Such an MO would have the form $\psi = p\pi_O + \lambda d\pi_X$. If λ were of the order of 1, this would be a simple π bond, i.e. the XO bond would be a customary double bond. But λ is generally believed to be considerably less than one, so that the π electron pair is predominantly on the oxygen atom, and only on the central X atom to a relatively minor extent. The cylindrical symmetry of the XO bond, in addition, suggests that there are two $p\pi$ orbitals on oxygen, in mutually perpendicular planes, and two $d\pi$ orbitals on X, and for each XO bond two such MO's can be formed. Hence, a description as a partial triple bond may be even more appropriate.

The conditions for the formation of such a partial multiple bond are of interest. Phosphorus, in PY_3, has a $^1/_2$ share of the six electrons forming the three bonds, and in addition a lone pair of electrons, that is a total of 5 electrons, and hence is neutral; similarly sulfur, in SY_2, with half of the four bonding electrons and two lone pairs, i.e. with six electrons, is neutral. In this case, the nucleus of the central atom has little if any attraction for additional electrons. Any such attraction for an electron in the 3d shell must arise from the fact that the 3d orbitals penetrate into the 3s3p shell. If, however, more bonds are formed, as in PY_4 or SY_4, by equal sharing of electrons, the central atom is left with a positive charge, $+1$ in the case of P, $+2$ in the case of S, and consequently has a residual attraction for electrons in any further orbital. The 3d orbitals in PY_3 or SY_2 is very diffuse, i.e. extend over a large space, and hence do not overlap strongly with the much less diffuse orbital of the ligands. But in PY_4 and SY_4 due to the positive charge, the d orbitals are contracted, and the overlap with the $p\pi$ orbitals of the ligand is greatly increased. As a consequence, multiple bonding is not important in such compounds as PR_3, but is generally observed in tetra-covalent phosphorus and sulfur compounds.

We have seen in the preceding paragraph that a condition for multiple bonding using the d orbitals of second row elements was the contraction of the d orbital due to a positive charge on the atom. In the cases discussed, this positive charge was generated by the formation of an excessive number of σ bonds. A further mechanism for generation of such a charge lies in the polarity of the single bonds, *i.e.* in the inductive effect. When the ligands are considerably more electronegative than the central atom, the electrons forming the σ bond are not equally shared; ionic structures with a positive charge on the central atom are important, and this atom acquires consider-able positive charge. Consequently the d orbital is contracted, and multiple bond formation occurs. This effect is particularly noticeable when the ligand is fluorine, the most electronegative element, as in PF_3 or SiF_4, less so with chlorine in PCl_3 and $SiCl_4$, and almost completely disappears with oxygen in SiO_4^{-4}, and PO_3^{-3}.

In the transition metals the d electrons also play an important role. In their ground state, these metals usually have two electrons in the s orbital of the valence shell, and a number of electrons depending on the atomic number in the d orbitals of the next lower shell. These electrons are roughly as tightly bound as valence electrons, and their orbitals extend in space also roughly as far as the valence electrons. Consequently they are frequently involved in bond formation. Since there are five of these d orbitals, quite a variety of bonding types may occur. A thorough discussion of these is beyond the scope of this chapter, but some brief indication of the principles will be given.

First, it is necessary to recall the form of these orbitals; these are given in Fig. 15. It is seen there that one orbital, d_{z^2}, is different in shape from the other four, d_{xz}, d_{yz}, d_{xy} and $d_{x^2-y^2}$, all of which are identical except for orientation in space. In the centrosymmetric field of the isolated atom all five are degenerate, but in the field of actual molecules differences in be-havior and energy arise.

The most common complexes of transition metals are six-coordinated, and the six ligands are arranged in the form of an octahedron about the central atom. Six hybrid orbitals pointing in the direction of the corners of an octahedron are readily formed from two d orbitals (d_{z^2} and $d_{x^2-y^2}$) and the s and three p orbitals. These d^2sp^3 orbitals are generally considered to be involved in forming the octahedral complexes. Many transition metals, particularly those toward the right end of the transition series, form tetra-coordinated complexes; these may be either tetrahedral or square planar in nature, *i.e.* the ligands may be arranged about the central atom at the corners of a tetrahedron, or at those of a square in one plane. Tetrahedral

Fig. 15. The d orbitals.

References p. 112

complexes are generally believed to involve simple sp^3 hybridization, although some admixture of d orbitals is possible, while the square planar complexes involve the use of four hybrids formed from the orbitals $d_{x^2-y^2}$, p_x, p_y and s (dsp^2). Many other coordination numbers occur more or less frequently including 5, 7 and 8, and various possible hybridizations for these have been worked out. But they are generally considerably more complicated than coordination numbers 4 and 6, and of lesser practical importance because they do not occur as frequently.

A complete MO treatment of such complexes is possible, and is in principle quite straightforward. The only difficulty lies in the need for a rather large number of integrals. In the lowest approximation of the LCAO method, one would require Coulomb integrals for the s, p and d orbitals of the central atom—and these could by no means be assumed equal—and Coulomb integrals for the ligand atoms. Also, resonance integrals for the interaction of each of the types of central atom orbitals with the ligand orbitals would be required. Although rather complete calculations are well within the realm of possibility, particularly since the advent of large and fast electronic computers, such semi-empirical calculations as were outlined for conjugated organic systems are unattractive because there would be too many integrals for which empirical values would have to be evaluated.

Fortunately, a method is available which, although not as extensive as a complete MO treatment, is able to shed considerable light on the complexes of transition metals, on their magnetic behavior and on their spectra. This method has become known as *ligand field theory*, or crystal field theory. It considers the complex as substantially electrostatic in nature rather than covalent, and focusses attention on the d electrons which are, fortunately, almost exclusively responsible for the magnetic properties and visible spectra of the compounds.

The ligand field theory considers the complex as made up of a central positive ion, surrounded by ligands which are either negative ions (*e.g.* Cl^-, OH^-, CN^-, etc.) or dipoles which have their negative end oriented toward the central ion (*e.g.* H_2O, H_3N, etc.). Such dipoles act substantially like negative ions, and do not need any special treatment. In the subsequent treatment we shall talk only of negative ions, and shall assume that dipolar ligands act similarly owing to the orientation of the negative end toward the central ion. The field of the ionic ligands has a symmetry characteristic of the geometry of the complex, and we shall consider only octahedral, tetrahedral and square planar coordination, but in every case this symmetry deviates from the centrosymmetric symmetry of the isolated ion. In the field of the ligands the degeneracy of the five d orbitals is split. Assuming all ligands equal, the manner of this splitting is readily worked out. Consider octahedral coordination, with the ligands placed at equal distances from the central ion, one on each of the positive and negative Cartesian coordinate axes. In this case the lobes of the d_{z^2} and $d_{x^2-y^2}$ orbitals are readily seen to point directly at the various ligands, and any electron in one of these orbitals is strongly repelled by the negative charge of the ligand. The lobes of the d_{xy} d_{xz} and d_{yz} orbitals, however, point in directions halfway between any pair of ligands, and any electron in one of these orbitals is repelled by the negative ligands to a much lesser extent. This difference in repulsion then leads to a splitting of the degeneracy of the orbitals. It can readily be shown by the methods of group theory that the repulsion of the first two orbitals is equal, and that the same is true for the last three. Consequently the five d orbitals split into two groups, two higher energy orbitals and three lower energy orbitals, as shown in Fig. 16(a).

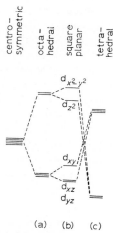

(a)   (b)   (c)

Fig. 16. Ligand field splitting in (a) octahedral, (b) tetrahedral and (c) square planar complexes.

Going on to square planar coordination, further splits occur. The plane of the ligands is generally chosen as the xy plane, and consequently all four lobes of $d_{x^2-y^2}$ point toward ligands, whereas the lobes of d_{z^2} along the z axis do not, and consequently the repulsions involving the latter orbital are less than those involving $d_{x^2-y^2}$, and these orbitals are split as shown in Fig. 16(b). Further, although none of the other three orbitals point toward the ligands, each of the lobes of d_{xy} lies halfway between pairs of ligands, but each lobe of d_{xz} and d_{yz} is found close to only a single ligand; the distance of the d_{xz} and d_{yz} lobes from the ligands actually is the same as the distance of d_{xy} from each of two ligands, and hence these orbitals (or the electrons occupying them) are repelled less than d_{xy}, leading to the splitting shown.

References p. 112

In tetrahedral coordination, the ligands lie at the corners of a tetrahedron having the Cartesian coordinate axes for twofold symmetry axes. Consequently d_{z^2} and $d_{x^2-y^2}$ are least repelled, d_{xz}, d_{yz} and d_{xy} are repelled more strongly. Again symmetry arguments can be used to show that the repulsions are equal for the first two and for the latter three orbitals, and the splitting pattern shown in Fig. 16(c) results.

Thus far the theory predicts two levels each for octahedral and tetrahedral coordination, and four levels for square planar coordination. The situation is, however, further complicated by electron repulsions. Thus, in octahedral complexes, up to three d electrons are readily accommodated by the three lower energy levels, and will, according to Hund's rule, occupy separate orbitals. But, as is well known, e.g. through Hund's rule, electronic repulsions are minimized when electrons occupy different orbitals. Consequently, when a fourth electron is to be accommodated by an octahedral complex, two possibilities occur. The splitting of the energy levels shown in Fig. 16(a) is proportional to the strength of the field of the ligands. If this field is strong, the so-called *strong field* case, the splitting is large compared to the extra electronic repulsion arising from double occupancy of one of the energy levels, and the electron configuration shown in the top half of Fig. 17(b) will result; this configuration will have two unpaired electrons. If the field is weak, in the *weak field* case, the configuration shown in the bottom part of the figure results, and gives rise to four unpaired electrons. With five d electrons one obtains the configurations shown in Fig. 17(c), with five and one unpaired electron in the weak and strong field case, respectively. The configurations for six and seven unpaired electrons are given in Fig. 17(d) and (e), and are seen to involve four and none, and three and one unpaired electrons for the two cases, respectively. With eight or more, just as with three or less d electrons, the two cases are not distinct, as shown in Figs. 17(a) and (f).

The strong and weak field cases correspond to the complexes of types differentiated by the magnetic criterion, which have previously been called ionic and covalent, respectively, by Pauling, and outer and inner orbital complexes by Nyholm. The terminology strong and weak field also may not be completely satisfactory since it is based on the assumption of a purely electrostatic interaction of ligand and central ion, which undoubtedly is a drastic oversimplification. Nevertheless, the results obtained here are consistent with what may be obtained by a MO treatment, and help to shed considerable light on the nature of complexes.

In tetrahedral complexes, similar situations are likely to occur, but the differentiation between the two cases would be expected to occur for central ions involving three to six d electrons, and ions with no more than six d electrons do not usually form tetrahedral complexes. In square planar complexes the situation is obviously considerably more complicated owing to the more extensive splitting, and will not be discussed further.

Owing to the approximation of purely electrostatic interaction between ligand and central ion, it is not possible to make absolute calculations of the ligand field splittings. But the configurations given graphically in Fig. 17,

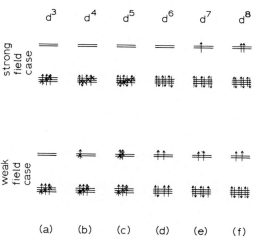

Fig. 17. The effect of electron repulsions in ligand field theory; the strong (top half) and weak (bottom half) field cases for (a) 3, (b) 4, (c) 5, (d) 6, (e) 7 and (f) 8 electrons.

and those similarly obtained from the level diagrams of Fig. 16 for other coordinations generally give rise to a series of electronic states, and energy differences between these can usually be expressed directly in terms of the splitting, and hence relations between different transitions arising from the ligand field levels can be predicted. The visible absorption spectra of most transition metal complexes are due to transitions between these levels, and such calculations have been eminently successful in predicting the observed relations between the various spectral bands, and hence in correlating, systematizing and identifying these spectra.

Many of the ligands involved in the formation of transition metal complexes have π orbitals available besides the σ electrons which form the primary bond of the complex. There can be little doubt that these π orbitals interact with the $d\pi$ (and possibly, when available, as in square planar complexes, the $p\pi$) orbitals of the central ion. Thus bond length, and force constants are consistent with the picture of partial multiple bonding between ligand and central ion. Also, the relatively high stability of such complexes as the cyanides, and the very existence of the metal carbonyls and acetylene complexes is strong evidence for such multiple bonding. Unfortunately ligand field theory has little to contribute to an understanding of this kind of inter-action. Standard MO theory qualitatively is in agreement with such π bonding, but quantitative calculations have been made in only very few cases.

REFERENCES

1 G. HERZBERG, *Molecular Spectra and Molecular Structure*, Vol. II, *Infrared and Raman Spectra of Polyatomic Molecules*, Van Nostrand, New York, 1945, pp. 1–12.
2 L. PAULING, *The Nature of the Chemical Bond*, 3rd ed., Cornell University Press, Ithaca, New York, 1960, p. 340 ff.
3 C. A. COULSON, *Valence*, Oxford University Press, London, 1958.
4 R. DAUDEL, R. LEFEBVRE AND C. MOSER, *Quantum Chemistry*, Interscience, New York, 1959.
5 G. W. WHELAND, *Resonance in Organic Chemistry*, John Wiley and Sons, New York, 1955.
6 Y. R. SYRKIN AND M. E. DYATKINON, *Structure of Molecules and the Chemical Bond*, Butterworth, London, 1950.
7 J. A. A. KETELAAR, *Chemical Constitution*, 2nd ed., Elsevier, Amsterdam, 1958.
8 R. D. BROWN, *Quart. Revs. (London)*, 6 (1952) 63.
9 J. S. GRIFFITH AND L. E. ORGEL, *Quart. Revs. (London)*, 11 (1957) 381.
10 D. P. CRAIG, A. MACCOLL, R. S. NYHOLM, L. E. DIGEL AND L. E. SUTTON, *J. Chem. Soc.*, (1954) 332.
11 C. A. COULSON AND H. C. LONGUET-HIGGINS, *Proc. Roy. Soc. (London)*, A 191 (1947) 39; A 192 (1947) 16; A 193 (1948) 447, 456; A 195 (1948) 188.
12 M. J. S. DEWAR, *J. Am. Chem. Soc.*, 74 (1952) 3341.

Chapter III

The Structure of Molecules

J. D. BERNAL

Department of Physics, Birkbeck College, University of London (Great Britain)

A. PHYSICAL AND CHEMICAL ASPECTS OF MOLECULAR STRUCTURE

1. Introduction

This chapter will deal with the structure of molecules as far as they are known, rather than with the methods of determining such structures which are detailed in other chapters. It will deal primarily with the *physical* structure of the molecule in its stable or ground state. This is essentially a spatial representation of the molecule expressed in terms of the lengths of the bonds by which its atoms are linked together, and of the angles between these bonds.

The physical structure of a molecule should be sufficient to account for all the behaviour of a molecule in the different states of matter, solid, liquid and gaseous, in which that structure remains intact. The *chemical* characteristics of a molecule do, on the contrary, imply a change in that structure. Somewhat paradoxically, the chemist is concerned with a molecule and, indeed, only infers something about it when it is changing into other molecules or is being synthesised from them. In other words, he knows it through its reactivity, through the kind of products from which it can be made or to which it will give rise in chemical change. Now, in this chemical approach, the structural formula of a molecule can determine its structure only in what we might call a logical sense — the logic of the organic chemist who determines even quite complicated structures by means of a network of reactions in which the particular kind of molecule is involved.

However, already from the beginning of the nineteenth century, there has been another way of investigating molecules, indeed, in some respects it was the original way — that is, the study of their physical properties. Mechanical, optical, electrical and thermal studies have led to the determination of such properties of a molecule as its weight, its refractive power, its dipole moment and its magnetic susceptibility. Now, all these physical constants of a molecule are also dependent upon its structure, but they have not, or rather, they did not until recently, give much information of that structure. It is only in the last years through more elaborate physical methods — those, for instance, of X-ray crystallography, or magnetic resonance — that the detailed structure of a number, but by no means a very large fraction of known chemical molecules, have been determined.

The difference between the physical and chemical method of approach was already apparent to Pasteur as he pointed out:

In order to approach the goal towards which so many efforts are striving, there are two paths to be followed. One can start from the chemical properties, properly speaking, alter the substance from various reagents, carefully study the resulting products, and then try to infer the dispositions of the atoms from the way in which their original arrangement dissociates. This analytical progress is powerfully aided by synthesis, that is the study of the processes necessary to reconstitute the arrangement in question starting from more simple ones. This is what can be called the *chemical method* proper, an extremely extensive method, which is that almost universally followed by chemists. But there is another way of tackling the problem. It consists above all of not altering the substance and of investigating scrupulously its properties as an intact unit (*interroger scrupuleusement ses propriétés toutes faites, si je puis ainsi parler*) notably those which are most directly dependent on the mode of its internal arrangement. And as certain physical characteristics, such as the crystalline form, or the effects of changes imposed on light when it passes through crystalline substances or solutions, must play the biggest part, this method of proceeding can be called the *physical method*. Even though it is more restricted than the chemical method, it is perhaps more precise and more certain[*].

In this chapter we will be dealing with the structure of molecules usually in the second or physical sense, that is, we will not be concerned so much with their reactivity as with their stable configuration. These limitations are implied in the general arrangement of this book in which such questions are treated elsewhere, but other limitations arise from its main concern with biochemistry. There are an enormous number of molecules known to organic chemistry that either are not formed in nature or have not been studied biochemically, and in a limited scope there would be little point in dealing with molecules other than those occurring in organisms. The molecules considered here will be organic, that is composed mainly of hydrogen, carbon, nitrogen and oxygen, but they will also include those containing as substituents such atoms as sulphur, phosphorus and the halogens. Salts and metal complexes will be considered only incidentally.

---

[*] Pages inédites de Pasteur, *Oeuvres*, Vol. I, pp. 392–3.

(a) Biochemical implications of molecular structure

Now although the structure of molecules is a subject extremely interesting in itself, here we are concerned primarily with those aspects of structure which either are known to have, or are likely to have, biochemical bearing. In living systems, the molecules are not necessarily the same as they are in the test tube and certainly not as they are in the solid crystal, and when we have to consider the function of the molecule, we must examine to what extent the element of constant or variable structure comes in.

In biochemistry practically no molecules are to be found in the free state, and relatively few are even constituents of pure liquids or crystals. The great majority occur in solution, and in general in solution in a medium mostly consisting of water. Unfortunately, it is practically impossible to determine, except in the simpler cases of molecules too rigid to be affected, what the precise structure of the molecule is in these conditions. The most we can do is to find the structure in conditions which can be determined, that is usually in a crystal and then use this information with appropriate changes to deduce what its structure would be like in its biological environment. The new knowledge of the inner structure of the cell, brought by the electron microscope, indicates that, except for the simplest molecules, they are as likely to be adsorbed on some structural element as to be free.

(b) Stages in the description of molecular structure

The structure of a molecule can be specified on several very different levels of precision. If we take for granted the result of chemical preparation in which the molecule appears either as forming a constituent of a pure substance or of a solution of one such substance in a known solvent, then we can begin with the most elementary physical property of the molecule, with weight. This already enables the purely arbitrary but convenient distinction to be made between those of small and those of large *molecular weight* — the so-called macromolecules. The division is rather hard to draw, but something of the order of molecular weight of 1,000 is a convenient line to divide one from the other. The next element in the description is the *composition* which, taken in conjunction with the molecular weight, provides the *constitutional formula* of the molecule — all that the organic chemist had before him in the middle of the last century. From that, and the knowledge of valence theory, the organic chemists have gradually built up the *structural formula*, that is the formal pattern in which the atoms in the molecule are bound together by a distinguishable and usually rather limited class of bonds — the homopolar valency bonds of the chemist. Now, these bonds taken together really represent only a topological arrangement of atoms.

In Fig. 1 they indicate, for instance, that atom C_2' is next to atoms C_3' and C_1', and the latter is bound also to atoms O_1 and N_3 (see also Figs. 22 a and b, p. 161). The next stage is to add the spatial element to produce the *stereochemical formula* of the molecule. All these are the common places of organic chemistry, and as such will be taken for granted in this chapter: the particular stereochemical functions will be the subject of Chapter 4.

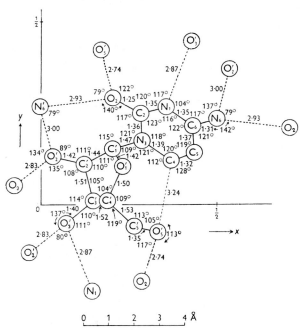

Fig. 1. Cytidine molecule showing inter-atomic distances and inter-bond angles. Note angle of nearly 90° between pyrimidine and pentose rings. (S. FURBERG, *Acta Cryst.*, 3 (1950) 325.)

The modern refined concept of molecular structure begins where these leave off, namely in producing a more or less accurate picture of the precise positions of the atoms, and in an ever higher grade of refinement, of the electrons, relative to each other. This is the kind of information which is provided by carefully carried out diffraction analyses by means of X-rays, electrons, or neutrons, as described in later chapters. The progressive stages of accuracy of representation can be presented in this order:

(1) The first is the determination of mutual atomic positions and rough inter-atomic distances. This at least establishes what atoms are joined to each other by easily distinguishable homopolar bonds as, for instance, by single or by double bonds. This information is hardly more than that provided

by the purely chemically derived stereochemical formula. However, it can give information on interference between different parts of the molecule.

(2) At the next stage bond lengths and inter-bond angles can be determined to a precision of about $1/100$ Å, or 1% of their normal length. This is the result of well-refined analysis, without any very special precautions. In many cases this will also include the location of the hydrogen atoms whose positions are assumed in the earlier stages.

(3) A final stage of analysis—final, that is, for all but the simplest molecules at the present moment but which may be exceeded in the near future—is that which gives all this information together with an electron density map indicating the deviation of the atoms from pure sphericity, due usually to thermal motions, and some indication of the location of electrons in single or double bonds. This kind of analysis can now only be achieved with enormous pains in rather simple molecules, and its value is probably less to the biochemist than to the theoretical organic chemist who may use it to check computations about bonds such as those which have been described in Chapter II.

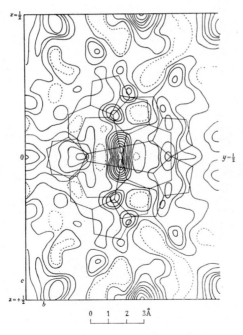

Fig. 2. Vitamin B_{12} showing different stages of analysis. (a) Early stage of Fourier analysis. (D. C. HODGKIN *et al.*, *Proc. Roy. Soc. (London)*, A242 (1957) 228.)

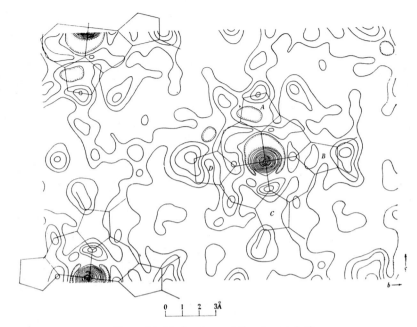

Fig. 2 (b). Early stage of Fourier analysis.

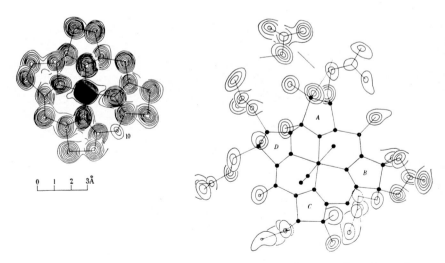

Fig. 2 (c). Showing the pseudo-porphyrin nucleus and surrounding atoms at an
intermediate stage.

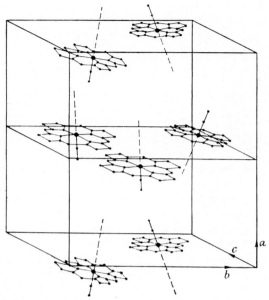

Fig. 2 (d). Showing positions of metal complex in crystal cell.

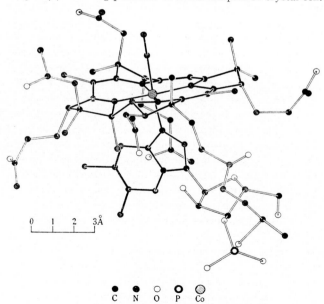

0 1 2 3Å

● ● ○ ○ ◍
C N O P Co

Fig. 2 (e). Showing complete molecule.

As an example of these levels of detail in description, we may take that of vitamin B_{12} which represents a high water mark of crystal analysis up to the present year. These stages are shown in Fig. 2 and its captions.

(c) Value of structural studies

In this chapter we shall be concerned mainly with the structure of molecules only up to the first of such stages, because it is only up to this degree of accuracy that the great number of molecules of biochemical interest are actually known. The greater precision available to special analysis will only be used when they have a definite bearing on biochemical questions, or on some questions of resonance. Now, it may well be asked, what has the structure, defined in this way, to do with the actual problems which appear in biochemistry; to what extent need a knowledge of the molecular structure enter into general considerations of the biochemical function of a molecule? In the past this would have been a very valid criticism because, until a few years ago, not enough structures were known that could have a useful bearing in such problems.

However, the situation is now changing very rapidly. One of the greatest discoveries affecting modern biochemistry, is that of the basic structure of the nucleic acids, particularly of deoxyribonucleic acid. Now, the physical elements of that structure, especially its double helical arrangement (Fig. 30, p. 175) are just those which give it its peculiar biological properties connected with precise reproduction of molecules. Further, these elements are determined less by the general chemical nature of the molecule than by details of its geometrical structure — the parallel packing of the purine and pyrimidine residues. Most of all, and this was the particular stroke of genius of Crick and Watson, does it depend on the convenient way in which the purine groups can be attached to pyrimidine groups by hydrogen bonds so as to link the two, otherwise independent, helical nucleotide chains (p. 176 ff.). A similar dependence of properties on structure, is also emerging in the structure of the proteins, much of which depends on the detailed geometry of the amino-acid chains as determined by hydrogen bonds between them, in the so-called Pauling α-helix (Fig. 25, p. 165). The overall structure of the quasi-spherical molecules of the crystalline proteins like haemoglobin also seems to be determined by the geometrical folding of a chain made of short α-helix links.

Both these examples point to one reason why the full geometrical description of molecular structures is especially desirable in biochemistry, namely, because so many important biochemical molecules are large and have overall arrangements inaccessible to purely chemical methods of analysis.

Another reason for the importance of geometrical structure, depends on the fact that the synthesis of molecules in biological systems always takes place at temperatures low compared to most organic chemical syntheses, and is usually, unlike them, brought about by specific protein enzymes. Now, although the nature of the operation of any of these enzymes has not yet been worked out on a molecular level, we have good reason to believe that it depends on the possibility of detailed fitting between parts of the enzyme and its substrate. This idea is reinforced by what we know of the antigen–antibody relation, in which a foreign molecule — the antigen — can in some indirect way determine the moulding of other molecules in the organism which, when formed as antibody, can combine specifically only with other antigen molecules. If we may ever hope to understand such reactions, it can only be on the basis of a full knowledge of the structures of the molecules concerned.

(d) Conformation

It is consequently worth while to examine the range of structures that appear in the types of molecules which the biochemist has to deal with, and to do this not only in respect to properties which have already been known to follow from these structures but to those which may subsequently emerge. At this point it is necessary to consider certain features of molecular structure which have been, for the most part, ignored in organic chemistry. The organic chemist is concerned primarily with determining the arrangement of the primary valence bonds uniting different atoms. There are other aspects of structure which are not distinguished by chemical formulae of this level, although they are now beginning to arouse interest. In the first place there are those that depend on what is called "conformation" — a more comprehensive term than "configuration" with which the stereochemist deals. Conformational properties are determined by the mutual interaction of parts of a molecule other than those immediately related by primary valence bonds. In the older chemical literature, these have been dealt with in a very vague and unsystematic way as effects of steric hindrance. We now have means of finding a more comprehensive description of structure which will explain the limitations, essentially secondary limitations, in molecular structure due to such interactions of distant parts of molecules over and above those due to conjugated double bonds. By distant I mean those which are not joined either directly or through one intermediary with a particular atom. The degree to which the structure of molecules may be considered to be determined by a primary chemical configuration will vary from molecule to molecule. In the smaller molecule the primary configuration can completely determine the structure, as, for instance, in a benzene molecule. But the larger the molecule the greater are the possibilities of alternative positions of the atoms even within the same bond patterns. For a large number of biological molecules, and particularly for those responsible for the reactions of metabolism, both definite and indefinite, alternative configurations are found.

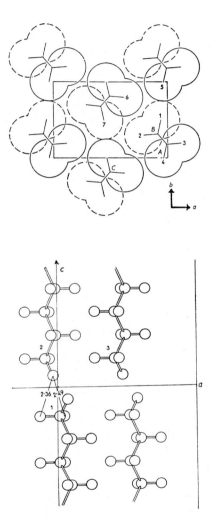

Fig. 3. Cross section and terminal positions of n-paraffin chains $C_{36}H_{74}$ showing H atom positions (atoms marked 1 and 2 lie below those marked 3 and 4 in upper diagram). (P. W. LEASE, *Acta Cryst.*, 12 (1959) 294.)

(e) Rigid and flexible molecules

The reason for the existence of alternatives, or wide ranges of possible conformation, is the limited degree to which the electronic nature of the bonds
fixes the mutual position of atoms more than two atoms apart. Molecules
can accordingly be divided into those which are flexible and those which are
rigid. Only the simplest molecules are completely rigid, such as, for instance,
methane. Others, even such comparatively simple molecules as hydrocarbon
chains, have the possibility of free rotation around all the single or s,p
bonds. In the case of double bonds, π bonds, then there are in general two
alternative configurations, *cis* and *trans*:

$$R^{\diagup C\,=\,C}\diagdown_{R'} \qquad R\diagdown_{C\,=\,C}\diagdown_{R'}$$

This has long been known, for which alternative actually occurs in any
particular case can be established by purely chemical methods. Where free
rotation is possible about any bond, the conformation of that part of the
molecule may be determined by the interaction between more remote parts
of the molecule on different sides of the particular bond. Here, the greatest
influence is most often exerted by the mutual relation of the atoms next to
the bond. For instance, in the hydrocarbon molecules, the alternating
positions of the methylene groups are determined very largely by the repulsion between the hydrogens and the next neighbouring carbon atoms (Fig.
3). But the conformations may be determined also by the extensive effects of the presence of conjugated or partially conjugated double bonds
which tend to produce plane arrangements; for instance, in the amide
group of the amino acids it is this configuration that determines the possible
alternatives in protein structure (p. 153).

For an isolated molecule, what determines the conformation is the sum
of the effects of the interaction of the more distant parts of the molecule.
These may, however, not always be sufficient to produce a stable conformation of minimum energy. Instead, there may be several conformations of
almost equal energy, all of which will appear together at higher temperatures
as in the case of rubber. In such cases the influence of the environment,
whether of similar molecules or of solvent molecules, may be the determining
factor in the distribution of different conformations, notably in the case of
rubber-like substances (Fig. 21, pp. 158–159). In general, these factors will be
most effective in long flexible molecules, especially in polymers. Here, over
and above specific conformations, there appear the two extreme cases—those
of the stretched out and the curled up form of molecule. The former of these
occurs where the reaction with the environment is strong, the latter where
it is weak.

Now, few of the factors determining conformation are treated in classical organic chemistry and then somewhat cursorily and in relation to particular cases. Consequently, it may be worth while to examine them here in a more systematic way.

(f) Van der Waals forces

The first and most important interaction is one which limits the possibility of certain conformations. This is the repulsive factor (b) of the Van der Waals forces, one which falls off very rapidly with the distance, approximately as $1/r^{12}$. Accordingly, it resists the approach of any two atoms, not actually bonded together, when this becomes closer than a certain minimum distance, usually referred to as the sum of their Van der Waals radii. The actual conformation taken up by the section of the molecule in question will be limited by the balance between the extra energy produced by too close an approximation and the bond distortion of the whole molecule needed to take this up. The energy of interaction of atoms pressed together may for another reason rise beyond a certain point; it cannot become greater than that required to form a homopolar bond between the atoms in question. Here

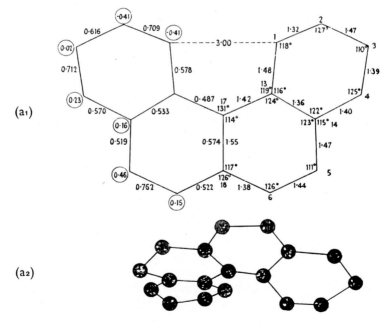

Fig. 4. Molecular overcrowding and distortion. (a).Benzphenanthrene: (a_1). Molecular dimensions; (a_2). Projection of molecule showing twist (S. M. J. SCHMIDT, *J. Chem. Soc.*, (1954) 3302.)

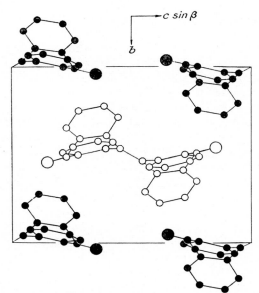

Fig. 4 (b). Dianthrolidene showing half molecules bent atoms centre line. (E. HARNIK AND S. M. J. SCHMIDT, *J. Chem. Soc.*, (1954) 3295.)

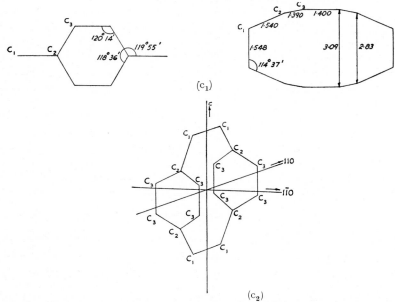

Fig. 4 (c). Di-*p*-xylene: (c₁). Molecular dimensions; (c₂). Projection of molecule showing bowing of rings due to repulsion. (C. J. BROWN, *J. Chem. Soc.*, (1953) 3278.)

awkward configurations may give rise to ring closure, as, for instance, in maleic anhydride and succinimide. Such positions are most likely to occur where a bond with some orienting power is found to link two relatively large and rigid sub-molecules as in cytidine (Fig. 1), that is, in the type of molecule which will be described subsequently as oligomeric or heteromeric.

These phenomena of steric hindrance can, to a certain extent, be studied by straightforward chemical methods, and, more particularly, by the method of the measurement of the energy of the molecule. A molecule in which there is an amount of steric hindrance will have a higher energy and consequently a greater heat of combustion. But this, although it indicates the presence of steric hindrance, does not indicate the actual atomic positions within the distorted molecule. These can only be determined by diffraction methods. Some examples of this in simple molecules are shown in Fig. 4.

The repulsive force fixes the limit of possible structures. Less determining in this respect is the attractive (a) part of Van der Waals forces — the so-called London or dispersion forces which act also between any pair of atoms. These, too, fall off rapidly, though by no means so rapidly as the repulsion potential, with the interatomic distance — as $1/r^6$ rather than as $1/r^{12}$. These forces are those which are responsible for the attachment of molecules together in non-polar liquids and solids. Inside complex molecules it is evident that Van der Waals forces must favour certain configurations rather than others, though the weakness of the forces means that the effect is of the same order as the heat motion at normal temperatures. Consequently, the determination of conformation by such forces is apt to be extremely temperature sensitive. This is the case for a very important set of molecules—those polymers, the so-called elastomers, in which free rotation is possible at many points along the chain. Certain configurations are more probable because they have slightly lower energy, but the difference is not so great as to compensate for the effects of the general disorder or entropy of the structure. Consequently, the usual shape of the molecule is a haphazard one and the combination of a large number of such shapes produces in general a curled up molecule which can only be straightened by the application of force. This is the basis of long-range or rubber-like elasticity.

(g) Hydrogen bonds

There exists, however, in a *hydrogen bond*, another kind of force more powerful than the Van der Waals but far less so than valency bonds. The hydrogen bond fixes the conformation of molecules, especially those which occur in biochemistry, to a considerable degree of rigidity. The electronic and electropolar nature of the hydrogen bond has already been discussed. For practical purposes here, it can be understood almost as if it were a valency bond of considerably lower energy, 6–1 as against 100–30 kcal/mole, for the major covalent bonds. Wherever there exists in a molecule OH or NH or NH_2 groups, then there is a strong possibility that a hydrogen atom of one of these groups, which are more or less highly polarised, will attach itself to the most electronegative part either of the same or of a different molecule — which is usually an O or OH group — forming a hydrogen bond.

The strength of a hydrogen bond can be measured by the closeness of approximation of the molecule it joins. The shorter the bond the stronger it is. The range is between 2.9 and 2.4 Å which lies between Van der Waals bonds of 3.7–3.2 Å and primary valence bonds of 1.6–1.1 Å. The bond strength depends on the degree of polarisation of the hydrogen atom itself which is a function of the electropositive character of the atom to which it is attached. The more negative the part of the molecule in which the OH or NH_2 group finds itself — that is the more acid the OH group — the more the proton is removed from its linked oxygen or nitrogen atom, the higher its effective charge and consequently the stronger the hydrogen bond that it forms. The strongest hydrogen bonds found in organic molecules are accordingly those in the carboxylic acids. Those between hydroxy groups, between hydroxy and nitrogen groups, and between NH and oxygen groups are definitely weaker. Hydrogen atoms attached to carbon do not, in general, form hydrogen bonds.

Hydrogen bonds are responsible, in the first place, for the solubility of molecules in water or in solvents containing hydroxyl, notably alcohols. Water itself is a liquid in which the molecules are held together at low temperatures almost entirely by hydrogen bonds, and only substances which can form hydrogen bonds can be readily accommodated into the water structure. The strength of hydrogen bonds is such that in most cases it counterbalances thermal movement to an extent that the Van der Waals bonds are quite incapable of, so that both external and internal hydrogen bonds are not so affected by temperature.

The possibility of forming hydrogen bonds with water does not imply the existence of OH groups in a molecule; the presence of negatively-charged groups like oxygen atoms, which can accept a hydrogen bond from water, will have the same effect. This accounts, for instance, for the effectiveness of dioxane as a solvent, though it can only act as an acceptor of hydrogen bonds. A molecule which can either donate to or accept from water hydrogen bonds over the larger part of its surface will be highly soluble in water. On the other hand, if it is covered by carbon-bonded hydrogen atoms, it cannot donate or accept hydrogen bonds, so that those of the water molecule are formed exclusively among each other and the neutral, hydrogen-covered or fatty molecules are pushed together as another phase. Oil and water do not mix.

Intermediate cases occur in which there are only a limited number of such sites in a molecule and particularly when there is only one such site, as in monocarboxylic acids. These unipolar molecules are of particular interest in biochemistry because they act as intermediates between water media and those of a fatty nature. Unipolar molecules are hence surface active; they will go to any boundary surface between water and air or any fatty liquid and tend to form monomolecular films. Such films are of great biological importance not only intra-cellularly but in various tissues such as nerve sheath (p. 188).

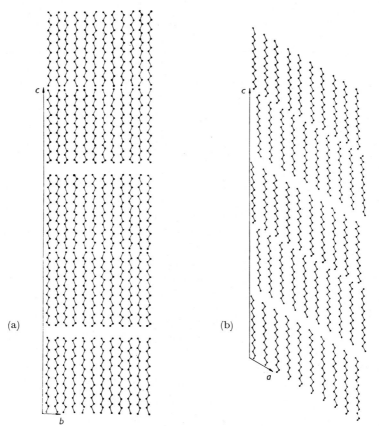

Fig. 5. Crystal structure of stearyl alcohol showing double layers with molecules held by hydrogen bonds. (a). Molecules shown extended and inclined. (b). Molecules shown at right angles to (a). (E. VON SYDOW et al., Acta Cryst., 13 (1960) 770.)

In the absence of sufficient surface to constitute a monomolecular film, the unipolar molecules aggregate in pairs attached by one or two hydrogen bonds or in bimolecular sheets (Fig. 5). In both cases the hydrogen bonds are effectively isolated in a fatty medium. The complicated phenomena of formation of *emulsions* and *detergence* depend on this mechanism.

One most important example of the activity of hydrogen bonds is to be found in the secondary structure of peptides and proteins (pp. 162 ff.). There it is different parts of the same molecule, rather than different molecules, that are attached together. As, however, hydrogen bonds are not specific, that is, any hydrogen bond donor can attach itself to any hydrogen bond acceptor, there are a great number of different ways in which the arrangement can be made, and consequently the number of different conformations is much multiplied.

The strength of the hydrogen bond, however, is so much less than those of covalent bonds that relatively small forces can counterbalance them or even change their positions. A most important example of this is the so-called α–β transition in the proteins which can be brought about by such a weak agency as mechanical stretching (p. 172).

If we include the ionic or coordination bonds with metals in certain organic molecules with the main covalent bonds as determining the rigid parts of the molecular structure, then the forces determining the less well-defined conformations are limited to: Van der Waals repulsion and attraction forces, and hydrogen bonds. Later (pp. 149 ff.) we will consider the effects of even weaker forces, so-called long-range forces, on associations of molecules, but they play no part in the actual conformation of the particular molecule as they are far less energetic even than the thermal motions.

2. Classification of molecular shapes

Having reviewed the nature of the forces that bind molecules together and may also modify their shapes if they are large and flexible enough, we can more profitably classify those shapes themselves.

Such a classification will be necessarily more physical than chemical but should nevertheless serve to bring molecular shape, to the extent that it is a determining factor, into relation with biochemical function. With this in view what is wanted is not so much a classification of all possible or even of all known molecules but rather one of the types most commonly occurring in living systems.

(a) Simple and compound molecules

For this reason a first major division of molecules must be made into two great groups — the simple and the compound. This is not the same division as between the small and the large, though naturally compound molecules tend to be larger than simple ones. A *simple molecule* or monomer is one like an alcohol, a sugar, or an amino acid, which does not contain recognisable sub-molecules as part of its structure. It may, however, contain small active groups or radicals — such as hydroxy or carboxy — which can be added to or subtracted from it. A compound molecule, on the other hand, consists of a number of parts which may be either the same or different, each of which can exist separately as molecules. When these are of the same nature, though not necessarily precisely identical, we speak of them as *oligomers*, with a few parts, or *polymers*, with a large number.

When the parts are of widely different kinds, I would propose the name of *heteromer*. The simplest types of compound molecule, and at the same time the simplest oligomer, are *dimeric* molecules consisting of two identical parts such as maltose, which consists of two α-glucose molecules joined together by a common oxygen atom. A corresponding heteromer would be sucrose—α,D-glucose, β,D-fructose (Fig. 10, p. 136).

The next stage of oligomer molecules is represented by the various oligosaccharides with from 3 to 30 α-glucose residues followed by poly-saccharides such as cellulose with up to ten thousand of these residues. In these cases the residues are identical; in others, like the amino acids, they only have one element in common, that of the α-keto amino group linked together by identical peptide bonds (Figs. 23, 24, 27, pp. 164, 165, 167).

Here, however, each amino acid residue is completed by one of twenty different side groups. These occur in a characteristic sequence in each oligomeric *peptide* or polymeric *protein* molecule (pp. 165 ff.).

At a more complex level the same modified or variegated polymerisation is found in the *nucleic acids*. Here the repeating part is the phosphate sugar (ribose or deoxyribose) pair, itself a compound *heteromeric* molecule (Fig. 29, pp. 173, 174) but each of the sugar molecules carries one of the five purine or pyrimidine groups in an order—not yet known—that gives every nucleic acid its specific properties (pp. 174 ff.).

The individual *nucleotides* which make up the nucleic acids may be taken as the type of heteromeric molecules in living systems. Here the three units, phosphate, sugar and purine or pyrimidine that are joined together are radically different and may thus enter into combinations independently. Similar heteromers are found among other co-enzymes, for instance co-enzyme-A (p. 175).

(a)

Compound molecules can usually, though not always, be distinguished from simple by the weaker nature of the link holding the parts together.

This is, for instance, through an etheric oxygen atom —O— in the poly-saccharides and the polynucleotides, or a peptide bond (formula a) in the proteins. Both the synthesis and the breakdown of oligomers and polymers in living systems occur typically through these links by the action of specific enzymes. This fact indeed justifies the conception of compound molecules in biochemistry.

In some cases, however, the links between the monomers are not different and have to be inferred from the mode of formation or biogenesis of the oligomer or polymer. The typical case is that of the lipids:

$$CH_3 \, (CH_2)_n \, COOH \quad \text{or} \quad -CH_2OH$$

Here the monomer can be shown to be the two ultimately indistinguishable

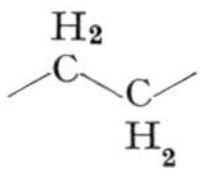

carbon ethylene radicles added successively in the form of acetic acid $H_3C-COOH$. In the sterols the corresponding unit is the isoprene unit squalene from which cholesterol can be derived.

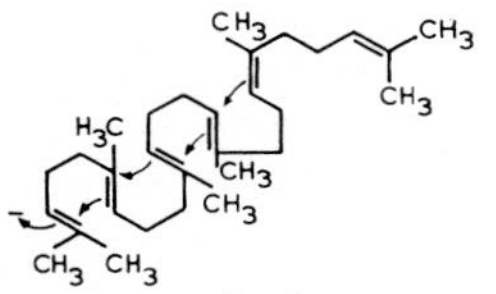

Squalene

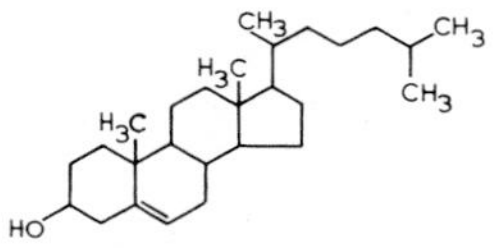

Cholesterol

In such cases, where there is no built-in weak place in the oligomer or polymer molecule, the biological pathways of build up and breakdown are often different.

(b) Classification of simple molecules

It is evident that the classification of compound molecules must be based on that of the simple molecules. As we are concerned here primarily with molecular *shape*, the classification will necessarily differ from that usual in organic chemistry but the difference will not be so great, as both will be based on the structure of the molecular *skeleton*. This is usually thought of as the carbon skeleton, but from the aspect of shape alone a nitrogen atom or occasionally an oxygen atom may take the place of a carbon atom — as for instance in the equivalence in shape of benzene and pyridine.

Benzene   Pyridine

TABLE I

TYPES OF SIMPLE (NON-POLYMERIC) MOLECULES

Molecular type	Examples (Number in brackets corresponds to figures)
1. *Small*	
(a) Single atoms	Ar, etc.
(b) Simple di-, tri-atomic	H_2, O_2, CO_2, H_2O (7)
(c) Short linear	C_2H_2, C_2H_4, C_2H_2HCOOH, CH_3CH_2OH, NH_2CH_2COOH
(d) Stellate	Triglycerides
2. *Long*	Long-chain molecules, lipids
(a) Saturated	Hydrocarbons (3); Alcohols (5); Amines; Mono- and dicarboxylic acids (8); Polyalcohols; Vegetable acids (9); Amino acids (18)
(b) Unsaturated	Carotenoids (21a); Isoprenoids (21b and c)
3. *Monocyclic*	Aliphatic: Cyclohexane, Sugars(10), Pyrimidines (19a and b) Aromatic: Benzene, Naphthalene
4. *Polycyclic*	
(a) Flat	Purines (19c and d); Porphyrins (2, 26c)
(b) Lath-shaped	Terpenes (12), Sterols (11)
5. *Basket-shaped*	Adamantane(6g); Hexamethylene-tetramine; Camphor (13); Alkaloids (22)
6. *Heteromorphic*	Sucrose (10b); Penicillin (14); Biotin; Vitamin B_{12}(2)

It is the arrangement or topology of the skeleton that determines how the shape and size of the molecule depend on the numbers of such atoms it contains (Fig. 6). The same number of atoms can, if stretched out, produce a long molecule; if grouped in rings, produce a flat molecule; or if grouped in a basket-shaped form, a more or less spherical molecule.

Based on the skeleton alone, the molecule shapes can be classified in the way shown in Table I. The table shows a classification of molecules into six major types: 1. Small; 2. Long-chain; 3. Monocyclic; 4. Polycyclic; 5. Basket-shaped; 6. Heteromorphic.

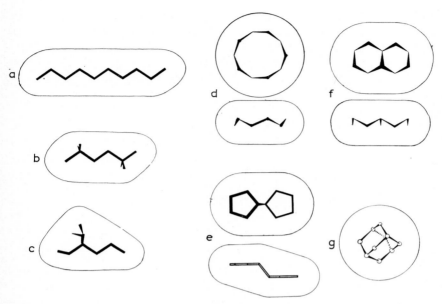

Fig. 6. Approximate molecular shapes and dimensions of saturated hydrocarbon molecules each containing ten C atoms.

    (a) *n*-decane
    (b) α, γ-hexamethylbutane   } $C_{10}H_{22}$
    (c) propyltrimethylmethane
    (d) cyclodecane $C_{10}H_{20}$
    (e) bi-cyclopentane
    (f) dekahydronaphthalene   } $C_{10}H_{18}$
    (g) adamantane $C_{10}H_{16}$

(i) Small molecules

The first is that of the *small* or *quasi-spherical* molecules which are already familiar even in inorganic chemistry. Here the structure is completely determined by the bond system — the bond lengths and the bond angles. Such molecules account for most of the small metabolites occurring in a biochemical system which are continually being produced and incorporated in other molecules, or the reverse, in various enzyme-active cycles. The skeleton of such molecules would, in general, contain up to eight carbon or equivalent nitrogen or oxygen atoms, but so arranged that no more than four atoms are linked in any row, that is, not enough to produce a normal cyclic structure (Fig. 7).

(ii) Long-chain molecules

In the next class are found the molecules with open rows containing more than four atoms. A typical linear molecule is that of the fatty substances, such as hydrocarbons, fatty acids, alcohols, amines, etc. The essential feature of this type of molecule is that it is extended in one direction and that it is fairly rigid. This rigidity proceeds from the orienting effect of one sub-

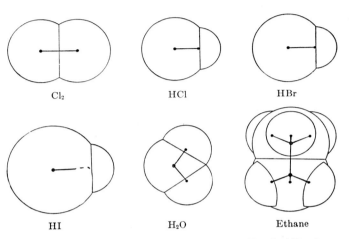

Fig. 7. Simple molecules. (L. PAULING, *Nature of the Chemical Bond*, p. 242.)

stituted carbon group on the next but one in the chain, tending to produce a flat zigzag arrangement (see Fig. 3, p. 122). Where double bonds are present a chain can be formed in *cis* or *trans* configuration, and this is in general more rigid than a simple hydrocarbon chain. This is the case for the carotenoids and isoprenoids (Fig. 21, pp. 158–159).

Linear organic molecules can be divided into two major sub-classes according to whether the carbon attachments along the chain are predominantly hydrogen or alkyl groups, or whether they are hydroxy, amino, or carboxy groups. The first group contains the typically lipid substances, the second the vegetable acids and non-cyclic sugars.

In the lipid-like molecules the effect of the shape is to produce a close-packed parallel alignment (see Fig. 3, p. 122) which persists to a certain degree even into the liquid. For pure or nearly pure substances where the molecules are all of one kind, this results in the formation of sheets or monomolecular layers. If end groups of the molecule are of an alkyl nature, these will be the simple layers of hydrocarbons. If, however, the molecules have one polar end group—such as hydroxy or acid—they will tend to form either double molecules or double sheets (Fig. 5, p. 128). These double sheets are, in biological structures, even commoner than single sheets. Finally, if they contain polar groups at both ends much more rigid structures will be formed (Fig. 8b).

Different kinds of structure result if the chains are branched. Small branches consisting of one or two atoms can be accommodated in the chain — for instance, ketones do not differ in physical properties very much from

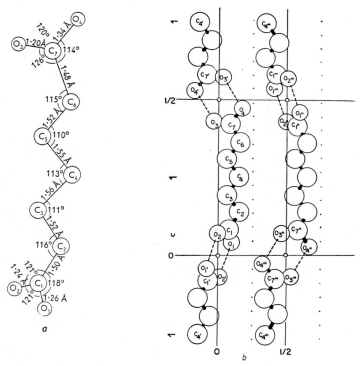

Fig. 8. α-Pimelic acid. (a). Molecular dimensions. (b). Crystal structure showing endless chain of hydrogen bonded carboxyl groups. (M. J. KAY AND L. KATZ, *Acta Cryst.*, 11 (1958) 289.)

their constituent hydrocarbon molecules. If, however, the branches are longer this results in a star-shaped molecule which is particularly difficult to accommodate in any regular way in a crystal. This is the case in a large number of oils. If the branches of the chain, however, are longer still, so that they can bond round and form a parallel bundle, then the whole system may revert to that of packing of simple chains. In the important triglycerides, for instance, the three stearic acid groups attached to the glycerin molecule are found in the crystalline form to be parallel to one another, and the whole triglyceride sheet not to be essentially different from a simple hydrocarbon. The second group of long-chain molecules are those of the open-chain

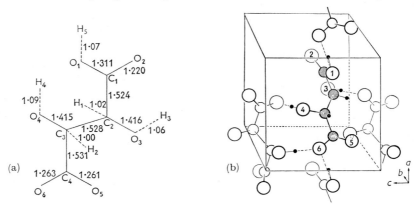

Fig. 9. Tartrate molecule in ammonium hydrogen tartrate. (a). Molecular dimensions. (b). Crystal structure showing network of H bonds. (F. STERN AND C. A. BEEVERS, *Acta Cryst.*, 3 (1950) 341.)

polyalcohols and vegetable acids such as erythritol or tartaric acid or their salts. Here both the internal structure of the molecule and its links with other molecules will be dominated by hydrogen bonds.

(iii) Monocyclic molecules

The next extremely important class is the monocyclic group, which contains not only all the simple aromatic molecules and the corresponding

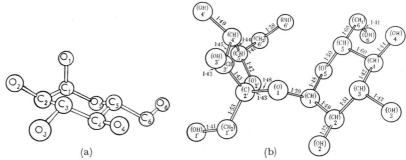

Fig. 10. Sugars. (a). α-D-Glucose. (b). Sucrose.
(A. W. COCHRAN, *Proc. Roy. Soc.*, *(London)*, *A*, 190 (1947) 257.)

heterocyclic molecules containing nitrogen or oxygen in their unsaturated and reduced states, but also the biologically important group of the cyclic sugars, where the ring is closed by an oxygen atom. From the point of view of molecular structure, these are more like the small quasi-spherical simple molecules than are the linear molecules. In monocyclic structures, even where the skeleton is flat as in the aromatic compounds, the sides of the pentagon or hexagon are short compared with the Van der Waals radii of the peripheral hydrogen atoms, so that the molecule as a whole behaves as a sphere, or as a slightly flattened sphere or ellipsoid (Fig. 6, p. 133).

Where the ring is puckered, as in the reduced derivatives or sugars, the resemblance to a spherical molecule is much increased. However, the major properties of such molecules are more determined by the nature of their side groups than by the shape of the molecule itself (Fig. 10). Of the aromatoid molecules, those without hydroxy groups behave on the whole like simple alkyl molecules, whereas those with hydroxyl groups form hydrogen-bonded associations.

(iv) Polycyclic molecules

Of the polycyclic compounds, by far the most numerous are those which

(a)

Fig. 11. Sterols and derivatives. (a). Cholesteryl iodide molecule. (C. H. CARLISLE AND D. CROWFOOT, *Proc. Roy. Soc. (London), A* 184 (1945) 64.)

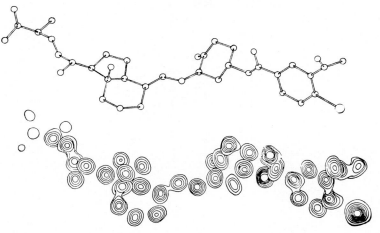

Fig. 11 (b). Calciferol iodo-acetate. (D. C. HODGKIN *et at., Chem. and Ind.,* (1957) 1148.)

contain only two cycles, either with five or six members. Here the planarity of the group is enhanced and a new tendency appears to form parallel arrangements. These appear in the crystalline state as needle-shaped crystals. A case of particular interest to biochemists is that of the purines; their flatness is largely responsible for the tendency of such molecular residues to form extensive complexes as in the nucleic acids, which will be discussed later (pp. 174 ff.).

This tendency is still further enhanced when several rings are joined together in a plane to form the larger aromatic complexes. These, though not usually common metabolites, are of importance as containing many of the carcinogenic substances. From the point of view of shape, though not of

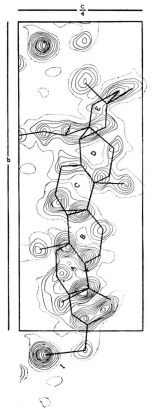

Fig. 12. Pentacyclic terpene. Oleanolic acid. (A. M. Abd el Rahim and C. H. Carlisle, *Chem. and Ind.*, (1954) 297.)

chemical composition, we must add to this group the most important class of porphyrins or porphyrinoid derivatives which consist of four ring molecules joined together through additional carbon atoms and coordinated to a central metal atom — although this is not strictly necessary structurally as hydrogen porphyrins can be made. Here the essential feature is the aromaticity of the porphyrinoid group which ensures its planar character, while at the same time permitting access by other groups to the central metal atom. An example worked out in detail of how such a plane complex works is shown in the case of vitamin B_{12} (Fig. 2, pp. 117–119); and another case is that of myoglobin (Fig. 26c, p. 166).

Lath-shaped molecules. Another important group of polycyclic compounds is furnished by those in which the rings are attached so as to form lath-shaped molecules.

Such lath-shaped molecules partake of the nature both of flat and of long molecules. The former property leads to the formation of needle-shaped crystals, the latter to that of molecular sheets. Accordingly the lath-shaped molecules of the sterols accommodate themselves with lipid molecules and form mixed layers with them.

This group contains a number of hydrocarbons, some of them carcinogenic. Their most important representatives biochemically are the sterols and their derivatives in all their multiplicity (Fig. 11).

Lath-shaped molecules are also found among the related terpenes and in some alkaloids (Fig. 12).

(v) Basket-like molecules

Where the rings are multiply-connected or cross-linked, the resulting molecule will be three- rather than two-dimensional in extent, and resemble, in its relations to other molecules, far simpler spherical molecules; accordingly they show none of the properties of sheet or needle formation attributable to long or flat molecules. One of the simplest of these is camphor (Fig. 13), but others are furnished by alkaloids (Fig. 22, p. 161).

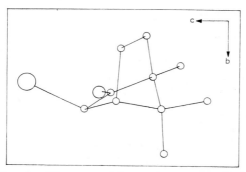

Fig. 13. *trans-d-α-*Camphor-Cl molecules, 'viewed in the direction of the a-axis. (E. H. WIEBENGA AND C. J. KROM, *Rec. Trav. Chim. Pays-Bas*, 65 (1946) 663.)

(vi) Heteromorphous molecules

Finally there are other types of molecular structure which cannot be readily assimilated into this classification or which could be given, with equal justification, a place in several different groups. I call these the heteromorphous forms, which present acutely bent molecules as well as curled and twisted molecules which defy any precise geometrical classification. In these cases, even for small molecules, the shape may be connected very much with biological activity. The most notable example fully worked out

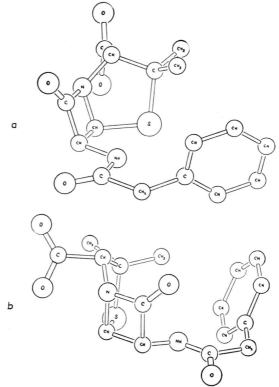

Fig. 14. Benzyl penicillin. Two views of molecule: (a). Showing thiazolidine ring; (b). Showing β-lactam ring. (D. C. Hodgkin *et al.*, in *The Chemistry of Penicillin*, p. 349.)

is that of penicillin (Fig. 14) which is a molecule with a most anomalous shape containing a four-membered ring. It may owe its activity to this as much as to its chemical constitution. A similar heteromorphous molecule, but even smaller, is that of biotin. Here there are two possible configurations, straight and curled, which may also be connected in a way we do not yet understand with its biological property.

(c) Compound molecules, oligomers and polymers

This completes the classification of relatively simple molecules, but there remains something to be said about the compound molecules which, as already explained, consist of several of these simple molecules attached together by usually relatively weak bonds.

The general nature of such compound molecules has been already discussed (pp. 129 ff.) as well as their classification into *oligomers* and *polymers*. On the general lines of molecular shape and rigidity both must be considered as a less or more extreme type of linear molecule. For this reason the *conformation* of the molecules — inaccessible to the organic chemist — must play a much larger part than in simple molecules. As here, however, the articulations at which bonding may take place are further apart, the linking of up to four-membered oligomers is fairly rigid. In biochemistry there is a practical distinction between the oligomers and the polymers with respect to their method of formation. The two, three, or four monomers may be joined together by different mechanics, but beyond that number the operations of adding further monomers become increasingly indistinguishable and lead to a sequence which can be quasi-indefinitely continued. In other words, in the process of polymerisation it is usual to pass from a few to very many without much transition. More careful study may reduce the gap between the oligomers and the polymers, but for the moment it is a convenient one.

Polymers

When we come to the polymers we reach a part of structural chemistry in which the conformation plays a decisive role and the information given by organic chemical methods is relatively limited. Here we can speak of the existence of organisation on different structural levels, an idea first introduced by Linderstrøm-Lang. A particular polymer can be characterised in the first place by the actual definition of the elements which constitute it and the order in which they are found in the chain. This is the so-called *primary* structure, which has been determined with such elegance for proteins by Sanger and his co-workers using chemical methods, and which has yet to be determined in the even more important nucleic acids.

Beyond the primary structure we have to consider the way in which non-adjacent parts of the polymer chain are linked together. This can only be by links which are weaker than those of the main chain, although certain covalent links of the character for instance of the S—S bond in the amino acid, cystine, are permitted. The commonest type of bond here is the hydrogen bond. The mutual arrangement of neighbouring groups in the chain of the order of 10 or 20 will be called the *secondary* structure of the polymer. In the case of the nucleic acids this is all the structure with which we have any detailed acquaintance. In the case of the proteins, on the other hand, it is only the first stage in complexity, that represented by the alternative of α-and β-configurations observed by long-chain or, fibrous proteins, and implied in the structure of many of the crystalline proteins as well (Figs. 24 and 25, p. 165).

To understand the nature of the possible arrangement of polymer molecules it is necessary to go a little into the geometry of long chains. The problem is how to make a line fill space. The simplest solution of this is

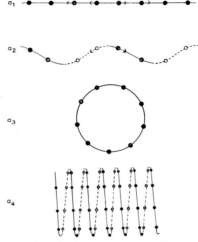

Fig. 15 (a). Coiling and twining of polymer molecules (diagrammatic only). (a_1). Straight chain polymer; (a_2). High-angled helix normal form if monomers are asymmetric; (a_{3-4}). Low angled helix; (a_3). Projection along axis leading to ring if angle is zero; (a_4). Open tube helix. (In real cases cf. Fig. 31 the monomers on alternate turns are staggered.)

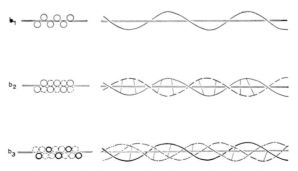

Fig. 15 (b). Twined high-angled helices; (b_1). Single; (b_2). Double; (b_3). Treble helix. Picture and section (note closer packing in b_3 cf. Fig. 28). (J. D. BERNAL, Discussions Faraday Soc., (1958) No. 25.)

equivalent to winding a thread into a ball or bobbin. In the first place any long thin object must have very much less rigidity than a shorter and thicker one of the same mass; in other words, it will be unable to maintain a straight form in the absence of some kind of constraint. Further, there will be a tendency in the various adjacent or nearly adjacent links of the molecule to adopt particular local conformations. Now in artificial molecules these will be at random, and the actual structure will be very mixed up. But in molecules formed by organic processes the arrangements are likely to have a certain mutual similarity and consequently the normal structure will be maintained from link to link and result in a helical form. That is, in the first place, the intrinsic structure of a long-chain polymer is likely to be helical. We must include in this helix the particular case of the half turn of the helix of 180°, this leads to a zigzag structure found in the polyethylenes.

Now such a helix can be stabilised in two ways, either by supporting it at the sides or collapsing it on to itself. For although an individual thread may be weak it can be put together with a number of threads to form a bundle, and this bundle by its very width can supply the rigidity that a single thread misses. Alternatively it can be wound in a coil. Both these forms are found with the same degree of sideways interaction between the two. In the first case the sideways interaction is between different molecules, or between parts of the same molecule widely removed from each other, as occurs in a long-repeating fold. In the second, the interaction is between near, but not quite adjacent, parts of the same molecule as in the α-helix of proteins (Fig. 25, p. 165). A very interesting example of the first case is provided by the arrangement of carbon chains in extremely pure (isotactic) polythene. Here the polythene molecules continue parallel over distances amounting to about 80 carbon residues and then bend over at regular intervals forming a folded structure.

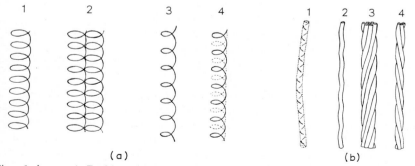

Fig. 16. $(a_{1,2,3,4})$. Packing of low-angled helices; (a_2). Juxtaposed; (a_4). Intertwined (cf. Fig. 30). $(b_{1,2,3,4})$. Coiled-coil arrangements; (b_1). Coiled-coil showing internal helix; $(b_{2,3,4})$. Association of twined coiled coils; (b_3). Sevenfold twist; (b_4). Threefold twist. (J. D. BERNAL, Discussions Faraday Soc., (1958) No. 25.)

Coiling and folding, therefore, are two ways of arranging long molecules, but there remains a third and that is *twining*. Here a limited number of linear molecules arrange themselves as constituents of a rope — they form a set of helices which are linked together, and as a whole form a thicker unit. The number involved in twining is usually fairly small. For geometrical reasons if the molecules are cylindrical (Fig. 15b) this number is more likely to be odd than even, because in this case a better fitting is achieved. Consequently we may expect a fair amount of triple chains as well as of double ones. This is notably the case in one important group of structural proteins — the collagens (Fig. 28, p. 171).

Coiling, folding and twining, are not necessarily exclusive methods of arrangement. It is possible that these processes can be applied one after the other; a molecule can first be coiled and then coiled again, as the so-called coiled-coil arrangement which may occur in the protein keratin (Fig. 16). To distinguish between the first and the second operation we talk here of a *secondary* and *tertiary* structure. Similarly a coiled molecule may be folded. This is what happens in a somewhat irregular way in the globular proteins of the haemoglobin group (Fig. 26a, p. 166). The possibility of further coiling and folding will depend on the dimensions of the groups. Naturally the shorter the resulting molecule the less likely it is to undergo further folding or coiling and there seems to be a natural limitation, at least in substances formed biologically, to two stages of this kind, although in the study of more structures more may come to light.

(d) Molecular aggregates and molecular compounds

A further complexity is produced in a different way by fitting a number of separate coiled and folded structures together to form *aggregate* molecules, as, for instance, in the larger proteins such as the globulins, and particularly the very large respiratory pigments of the haemocyanin group. We must distinguish here between what may be called the intimate complexities produced by twining and the external apposition of molecules of this kind; I would use the word convoluted polymer for the former and aggregated polymer for the latter (Fig. 26d, p. 166).

The concept of *molecular aggregates* is closely linked to that of molecular compounds. The former strictly applies to a larger unit composed of several molecules of the *same* (or very similar) kind, held together by secondary valencies but capable of at least temporary existence as an independent unit. The latter, the true *molecular compounds*, may be physically similar but consist of *different* molecules. Both types must be distinguished from the compound molecules just discussed for in these the various parts are held together by primary valency bonds.

Indefinite and regular molecular aggregates are by definition crystals, so also are indefinite molecular compounds. Indeed, the very few that have been studied carefully, such as quinhydrone or the picric acid complexes of hydrocarbons, have been in this form. They need not, however, extend indefinitely and may instead form limited complexes, such as the globular proteins just discussed. Such limitation in extent does not imply absence of symmetry but it is limited to rotational rather than translational symmetry. In this case the limitation of rotational symmetry to those allowed in crystals with their 2-, 3-, 4- or 6-fold axes is lifted and other periodicities, particularly 5-fold rotation, are admissible and actually occur in all of the globular viruses hitherto studied. Where translation symmetry does occur it is of a one-dimensional irrational helical kind as found in the rod-shaped viruses (Fig. 31, p. 179).

At a much simpler level in biochemistry molecular compounds must play a very important part although it has been exceptionally difficult to isolate them. In particular the temporary existence of a compound between an enzyme protein and its co-enzyme — usually a nucleotide or similar molecule — is postulated to account for enzymic action, but such complexes have not yet been studied in isolation. More recent knowledge of molecular aggregation in liquids indicates that the reason for this is a fundamental one — that the attachment between one molecule and its different partner is of a kind which by its very nature is saturated, that is, it is not easy for other molecules to attach themselves, and therefore not easy for the complex to crystallise. Though such associations may exist in solution they need not be of a permanent nature. In fact the effectiveness of the enzyme–co-enzyme system will depend on the ease in which such molecular compounds are formed and broken up. Molecular compounds are particularly easily formed when aromatic or aromatoid groups are present, and here the mutual relations of the π electron systems may play an important part in determining the total reaction of the joint system. In other words, two substances may be separately colourless and as a compound form a highly coloured system; this is, for instance, the case for the quinone–hydroquinone compound which forms the quinhydrone redox system. Such systems are apt to be very easily affected by the environment and furnish the basis for the activities of the oxidation–reduction type.

3. Physical properties of polymer aggregates

These geometrical varieties of the packing of extended and globular polymers reveal themselves in their physical appearance and properties. Arrangements of extended parallel molecules, whether in bundles or twined, give rise to fibrous structures. These are the bases of the structural tissues of biological systems whether of vegetable cellulose or animal protein as found in supporting fibres, skin, hair and muscle (pp. 181 ff.).

Coiled and folded types on the other hand, whether simple or aggregated, can give rise to definite molecules as in the crystalline proteins. These two aspects are, however, closely inter-related and there is more than one way in which a globular arrangement can turn into a fibrous one.

(a) The globular–fibrous G–F transformation

The simplest form this can take is by the unfolding or conversely the rolling up of a long polymer chain. This can be brought about in solution by appropriate changes of ionic environment or pH, for instance, in albumen. As long as no cross links are formed this process is reversible.

On a higher level, globular molecules, without unrolling, may associate reversibly themselves not into crystals but into relatively weak fibres. The process has been particularly well studied in the cases of fibrous insulin and fibrous actin. This indeed is the classical G–F transformation of Szent-Györgyi.

When fibrous aggregates are formed from globular they can be fixed irreversibly in this state by appropriate agents which may be enzymic. In the fibrinogen–fibrin transformation, the enzyme thrombin removes part of the fibrinogen molecule and thus enables the remaining parts to join up through true homopolar bonds to form the polymerised fibrin.

When a similar process is brought about by heat or acids, cross linking may occur irregularly leading to irreversible *denaturation* to a flocculated network of fibres. It is only if the new links are much weaker than the old that they can be preferentially broken and the denaturation is temporary and reversible.

A still further variant in polymer organisation is the formation of spherulites favoured by many synthetic polymers where it would appear that the molecules are usually arranged parallel to the faces of the spherulites rather than perpendicular to them. These spherulites may be of a crystalline nature — that is rigid — or they may represent a kind of internal liquid as in the case of the many lipoproteins or in the higher aggregations formed by nucleoproteins, as for example, in chromosomes.

Polymer molecules need not be definitely or indefinitely extended simple linear aggregates of monomers; they may be *cyclic, branched,* or *cross-linked.*

In these more complex types of association, it is necessary to depart still further from the earlier chemical conception not only of a molecule but of a pure substance. A chemical molecule was originally conceived of as a definite entity which could be precisely described and which could be consequently associated together to form a pure substance, normally a pure crystalline substance. However, in biochemistry we may often have to deal with molecules of indefinite shape and composition for instance, in the starchy, mucous and glutinous substances. Here it is impossible to talk about molecular structure, except in a statistical sense, but the distinctions for instance between the starches of simple and branched forms — the amyrins or the amylopectins — can be made not only chemically but by diffraction studies. The full analysis of cross-linked or anastomosing polymers, typically hard amorphous substances, such as keratin, is still more difficult.

(b) Isotactic polymers

The mutual relations of polymers are very largely determined by the degree of perfection of the individual units and this is the more so the longer and more complicated the polymer is. Naturally, any kind of irregularity which can be rejected in the case of individual molecules has to be somehow incorporated into a structure composed of several polymer molecules. Consequently the resulting material will have a more or less crystalline character according to the regularity or irregularity of these individual polymers. This now has very important industrial consequences in the various new kinds of regular polymers which have been produced by solid state catalysis by the Ziegler or Natta processes — the so-called *isotactic* polymers. The first obvious effect of these polymers is to produce the solid substances which are much stronger and more difficult to melt than the normal casually produced polymer.

Both artificial and natural polymerised substances contain a variable amount of so-called crystalline and amorphous regions. This is not only a function of the molecular shape, it also depends on the state of the environment. Polymers having definite connections extending over large distances are susceptible not merely to the ordinary conditions of temperature and pressure but also to the physical conditions, whether permanent in the nature of tensile stress, or variable as in shear applied to polymer liquids.

In the first case it is evident that tension promotes the parallelism of chains and consequently crystallinity. Rubber-like substances can generally be crystallised even at fairly high temperature when stretched, and they revert to the amorphous form on contracting. In solution, polymer molecules, if of sufficient length, tend to react to the stresses in the medium by aligning themselves, in relation to the direction of shear or flow. If they are long enough this alignment is parallel. If they are of intermediate length, they set at some definite angle, the so-called angle of isocline, to the flow, which reveals itself in *flow birefringence*. Many biologically interesting polymers show these properties very markedly; most animal or vegetable fibres have a birefringence depending on the stress, whereas biochemical polymers in solution, particularly proteins, polysaccharides, and nucleic acids, give very marked flow birefringence.

(c) Colloidal properties of polymers

Not only have polymer molecules peculiar properties when they are in a fairly dense state, but also they exhibit them in dilute solutions where the molecules are in general fully separate. Many of these properties are dealt with in other chapters of this series. They form the essence of colloid science. However, something must be said here about the effects of the nature of the molecular structure on the colloidal properties. Here very much depends on the shape of the polymer molecule and on the nature of its surface. As to the first, in general, polymer molecules can be classified, just as can simple molecules as quasi-spherical, elongated, or planar (p. 131). Mutual relations of quasi-spherical molecules are the same in all directions, while those of the other types of molecules show a marked anisotropy of grain. The surface of a polymer molecule will, in general, be highly dependent on the medium in which it is placed. According to the relation between the medium and the major elements covering the surface of the molecule, the molecule will tend to produce either a maximum or a minimum surface. It will be either curled up or extended. An even stronger determining force will be provided by the presence in the molecular environment of any surfaces, either those of larger molecules or actual free surfaces, or inter-surfaces, or crystals. In most of these cases there will be a tendency to produce the maximum common surface; those parts of the molecule which are particularly attachable to one medium will tend to stretch themselves out on to it in the form of a film. Thus, for instance, we know from crystalline studies that many protein molecules can be found in more-or-less globular conformation. However, it is more likely that in the cell where they are functioning as enzymes, for instance in mitochondria, they are probably stretched out on the lipoid layers of the cell.

The variability of molecular structure imposed by the medium is of particular importance in biochemistry, where the medium varies so much in chemical and physical composition. The precise determination of structure of complex molecules is at present only possible where the substance can be obtained in crystalline form. The results of diffraction analysis based on crystals (p. 115), even if successful, cannot be transferred safely to the molecule *in vivo* without other evidence such as spectroscopic, which indicates that at least the optically-reacting part of the molecule is the same in the crystal as in the cell. This, for instance, has been shown to be the case in haemoglobin.

(d) Long-range forces

The nature of the polymer surface determines in turn whether the interaction between different polymer molecules will be limited to contact or will extend through the medium. In aqueous media, which are for the most part the only ones of concern to the biochemist, the possibility of long-range action depends on the presence of charges on the surface of the molecule. Where the molecules contain separated positive and negative charges, as in the so-called ampholytes, the range of those forces may be very large. It depends on the size of the particles, and in general the larger the particle the larger relatively is its range of action. Particles of a few hundred Ångströms in dimensions can interact over distances of some thousands of Å, whereas particles of only ten Å in dimension hardly affect each other at distances greater than their diameters. Consequently radically new properties appear, once the size of a colloidal aggregate has reached a critical value, something in the order of 100–500 Å. Now this is the actual size adopted by particles of great biological importance such as microsomes, viruses, plastids, and a number of other active constituents of cells. They are probably responsible for most of the easily disturbed micro-structure of cells.

Where the particles are spherical and exert an isotropic reaction on each other, these long-range forces may provide a possible stability which is independent of the total concentration of the large molecules, in which

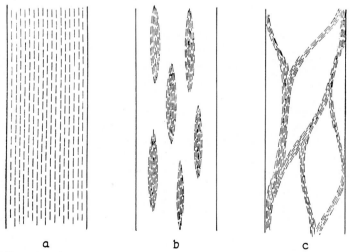

a   b   c

Fig. 17. Tactoids. (a). Oriented solution of long molecules (Tobacco mosaic virus). (b). Concentration by change of pH into tactoids. (c). Effect of stirring, fusion of tactoids to form gel (rheopexy). (J. D. BERNAL AND I. FANKUCHEN, J. Gen. Phys. 25 (1941) 111.)

case the system will divide into two phases—one containing a concentration which may actually be as low as one per cent of the colloidal material, and a liquid containing practically none of it. These arrangements consequently form little drops or fine emulsions in the media. They are the so-called *coacervates* which have been postulated by Oparin as one of the stages in the origin of life. The range of activity is markedly greater if the particles, instead of being quasi-spherical, are elongated or planar as in many intra-cellular or extra-cellular processes such as cilia or endothelial membranes (p. 185). When the particles are elongated, instead of a spherical drop, with the structure of a coacervate, there is formed a spindle-shaped drop or a *tactoid*, in which all the particles are oriented with their long directions in parallel (Fig. 17). These tactoids, which can be studied in struc-tures formed from tobacco mosaic virus, can exist as separate spindle-shaped bodies, or they can be fused together to form a network which corresponds to what has been called for many years a gel of greater or less rigidity according to the amount of liquid contained. Now X-ray studies have shown that in tactoids formed of homogeneous materials the individual particles which are of the order of 150 Å in diameter, are arranged not only in parallel but also equidistant—the distance between them being determined by the ionic character of the liquid and not in general by the concentration of the colloidal particles. Similar equidistant structures are particularly evident in cellular structures, especially in muscle where, as Huxley has shown, there is the further complexity of a linear molecular compound between large and small fibres, giving a beautiful hexagonal arrangement (Fig. 33b, p. 183).

Where the particles are flat, another kind of tactoid is formed, and here the arrangement also preserves equidistance over large lengths. In fact these kinds of tactoid were first observed in inorganic systems—in iron oxide and hydroxide gels, where the regularity was so great that they could act as diffraction gratings for ordinary light. These are the so-called iridescent gels. Iridescences of this kind are also found in a variety of biological systems responsible for many evanescent colours of living marine organisms, or are found crystallised in their shells—mother of pearl is a typical example. It would be useless at this stage to go further in the discussion of the molec-ular features of intracellular organisation, as this subject, thanks to the use of the electron microscope in conjunction with X-ray studies, is advancing so rapidly that anything said now would be out-of-date by the time this book is printed. But there is no doubt that here is a vast field in which an appreciation of the function of molecular structure will be important, and which in return will provide new ideas about that structure.

B. STRUCTURES OF THE MAJOR CLASSES OF BIOCHEMICAL MOLECULES

The brief account just concluded of the structures of molecules from the simplest to the most complex was carried out to illustrate the general principles of molecular structure. The sequence followed, however, was essentially a geometrical one. From a more biochemical point of view it may be

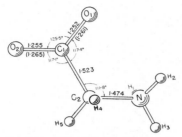

Fig. 18. Amino acids. (a). Glycine molecule (in Zwitter-ion form). (R. E. MARCH, *Acta Cryst.*, 11 (1958) 654.)

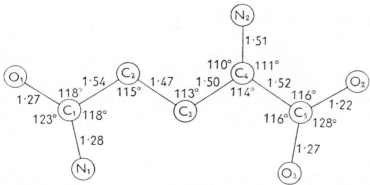

Fig. 18 (b). L-Glutamine molecule. (W. COCHRAN AND B. R. PENFOLD, *Acta Cryst.*, 5 (1952) 644.)

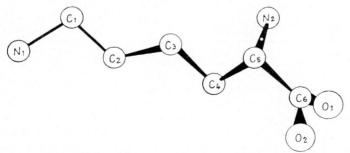

Fig. 18 (c). L-Lysine molecule. (S. RAMAN, *Z. Krist.*, 9 (1959) 301.)

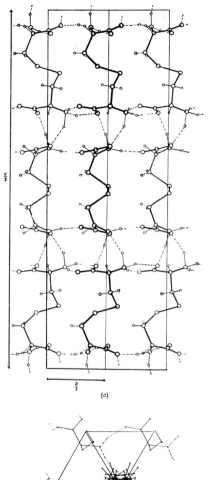

(a)

(b)

Fig. 18 (d). L-Cystine. Two projections of crystal structure showing sixfold helical twist of molecules held together in piles of columns by hydrogen bonds. (B. M. OUGHTON AND P. M. HARRISON, *Acta Cryst.*, 12 (1959) 396.)

useful to look over the field again, this time according to the different biochemical types of molecules.

Inevitably there will be an overlap between the two sections, but it may serve to bring out the different kinds of relationships, geometrical and chemical that may exist in such a biologically selected set of molecules. Here, for the purposes of this discussion, I propose to divide the biological molecules into seven classes: (a) nitrogen compounds, (b) carbohydrates, (c) lipids, (d) sterols and terpenes, (e) alkaloids, (f) peptides and proteins, and (g) nucleotides and nucleic acids. The first five of these correspond to relatively simple arrangements, although they also include some regular polymers such as the polysaccharides. The last two groups contain the biologically complex polymers, the proteins and the nucleic acids.

In discussing these structures little will be said about the question of the biogenesis of the molecule in question and as far as possible only of such features of their structure as seem to have some relation to their properties will be discussed.

1. Simple nitrogen compounds

The nitrogen compounds referred to very briefly here will be firstly the amino acids and then the cyclic nitrogen compounds, the pyrimidines, purines and porphyrins.

(a) Amino acids

The structure of α-amino acids has now been very carefully studied by X-rays, and some dozen out of the twenty are known with a very considerable

TABLE II

AMINO ACIDS

α-Glycine	R. E. Marsh, *Acta Cryst.*, 11 (1958) 654.
β-Glycine	Y. Jitaka, *Acta Cryst.*, 13 (1960) 35.
γ-Glycine	Y. Jitaka, *Acta Cryst.*, 11 (1958) 225.
DL-Alanine	J. Donohue, *J. Am. Chem. Soc.*, 72 (1950) 949.
D-Isoleucine-HCl·H₂O and -HBr·H₂O	J. Trommel and J. M. Bijvoet, *Acta Cryst.*, 7 (1954) 703.
DL-Serine	D. P. Shoemaker, J. Donohue, R. E. Barieau and C. S. Lu, *Acta Cryst.*, 6 (1953) 241.
L-Serine phosphate	S. H. McCallum, J. M. Robertson and S. A. Sim, *Nature*, 184 (1959) 1863.
Lₛ-Threonine	D. P. Shoemaker, J. Donohue, V. Schomaker and R. B. Corey, *J. Am. Chem. Soc.*, 72 (1950) 2328.
L-Tyrosine-HBr	R. Srinivasan, *Proc. Indian Acad. Sci.*, A, 49 (1959) 340.
L-Glutamine	W. Cochran and B. R. Penfold, *Acta Cryst.*, 5 (1952) 644.
L-Glutamic acid	S. Hirokawa, *Acta Cryst.*, 8 (1955) 637.
L-Lysine-HCl·2H₂O	S. Raman, *Z. Krist.*, (1959) III, 301.
L-Hydroxyproline	J. Donohue and K. N. Trueblood, *Acta Cryst.*, 5 (1952) 419.
Histidine-HCl·H₂O	J. Donohue, L. R. Lavine and J. S. Rollett, *Acta Cryst.*, 9 (1956) 655.
DL-Methionine-(α)	A. McL. Mathieson, *Acta Cryst.*, 5 (1952) 332.
L-Cystine	B. M. Oughton and P. M. Harrison, *Acta Cryst.*, 12 (1959) 396.
Cystine-2HBr	J. Peterson, L. K. Steinrauf and L. H. Jensen, *Acta Cryst.*, 13 (1960) 104.
Aspartate ion in Zn, Co, Ni salts + 3H₂O	J. Doyne, R. Pepinsky, and J. Watenabe, *Acta Cryst.*, 10 (1957) 438.

degree of precision. A list of amino acids whose structures have been accurately determined by X-rays are shown in Table II and some of their structures are shown in Figs. 18 (a–d). The major structural feature of amino acids which is important for that of protein, first brought to light by Pauling's discussion of their chemistry, is the planarity of the amide groups. This is, as he points out, a consequence of the partial resonance between the carboxy and the C–N group in the α position. In Fig. 24, p. 165 it can be seen that the N–C(O) bond is 1.32 Å, as against 1.47 for the N–CHR bond. This means, effectively, that when amino acids are joined together into polypeptides through the peptide link, there can be no rotation about the C(O)–N(H) link. In other words, the degrees of freedom of the polypeptide chain are the same as that of the hydrocarbon chain with the same number of atoms as the polypeptide chain has of amino acid residues.

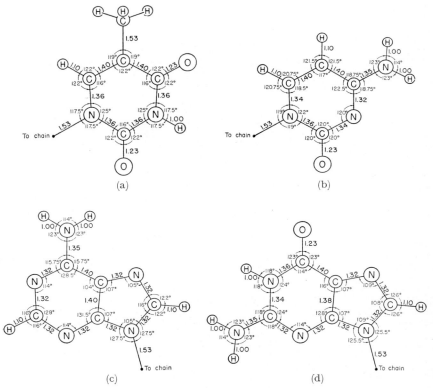

Fig. 19. Purines and pyrimidines showing relation to deoxyribose nucleic acid chains. (a). Thymine. (b). Cytosine. (c). Adenine. (d). Guanine. (L. PAULING, *Nature of the Chemical Bond*, p. 306–308.)

(b) Pyrimidines, purines and porphyrins

The structures of these compounds have been studied almost as closely as those of the amino acids themselves, as is shown in Table III and Fig. 19. The peculiar stability of the canonical five purines that are constituents of the nucleic acid, are due to the 6,5 fused ring system they share with uric acid (Figs. 19 and 29, pp. 173–174).

The variety of these structures only emphasizes their common ring skeleton, which must be a peculiarly stable one.

Another example of stability is furnished by the porphyrins and their derivatives, such as the biliverdins and bilirubins. Here we have to deal with the linkage of pyrrole groups, but in the tetrapyrroles a predominant part is also probably played by the central metal atom which ensures the planarity of the group and its general aromatic character.

There have as yet been few detailed studies by X-rays of the structure of naturally occurring porphyrins (Table III), although the structure of the related artificial phthalocyanin dyes are classics of crystal analysis. Evidence for the relation of porphyrins to other molecules has been found in the haem group of myoglobin (Fig. 26c, p. 166) containing but the anomalous reduced porphyrinoid nucleus of vitamin B_{12} (Fig. 2, pp. 117 ff.).

TABLE III

PYRIMIDINES, PURINES AND PORPHYRINS

Pyrimidines

2-Amino-4-methyl-6-chloropyrimidine	C. J. B. CLEWS AND W. COCHRAN, *Acta Cryst.*, 1 (1948) 4.
4,6-Dimethyl-2-hydroxy-pyrimidine	C. J. PITT, *Acta Cryst.*, 1 (1948) 168.
4-Amino-2,6-dichloro-pyrimidine	
5-Bromo-4,6-diamino-pyrimidine	C. J. B. CLEWS AND W. COCHRAN, *Acta Cryst.*, 2 (1949) 46.
4,5-Diamino-2-chloropyrimidine	N. E. WHITE AND C. J. B. CLEWS, *Acta Cryst.*, 9 (1956) 586.
Uracil	G. S. PARRY, *Acta Cryst.*, 7 (1954) 313.
Thymine monohydrate	R. SERDIL, *Acta Cryst.*, 14 (1961) 333.

Purines

Adenine-HCl	J. M. BROOMHEAD, *Acta Cryst.*, 1 (1948) 324.
	W. COCHRAN, *Acta Cryst.*, 4 (1951) 81.
Guanine-HCl	J. M. BROOMHEAD, *Acta Cryst.*, 4 (1951) 92.
Theophylline	D. J. SUTOR, *Acta Cryst.*, 11 (1958) 83.
Caffeine	D. J. SUTOR, *Acta Cryst.*, 11 (1958) 453.

Porphyrins

Ni-etioporphyrin	M. B. CRUTE, *Acta Cryst.*, 12 (1959) 24.
Phyllochlorinester	W. HOPPE AND S. WILL, *Z. Krist.*, 113 (1960) 104.

The porphyrinoid substances, other than the haemoglobin group, that are most important biologically are the chlorophylls. It is evident that the structure of chlorophyll determines its reaction to light, but the nature of this mechanism has not yet been fully established.

2. Carbohydrates, vegetable acids and aldehydes

The structures of these molecules are by no means so well known as those of the nitrogen compounds. This is not only because of the lack of interest, but also because they are structures particularly difficult to work out, being essentially compounds of an aliphatic kind with considerable freedom of internal movement. Also they are, by definition, covered with hydroxyl groups which lead to very open work and complex structures. The notable feature is the way in which these acidic or alcoholic hydroxyl groups, are linked together. The strength of the hydrogen bond makes for the closest junction between the acidic hydroxyls of the molecule. Of these, by far the best studies concern oxalic acid. The interest here is essentially that of precise measurement of interatomic distances; probably no organic molecule has been studied in such detail.

Structures which have been studied almost as much but with less success because of their complexity, are some of the vegetable acids, and notably tartaric acid and its salts (Fig. 9, p. 136). Here again this is rather because of the industrial importance of the salts than on account of their biochemical functions. The precise structure of pyruvic acid, for instance, probably the most important vegetable acid in the process of metabolism, has not been studied.

The determination of the structure of sugars has presented enormous difficulties, and in fact most of them have only been determined in the form of complexes with salts (Fig. 10, p. 136). Enough, however, is known to bring out their essential characters as quasi-spherical, hydroxy-covered molecules.

Polysaccharides

More interest has centered on the polysaccharides but also largely for their industrial rather than their biochemical importance. Here the structure is evidently essential to the understanding of the properties, because a purely chemical approach is limited to the primary structure. Cellulose in its various forms and modifications has been particularly well-studied for a large number of years, but it must be admitted that the details of the structure, particularly the hydrogen bonding between the parallel chains, is not well known. Nor do we understand the relations between the length of the cellulose chains and the amorphous parts of natural cellulose textures. However, with the combination of electron microscope studies, some idea of the nature of the cell wall, both of bacteria and plants, has been elucidated, and it appeared that cellulose occurs not so much in single molecular chains as in a chain aggregate containing something of the order of a hundred chains in parallel.

The formation in the harder parts of plants of a combination between cellulose and various polyphenols—the so-called lignins—to make a woody substance is through a mechanism which is still largely unknown. This appears to be of the industrially well-recognized cross-linked type of polymeric structures but evidently not well enough crystallised for existing methods to disentangle.

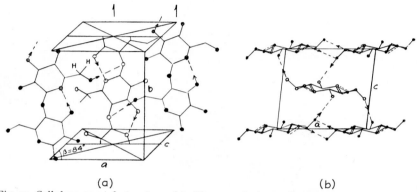

(a)   (b)

Fig. 20. Cellulose crystal structure. (a). View nearly normal to rings showing internal hydrogen bonds. (b). Projection along fibre axes showing cross hydrogen bonding. (C. Y. LIANG AND R. H. MARCHESSAULT, *J. Polymer Sci.*, 37 (1959) 385.)

Even more complicated are the structures of the starches, which have also been extensively studied without very conclusive results. The X-ray pictures of starches are peculiarly vague and electron methods have not yet had time to be applied thoroughly, but it would appear that the general distinction between the amyrins, which have straight chains, and the amylopectins, which have branched ones, can be substantiated on the X-ray evidence.

Of greater interest from a general theoretical point of view is the essential difference between celluloses, or other straight polysaccharides, on one hand, and starches and pectins, on the other. In the latter sugar residues are set at an angle and can therefore be curled around other small molecules notably in the case of iodine which gives the characteristic blue colour for starch.

3. Lipids

It is in the great class of lipids, which for the most part consist of hydro-carbon chains with different terminations, that the importance of the physical aspect of structure of molecules is most evident. Chemically, lipids are useful as the concentrated storers of oxidation energy. But probably in the origin of life and the subsequent development lipids had been even more important because they have furnished a type of structure which no other biochemical compound can give rise to, namely a discriminatingly permeable membrane such as occurs both inside and on the surface of cells. This is a consequence, as already indicated, of the length of the molecules and the way in which they normally tend to pack together side by side to form sheets.

The structures of lipids are, for this reason, comparatively simple and they were in fact almost the first of organic compounds whose structures were fully determined (Figs. 3 and 5, p. 122 and p. 128). Another aspect of the structure of lipid substances is the prevalence of liquid crystal forms among

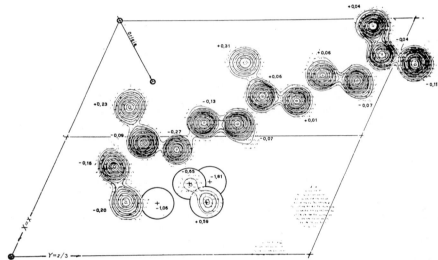

Fig. 21. Isoprenoid molecules. (a). *Trans* isomer of β-ionylidene crotonic acid related to Vitamin A. Molecule in cell. Numbers refer to heights above or below mean plane. Note single and double bonds.

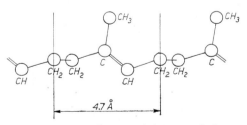

Fig. 21(b). Part of *trans*-polyisoprene chain.

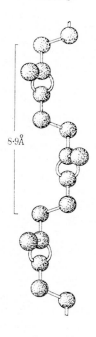

8·9Å

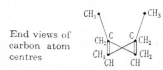

End views of
carbon atom
centres

Fig. 21 (c). Part of *cis*-polyisoprene chain. Gutta percha. (E. L. EICHHORN AND C. H. MACGILLAVRY, *Acta Cryst.*, 12 (1959) 872.)

them. Effectively this means that a lipid layer has at the same time the properties of a crystal and a liquid; it can have a certain rigidity but it can also fold round other surfaces.

Carotenoids

Although the major lipids that occur in cells are either saturated or have one or two double bonds, the structures containing a large number of conjugated double bonds are clearly related to them, and are also necessarily fat soluble. These are the carotenoids which, as organic coloured compounds, have such a large part to play either acting as co-enzymes or in various types of receptors. These compounds, however, differ very much from the fats in their rigidity of the molecule due to its double bond character and the corresponding high crystallinity of the compounds formed. They, however, do form structures such as those found in the retina of the eye in which the optical properties are related to the kinds of crystalline arrangement (Fig. 36b, p. 190).

4. Sterols and terpenes

Closely related to the lipids, physically as well as chemically, are the sterols. The most physiologically active sterols—heart poisons, the sex hormones, and other endocrine types, such as corticosterol—have all in common a molecular skeleton consisting of linked rings terminating in some active group, and consequently have an elongated shape similar to that of the hydrocarbons. They are also usually, except for terminal groups, hydrogen covered. Consequently sterols will normally insert themselves in lipid layers, and probably exert their extremely highly specific physiological functions when acting in such a way.

The structures of sterols have been most intensively and extensively studied. Diagrams of sterols of particular importance — cholesterol and calciferol or vitamin D have been shown in Fig. 11, p. 137. The specificity of sterols clearly arises not only from their shape or their terminal groups, but also depends on the degree of saturation, that is the presence of double bonds in different parts of the molecule. This, for instance, seems to be part of the carcinogenic character of sterol-like hydrocarbons — some of which have very high carcinogenic activities. Their structures do not differ at first sight from those with low activities, but all of them are found to have certain specific electronic configurations. This will be discussed in another chapter.

The sterols are for the most part optically active substances, and this, combined with their tendency to form layers and liquid crystals, gives the sterols a particular importance in producing a layer structure which is at the same time twisted. These twisted structures have long been studied by physicists in the so-called cholesteric phenomena, and the colours they produce can be seen by anybody, for instance, on the surface of white fish muscle. Detailed studies have shown how the appearances of colours are limited to the degree of twist of successive layers, but the biochemical importance of this, if any, has yet to be found.

Closely related to the carotenoids and the sterols, and making a link between them and the lipids, are the terpenes, many of which have essentially the same skeleton as sterols while others have simpler ones. Terpenes have not been structurally very much studied, although a few have been fairly completely analysed — notably geranylamine and the oleanolic acids (Fig. 12, p. 138). Polymerisation of terpenes in vegetable cells gives rise to various kinds of resins, of which the most interesting industrially are the latexes of the rubbers.

5. Alkaloids

The alkaloids have attracted interest for a long time on account of their extremely violent physiological activities. Their structures, however, are very complex and their full elucidation has made considerable calls on X-ray analysis. This is largely because their molecules have typical three-dimensional basket-linked skeletons which are refractory to ordinary chemical methods of analysis. In a few cases X-ray analysis has verified accepted structures but in a number of others has served to put forward new structures or to decide between old ones. The known structures of alkaloids are set out in Table IV and Fig. 22. However, we still lack any serious understanding of what is the relation between these complex structures and the physiological activity of most alkaloids, though this undoubtedly presents a fascinating problem for the future.

With the alkaloids one may take a few other extremely physiologically active compounds, particularly some of the antibiotics. The antibiotics are not a particular chemical or structural group, some of them seem to be

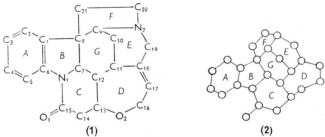

Fig. 22. Alkaloids. (a). Strychnine. (1) Chemical formula. (2) Structure. (C. BOKHOVEN, J. C. SCHOONE AND M. BIJVOET, *Acta Cryst.*, 4 (1951) 275.)

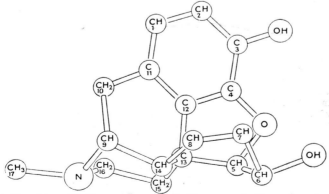

Fig. 22 (b). Morphine. (M. MACHAM AND D. C. HODGKIN, *J. Chem. Soc.*, (1955) 3261.)

TABLE IV

ALKALOIDS

Morphine	M. MACKAY AND D. C. HODGKIN, *J. Chem. Soc.* (1955) 3261.
Codeine-HBr·2H$_2$O	J. M. LINDSAY AND W. H. BARNES, *Acta Cryst.*, 8 (1955) 227.
Quinine (prelim. report)	H. MENDEL, *Koninkl. Ned. Akad. Wetenschap., Proc., Ser. B*, (1955) 132.
Hydroxydihydroeremophilone	D. F. GRANT AND D. ROGERS, *Chem. & Ind., (London)*, (1956) 278.
Annotinine bromohydrin	M. PRZYBYLSKA AND L. MARION, *Can. J. Chem.*, 35 (1952) 1075; M. PRZYBYLSKA AND J. R. AHMED, *Acta Cryst.*, 11 (1958) 718.
Erythraline hydrobromide	W. NOWACKI AND G. F. BONSMA, *Z. Krist.*, 110 (1958) 89.
Muscarine iodide	F. JELLINEK, *Acta Cryst.*, 10 (1957) 277.
(—)-Aspidospermine-N(b)-methiodide	J. F. D. MILLS AND S. C. NYBURG, *J. Chem. Soc.*, (1960) 1458.
Ibogaine-HBr	G. ARAI, J. COPPOLA AND G. A. JEGGREY, *Acta Cryst.*, 13 (1960) 553.
ψ-Conhydrine-HBr	H. S. YANAI AND W. N. LIPSCOMBE, *Tetrahedron*, 6 (1959) 103.
Calycanthine-2HBr·2H$_2$O	J. A. HAMOR, J. M. ROBERTSON, H. N. SHRIVASTAVA AND J. V. SILVERTON, *Proc. Chem. Soc.*, (1960) 78.
Jacobine bromohydrin	J. FRIDRICHSONS, A. McL. MATHIESON AND D. J. SUTOR, *Tetrahedron Letters*, 23 (1960) 35.
Isoclovene-HCl	J. S. CLUNIE AND J. M. ROBERTSON, *Proc. Chem. Soc.*, (1960) 82.
Gelsemine-HCl and -HBr	F. M. LOVELL, R. PEPINSKY AND A. J. C. WILSON, *Tetrahedron Letters*, 4 (1959) 1.
Cevine-HI	W. J. ECLES, *Tetrahedron Letters*, 7 (1960) 24.
(+)-Demethanol acconinone-HI·3H$_2$O	M. PRZYBYLSKA, *Acta Cryst.*, 14 (1961) 429.
(+)-Des-(oxymethylene)-lycoctonine-HI·H$_2$O	M. PRZYBYLSKA, *Acta Cryst.*, 14 (1961) 424.
Narcotics	
Miroestrol-HBr	N. E. TAYLOR, D. C. HODGKIN AND J. S. ROLLETT, *J. Chem. Soc.*, (1960) 3658.
Ephedrine-HCl and -HBr	D. C. PHILLIPS, *Acta Cryst.*, 7 (1954) 159.
Tropine-HBr	J. W. VISSER, J. MANASSEN AND J. L. DE VRIES, *Acta Cryst.*, 7 (1954) 288.
Colchicine (methylene bromide and iodide)	M. V. KING, J. L. DE VRIES AND R. PEPINSKY, *Acta Cryst.*, 5 (1952) 473.
Ergine-HCl and -HBr	J. L. DE VRIES AND R. PEPINSKY, *Nature*, 168 (1951) 431.
Strychnine-HBr	J. H. ROBERTSON AND C. A. BEEVERS, *Acta Cryst.*, 4 (1951) 270.
Strychnine isomorphous sulphate and selenate pentahydrate	C. BOKHOVEN, J. C. SCHOONE AND M. BIJVOET, *Acta Cryst.*, 4 (1951) 275.
(+)-Isocryptopleurine	J. FRIDRICHSONS AND A. McL. MATHIESON, *Acta Cryst.*, 8 (1955) 761.
α-Isoparteine	M. PRZYBYLSKA AND W. H. BARNES, *Acta Cryst.*, 6 (1953) 377.
D-Methadone-HBr	A. W. HANSON AND F. R. AHMED, *Acta Cryst.*, 11 (1958) 724.
DL-Alphaprodine-HCl	G. KARTHA, F. R. AHMED AND W. H. BARNES, *Acta Cryst.*, 13 (1960) 525.

definitely polypeptides and will be dealt with in the next section, but the first natural antibiotic, penicillin, can be taken in this group. The analysis of the structure of penicillin (Fig. 14, p. 140) is one of the triumphs of X-ray analysis (see Vol. 3, Ch. II), but there again the relation of this now well-known structure to its activity on bacteria is not known.

6. Peptides and proteins

Peptides and proteins correspond respectively to oligomers and polymers composed largely, but not entirely, of a variety of amino acids. The distinction between the two is somewhat arbitrary and based essentially on the physical properties of the molecules. The smaller peptides, ranging up to thirty amino acid residues, have fairly rigid molecular skeletons, many of them cyclic, such as gramicidin. They are not distinguishable in physical properties from other amphoteric water soluble molecules of the same molecular weight. The proteins on the other hand with the number of residues

TABLE V

PEPTIDES

β-Glycylglycine	E. W. Hughes and W. J. Moore, *J. Am. Chem. Soc.*, 71 (1949) 2618.
N-acetylglycine	S. B. Carpenter and J. Donohue, *J. Am. Chem. Soc.*, 72 (1950) 2315.
Glycyl-L-tryptophan· 2H$_2$O	R. A. Pasternak, *Acta Cryst.*, 9 (1956) 341.
Glycyl-L-tyrosine·HCl	D. W. Smits and E. H. Wiebenga, *Acta Cryst.*, 6 (1953) 531.
Glycyl-L-asparagine	R. A. Pasternak, L. Katz and R. B. Corey, *Acta Cryst.*, 7 (1954) 225.
N,N'-diglycyl-L-cystine· 2H$_2$O	H. L. Yakel and E. W. Hughes, *Acta Cryst.*, 7 (1954) 291.
Diglycylglycine ethyl ester·HCl	K. B. Dyer, *An X-Ray Study of Certain Peptides, Ph. D. Thesis*, University of Cambridge, 1951.
L-Leucyl-L-prolyl-glycine monohydrate	Y. C. Leung and R. E. Marsh, *Acta Cryst.*, 11 (1958) 17.
Tosyl-L-prolyl-L- hydroxy-proline monohydrate	A. F. Beecham, J. Fridrichsons and A. McL. Mathieson, *J. Am. Chem. Soc.*, 80 (1958) 4739.
Glutathione	W. B. Wright, *Acta Cryst.*, 11 (1958) 632.

ranging into the hundred thousands form solutions which are colloidal (to less or greater extent) as the size of the molecule increases, giving rise to long range forces. They also show the characteristic phenomenon of denaturation with heat or drastic pH changes (see below).

(a) Peptides

The molecular structures of a number of peptides have been determined by X-rays; some like glutathione for intrinsic reasons, as have been anti-

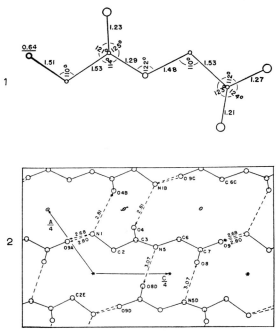

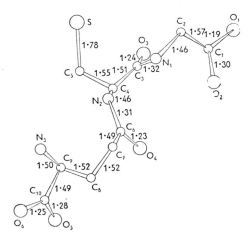

Fig. 23. Peptides. (a) β-Glycylglycine, (1) Molecule, (2) arrangement in cell showing hydrogen bonds. (E. W. HUGHES AND W. J. MOORE, *J. Am. Chem. Soc.*, 71 (1947) 261.)

Fig. 23 (b). Glutathione molecule. (W. B. WRIGHT, *Acta Cryst.*, 11 (1958) 632.

biotics like gramicidin or important metabolites, others as first steps to the elucidation of protein structure. Some of these are shown in Fig. 23 (see also Table V).

Their structures conform to expected pattern and show the planarity of the amide groups of their constituent amino acids giving weight to Pauling's thesis that this was also maintained in the proteins.

(b) Globular and fibrous proteins

The protein molecules extracted from living systems, and by implication occurring in them, have characteristic and highly specific ordering of different amino acids in one or more chains. The number of chains in each kind of

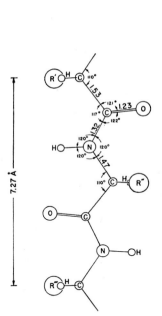

Fig. 24. Polypeptide chain fully extended. (L. PAULING, *Nature of the Chemical Bond*, p. 498.)

Fig. 25. α-Helix of polypeptide chain. (L. PAULING, *Nature of the Chemical Bond*, p. 500.)

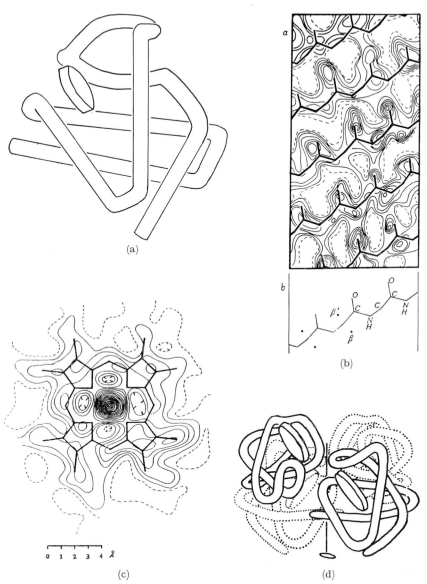

Fig. 26. Globular protein. (a) Sperm whale myoglobin molecule. Diagram showing folded α-helices and haem group. (b) Electron density map of part of α-helix from myoglobin. (c) Haem group from myoglobin. (J. C. KENDREW et al., Nature, 185 (1960) 422.) (d) Haemoglobin molecule (drawn to compare with a) showing two pairs of molecules related by vertical symmetry axes (M. F. PERUTZ et al., Nature, 185 (1960) 416.)

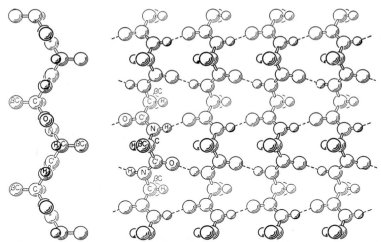

Fig. 27. β-Type fibrous protein. (a). Pleated sheet form. (L. PAULING, *Nature of the Chemical Bond*, p. 501.)

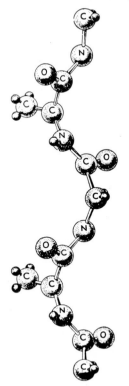

Fig. 27 (b). Glycine -alanine sequence in natural silk. (R. E. MARSH, R. B. COREY AND L. PAULING, *Acta Cryst.*, 8 (1955) 713.)

protein molecules and the precise ordering of the amino acids in them have been established by chemical methods for a few protein varieties. This constitutes the *primary* protein structure; beyond that lie the higher orders of conformation which determine the physical rather than the chemical properties of proteins.

Long before there was any clear idea of what these structures were, it was clear that proteins could be divided into those showing normal isotropic character in solution and which could often be crystallised, and these which were either insoluble fibres or, if dissolved, showed marked anisotropic character in solution such as flow birefringence, anomalous viscosity and tendency to form gels (see Vol. 3, Chap. IX). The type of these is gelatin itself. All these properties correspond to quasi-spherical molecules in the former case and elongated chain molecules in the second. Proteins are accordingly divided into globular and fibrous types. The former are sometimes referred to as crystalline proteins but this is a narrower definition, for while all truly crystalline — excluding paracrystalline — proteins are globular, only a few globular proteins have been crystallised.

A further complication is that this distinction refers not to the chemical protein variety, but rather to its particular physical state. Many, possibly all, pure proteins can be made to change from the globular to the fibrous state and sometimes reversibly in the way already described (p. 146). The best studied case of this G → F transformation is that of crystalline and fibrous insulin.

(c) Active and structural proteins

The physical distinction between globular and fibrous proteins runs, but only roughly, parallel to another biochemical division. The natural proteins can be divided functionally into two classes — the chemically *active* proteins, essentially enzymes, and the other soluble proteins of unknown function, possibly only nutritional or physical–chemical, such as the albumens. These are usually globular and crystalline proteins but one important enzyme, adenosine triphosphate (ATP-ase), seems to be the fibrous protein, myosin. The other major group of proteins are the *structural* proteins which appear in cell walls and in such functional protective structures as connective fibre, muscle and skin; these are necessarily fibrous proteins.

Various aspects of the structure of proteins have already been alluded to in this chapter, but this is very much at present a work in progress. The first general picture of the structure of a protein molecule was established only two years ago, and in any detail only a few months before writing. What has emerged, however, from these preliminary studies is the picture of a protein as an instance of a highly complex linear polymer of amino acids coiled and folded in an elaborate but highly precise way.

The primary structure, essentially a chemical one, appears as a consequence of elaborate biochemical and genetically controlled processes. There was for some time a doubt as to whether the particular structure of each protein was due to some peculiar physical property or was essentially of biological origin. The study of even the first protein to be analysed answers this question by agreeing to both propositions. The primary structure would seem to be essentially a biological one, due to the sequence of enzymic reactions controlling the addition of each amino acid in turn; the secondary structure on the other hand seems to be almost purely physical. The protein molecule can only be studied by diffraction methods in its crystalline form, and here it is usually more condensed and curled up than it would be in its active state inside a cell. The secondary coiling into Pauling helices, where it occurs, follows from the shapes of the peptide chain and from our knowledge of hydrogen bonding. The tertiary folding of chains or helices is likely to be more indeterminate; it is certainly more irregular, but that irregularity is still remarkably reproducible, as is shown by the ease with which the globular proteins crystallise.

(d) Denaturation

The characteristic physico–chemical property of proteins — the ease by which they are denaturated — also follows fairly simply from such a model. This extremely regular way of coiling and folding can only be achieved under conditions of relative lack of disturbance — mild disturbance, thermal or chemical, will produce errors in hydrogen bond formation, particularly cross-linking between parts of different molecules. This would correspond to reversible denaturation. More severe disturbances would lead further to the formation of covalent bond cross-links which would produce irreversible denaturation. It is significant that the smaller proteins such as insulin are very difficult to denature. It would be difficult to break such cross-links without profoundly disturbing the sequence of amino acid residues. As this is the consequence of the biogenetic process, restoring the original sequence would require digesting the protein into its constituents peptides or amino acids and putting it together again, something that can only occur in a living organism. In other words the Humpty Dumpty story is as true for boiling, as for breaking an egg.

(e) Crystalline proteins, myoglobin and haemoglobin

The structures of these proteins have been the first to be worked out in all their essentials by X-ray diffraction methods. This is a notable triumph of persistent research carried out over more than twenty years, first by Perutz alone and then by Perutz, Kendrew and others. The present state of the analysis is shown in Fig. 26 (p. 166). There is clearly no room here to discuss these in detail. What can be done is to bring out some leading features found in these proteins which are likely to have general application to other crystalline proteins. It is almost certain that the general arrangement holds closely for the whole haemoglobin group and to a large extent in the closely related respiratory pigments such as the cytochromes and catalase. How far it will need to be modified to include other groups of proteins remains to be seen. There is some evidence that the arrangement of peptide chains in proteins like ribonuclease is different in that Pauling α-helices play a smaller part in the secondary structure.

What the analysis definitely shows in myoglobin is firstly that Pauling α-helices account for the majority of the single polypeptide chain. Only at the turns of the tertiary structure — the folding of the coils — are there inevitably some uncoiled amino acid residues. The folding is so arranged that a quasi-spherical molecule is formed. This would seem to be largely a physical effect conditioned by the need to present a minimum surface to the solution. The clearly identified haemin group is shown to be surrounded by the poly-peptide coils but it is impossible as yet to get enough detail of the precise surrounding of the iron atom in such a way as to explain its oxygen attaching function.

The structure of haemoglobin (Fig. 26, p. 166), though not worked out in such detail, is important as bringing out the structure of an aggregate protein molecule. Here the four parts are divided into two pairs of identical sub-molecules. Those in each pair differ slightly but all are very similar to those of myoglobin. Further they pack extremely neatly into a nearly spherical aggregate in the form of a rounded tetrahedron. If this arrangement may be taken as characteristic of large protein molecules made up of identical or quasi-identical sub-molecules, an explanation is provided for Svedberg's rule of the multiplicity of protein molecular weights. It now appears not valid, as he thought, for all proteins, but only for those belonging to the same family — here the haemoglobin–cytochrome family.

In such molecular aggregates, because no indefinite repeats occur, the rules of regular crystallography need not hold. Symmetry is no longer limited to symmetries of 2, 3, 4, and 6. But other more complicated rules still remain, but need to be elucidated. It has long been known from studies of molecular weight by sedimentation or electrophoretic methods, that many, in fact most, of the larger proteins can be disaggregated reversibly into units of smaller size. A notable case is that of haemocyanin which can be broken down into 2, 4, up to 16 separate molecular parts. The advent of the electron microscope has shown these parts in these big molecules, and indicated that such clustering is a very frequent occurrence, and, of course, occurs *in vivo*.

Besides the splitting of protein aggregate molecules, certain physical conditions can cause a limited degree of uncoiling of loops or free ends of poly-peptide chains of protein which is detectable by viscosity measurements and the scattering of light and X-rays (Vol. 3, Chap. II). This effect rep-resents a smaller alteration of protein molecular structure than does the reversible denaturation mentioned above (p. 169).

With the rapid development of analytical methods and the interest of the first successes of Kendrew and Perutz, our knowledge of protein structure will rapidly increase; and this is where we may expect the clearest evidence of the physically-determined structure on the biological properties.

(f) Fibrous proteins

In contrast to the globular proteins, the fibrous proteins are far less easily characterised. They lack full three-dimensional crystallinity. The nearest they approach to it is in bundles of parallel linked chains which may have a hexagonal cross-section as in muscle (Fig. 33b, p. 183).

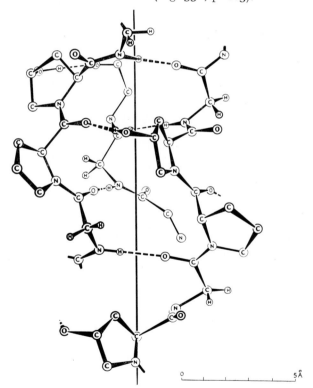

Fig. 28. Collagen. Treble twined chains of proline–glycine residues. (F. H. C. Crick and A. Rich, Nature, 176 (1955) 915.)

The fibrous proteins are found to occur in three major groups. The first, the β type of Astbury are those characterised by the fully-extended peptide links. These usually occur outside cells in extruded and repolymerised proteins of the type of silk (Fig. 27, p. 167). The next group are those that are in the form of a coil, usually the Pauling α-helix (Fig. 25, p. 165) which apart from details such as coiled coiling seem to explain the structures of proteins of the keratin, myosin, actomysin and fibrin varieties. However, these two groups are only apparently distinct and it has been possible in most cases to effect reversible transformations between them. They only differ by the arrangement of the hydrogen bonds. In one case the hydrogen bonds can tie the molecules into short coils which are relatively isolated from each other, while in the stretched form the hydrogen bonds exist between the chains holding them together. Tension can turn the second group into the first, as Astbury showed long ago, and this is the basis for such practical processes as making shrink-proof wool or setting permanent waves. The alpha-beta transformation therefore is a very common one for fibrous proteins.

There is one important group of such proteins that does not fit into this pattern and is of a substantially different structure; it is that of the supporting proteins of collagen type. Here there are three somewhat simple protein chains containing a very large amount of the amino acid proline, which are twined together to form a triple non-extensible chain (Fig. 28). This means that these supporting proteins lack the elasticity of the alpha type, but on the other hand are remarkably permanent and can be disaggregated by heat and re-aggregated remarkably easily. This is the basis of the production and use of gelatin and in general of the animal gel forming substances; the corresponding function in the vegetable world is played by the polysaccharide pectins.

There are many other proteins of somewhat indefinite character which cannot as yet be crystallised. This may be because of impurities, and in this case it is difficult to know whether these impurities are, or are not, essential components of the molecule. These include the glutinous proteins of grains, on which, more than any other protein, human beings feed. In other cases the non-protein element probably plays a predominant role. These include complex lipoproteins and mucoproteins, which have a large part to play both intra-cellularly and in various secretions. The physical properties of all these, however, particularly their possibility of extension and a certain degree of rubber-like elasticity, indicate the presence of long molecules which can be coiled in different ways. We may say that the study of protein structure has only just passed its initial stage, and the great triumphs which will link the knowledge of structure with that of function must be reserved, let us hope, for the near future.

We are still very far from understanding the relation of the structure of proteins to their physiological functions, particularly in the case of the all-important enzymic proteins. Their more physical properties, particularly their poly-electrolyte properties and the models of structures do give a fair picture of a molecule which can associate itself with a number of layers of water molecules. The characteristic swelling of protein crystals was shown by Perutz to be resolvable into a number of definite steps indicating that there are protein water complexes of various degrees of complexity, and this is also found in the rather complicated peptide, vitamin B_{12}, where the association with the water molecules in the partially dried and totally dried form has been particularly beautifully brought out by Mrs. Hodgkin.

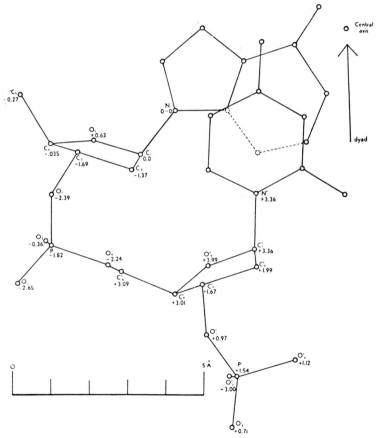

Fig. 29. Nucleosides and nucleotides. (a) Arrangement of purine and pyrimidine nucleotides in part of the DNA chain. (M. H. F. WILKINS et al., J. Mol. Biol., 2 (1960) 38.)

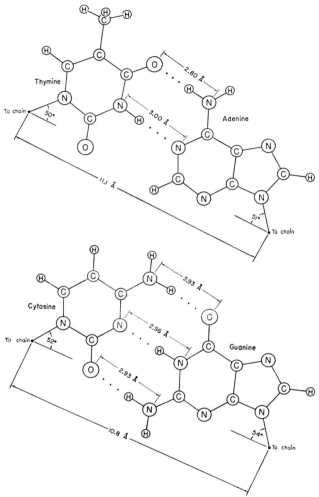

Fig. 29 (b). Linking of purines and pyrimidines by H bonds to form double chain DNA.
(L. PAULING, *Nature of the Chemical Bond*, p. 502.)

7. Nucleotides and nucleic acids

Before considering the structure of the nucleic acids, something more must
be said about that of their component nucleotides. As already described
(p. 130) nucleotides are typical hetero oligomers composed of a purine or
pyrimidine, a sugar, ribose or deoxyribose, and a phosphate group. The
structure of one nucleoside, cytidine, was first determined by Furberg (Fig. 1,
p. 116) and this was to prove a clue to the structure of the nucleic acids.

Quite apart from their function as constituents in nucleic acid, these compounds, and others that are not included in nucleic acids, seem to have a very large biochemical role to play and possibly one actually anterior in the development of life to those of the nucleic acids. Some of the major co-enzymes in biochemical systems are of this type — notably adenosine in its monophosphate (AMP), diphosphate (ADP), and triphosphate (ATP), forms. So far the conformation of this most important co-enzymic substance, through which most energy transfers in living systems seem to be channelled, has remained obscure.

Many of the co-enzymes contain a nucleotide as one member of a pair linked through pyrophosphate to a similar molecule in which the purine group is replaced by a pyridine group as in diphosphopyridine nucleotide (DPN), by flavin as in flavin-adenine dinucleotide (FAD) or by pantothenic acid in co-enzyme A.

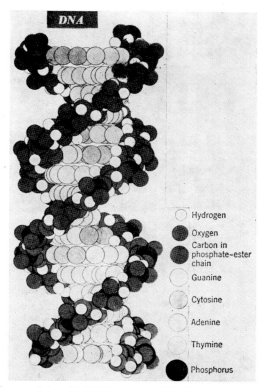

Fig. 30. Deoxyribosenucleic acid, DNA, showing linked purines and pyrimidines piled along axis and unequally spaced double helices of phosphate and sugar. (F. H. C. CRICK AND J. D. WATSON, *Proc. Roy. Soc.*, (*London*) *A*, 223 (1954) 80.)

Though the chemical structure of these and similar biochemically active molecules are known, none has been studied sufficiently to determine their conformation. This knowledge may be worth taking some trouble to get; one possibility is that by a change in conformation a phosphate group may approach part of a purine (pyridine etc.) end group and thus help to further proton transfer, a major element in enzymic reactions.

Much interest will be attached at a later date when it is possible to make a precise analysis of these pyrophosphate chains because the length and corresponding stability of the links through oxygen may determine the nature of the so-called energy-rich phosphate bonds, but it is too early now to make any statement on it because it must depend on refined methods of measuring inter-atomic distances.

(a) Nucleic acids

The study of the structures of nucleic acids came later than that of the proteins, but has made a more rapid progress up to a certain stage. Structural knowledge of nucleic acids is on a lower level of accuracy than that of the proteins for the obvious reason that no nucleic acid has been crystallised as yet. Nevertheless our knowledge of the essential features of nucleic acid structures is actually greater than that at present available from the proteins. The reason for this is that the secondary structure of the nucleic acids — considered as sugar-phosphate chain polymers with substituted purines and pyrimidines consisting of four essentially similar flat units — is in fact more regular than that of the protein with its very different R groups in the polypeptide form. Consequently, at least in the cases where the nucleic acid chains are found in a single or double helical form, the resulting structure is actually simpler than that in the protein. It is this simple bihelical secondary structure of DNA (Fig. 30) that has shed such light on biology, especially in genetics. So far no tertiary structure has been determined, although there is evidence that some must exist in, for instance, the nucleic acids packed in the capsule of the bacteriophages, far too short to accommodate the whole helix.

The very viscous properties of nucleic acids led to their study by X-rays using the methods of fibre structure studies already established for proteins and other linear polymers. The very first studies of these by Astbury showed that here the chain was such that the purine and pyrimidine molecules were arranged parallel to each other in piles normal to the axis. A little later Furberg showed that in the nucleoside cytidine the sugar molecule planes were at right angles to those of the pyrimidine, and at this stage both he and Pauling suggested that the structure might be a helical one. However, no simple helical structure seemed to fit the observations, and it was here that the genius of Watson and Crick, by introducing the idea of a double helix, provided the clue to the structure of the nucleic acids or at least of those known in a helical form. These included the deoxyribonucleic acids which appear to be the essential carriers of genetic information in all cellular organisms, and possibly in certain viruses as well. The structure of the simpler ribose nucleic acid is not so well understood, because it does not seem to form, at any rate in organic systems, any helical arrangement.

It was the study of the helical models proposed by Pauling for the proteins, and the consequent working out of their diffraction patterns, that made it possible to understand the essential features of the X-ray photographs of the nucleic acid. The helical structure is organised in one dimension instead of three, as in the case of the regular crystals, but now that methods of diffraction analysis of such one-dimensional helical structures are available, a great deal of information can be obtained from them, though naturally never to the same degree of accuracy as that obtained in proteins. However, for many purposes the general lines of the structures of the nucleic acid is all that is wanted and further it is possible to note differences between one structure and another without necessarily understanding the complete structure of either of them.

The general character of the nucleic acid double helical chains is determined on the one hand by the forces by which the nucleotide pairs, attached to each other by hydrogen bonds, are piled, and, on the other, by the shape adopted by the helical chain of phosphate-sugar groups which surround the whole structure. A helical structure permits several degrees of freedom, and it is evident from the various structures observed in the different salts of the nucleic acids — lithium salt being one which gives peculiarly definite information — that these local arrangements are somewhat variable. In other words, that the helix of the chain can be more or less open, allowing more elements to form in a single turn; it can be imagined as a spring that can be tightened up or loosened out by twisting along its axis while keeping the pitch approximately the same (Fig. 29, p. 173).

Although natural ribosenucleic acids do not appear to have this helical configuration, artificial ones are known to have essentially similar arrangement, and here it is possible to observe and study by means of X-rays the interaction of two such chains. If polyadenylic acid is mixed with polyuridylic acid, the resulting solution rapidly becomes viscous on account of the formation of double helices in which the adenylic and uridylic parts are twined together. This twining or untwining is a function of the pH of the medium and thus it is possible to reproduce *in vivo* some of the postulated methods by which chains in an organism can coil and uncoil, and at the same time make duplicate pictures of themselves.

(b) Nucleoproteins

The study of nucleic acids leads to that of the most complicated of molecules — those of the nucleoproteins, which lie on the border between non-living and living systems. The nucleoproteins are found in two forms: one is an intimate association of nucleic acid and protein in which the dominant structural role is played by the nucleic acid. In the other, the two elements of the structure are more loosely attached and the protein plays the leading structural role though it is the nucleic acid that has the biogenetic role.

The first of these types is found in the nucleoproteins of sperm, where it can be readily studied by X-rays as it exists almost in a pure form, and is also probably found in the chromosomal part of the nucleus, but here methods of study have not revealed the relation of the two parts. In sperm the study of the intact sperm head indicates the filling in of the nucleic acid helices by the addition of bodies which are essentially small proteins — so-called protamines or histones—containing a large number of basic arginine groups.

The work of Wilkins has shown that these are to be found embedded in the third or "open" groove of the DNA helix. They may even have been synthesized in that position through the effects of the nucleic acid itself. This may be a model for the synthesis of proteins by nucleic acids. However, it would appear from other studies that this could only be the case for very simple proteins because more elaborate proteins are synthesized by a step-by-step mechanism in which nucleic acid appears to play the underlying role of providing the information but not necessarily the active one of carrying out the operations of synthesis. A nucleoprotein of this kind is of the true type of a molecular compound in which the element of the nucleic acid and that of the protein are on an equal footing.

(c) Virus nucleoproteins

There exists, however, an entirely different kind of nucleoprotein — that found in most viruses in which the association is a very much looser one, and should strictly be discussed in relation to the structures found in cells. However, its study has been carried out by the same X-ray methods that have been used for the nucleic acids and for the proteins, and it is appropriate to treat it here. The virus nucleoproteins seem to be of two types — those in which the virus particle is elongated, and those in which it is approximately spherical. The only viruses studied in any structural detail are the smaller viruses of the ribosenucleic acid type rather than the deoxy-ribonucleic acid type of the larger viruses such as vaccinia or the bacterio-phages. These used to be called plant viruses but as we now know they also include such important animal viruses as poliomyelitic virus.

(i) Rod-shaped viruses

The structure of tobacco mosaic virus was the first to be studied, and has yielded the most detailed information. The virus particle is around about 3000 Å long and 152 Å wide and is built out of a helical arrangement of identical or quasi-identical protein molecules packed rather like the sections of a pineapple with 39 units in three turns of the helix. As this virus can be modified in various ways so as to separate the nucleic acid from the protein it is possible to locate the position of the nucleic acid which turns out to lie, not as was expected in the hole through the middle of the helix, but buried in the wall of the helix, or possibly in the deep groove going into its interior surface (Fig. 31).

The measurement of the weight of the ribonucleic acid indicates that this does not form a double-coiled system but is a single chain wound in the same helix as are the protein molecules, that is a helix of 80 Å diameter and 23 Å pitch. The structure of the protein shell helix is not strictly dependent on the presence of the nucleic acid because it is possible to remove the nucleic acid enzymatically, to disaggregate the protein into individual particles and to re-aggregate them again into an approximately, but not quite identical, helical structure. But this may be, significantly, of indefinite

Fig. 31. Structure of tobacco mosaic virus showing helically close-packed protein sub-units and ribonucleic acid, RNA, passing between them. (A. KLUG AND D. L. D. CASPAR, *Adv. Virus Res.*, 7 (1961) 274.)

length. The protein is characteristic of the particular strain of virus, and seems to be independent of the nature of the infected plant.

(ii) Spherical viruses

Small spherical viruses are arranged in a different way. Here the protein molecules form a kind of polygonal cage — in all cases hitherto studied essentially of a pentagonal, dodecahedral or icosahedral character, that is with ten three-fold axes and six five-fold axes. The actual arrangement of the particles varies considerably between the different viruses. In some cases the complexity is very great, there being as many as 252 protein molecules in the shell, and, as can be seen, not all of these are in identical geometrical positions. However, the difference between them does not seem to justify the idea that there is more than one kind of protein involved. The pentagonal arrangement is essentially one which any set of quasi-equal particles will adopt if they lie on the surface of a sphere; and what determines their number and arrangement will be largely the ratio of the diameter of the protein particle to that of the sphere they lie on (Fig. 32).

The position of the nucleic acid in this type of virus is not known, but may soon come to light. If it consists of a single chain it must, somehow or other, be rolled up like a ball of wool inside the protein cage because it is

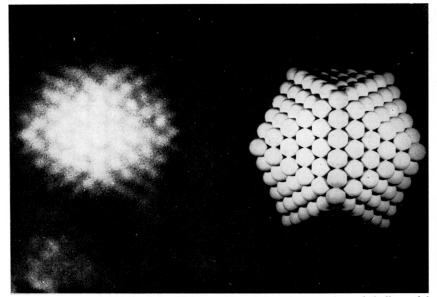

Fig. 32. Polyhedral adenovirus. Electron-microscope photograph and ball model. (R. W. Horne, S. Brenner, A. P. Waterson and P. Wildy, *J. Mol. Biol.*, I (1959) 84.) (Magnification: 644,000 ×)

impossible to arrange a single fibre with the symmetry which the cage possesses. Arrangements not essentially different from those of the virus shells are found in a number of biological structures, notably, in the skin of the earthworm. It may in fact be a perfectly general feature of all structures based on quasi-spherical protein molecules.

8. Molecular structures in relation to cells or tissues

This completes, in our present stage of knowledge, the description of the structures of molecules which can be found or extracted from biological sources. Nevertheless, before leaving the picture of molecular structure in biochemistry, it is desirable to say something of the relation of molecules to the fine structure of biological tissues themselves. The full description clearly belongs to the new extension of histology which might be called ultra-histology or electron microscope histology. However, as the development of biochemistry is proceeding very rapidly in the direction of determining the microchemistry of such parts of cells, studied either in intact cells or in extracts, they should be mentioned for completeness, at least insofar as their structure has been determined or can be inferred from that of other molecules. These can be divided into two major groups — those which are found inside nearly all cells, the *intracellular structures*, and those which are formed by special cells, of which they form the bulk and constitute the *tissues*.

(a) Intracellular structures

These can be divided into particles, fibres, and membranes, according to their degree of association. Cells are usually full of a great variety of particles, only some of which have been studied in any detail. Some are definitely of a non-crystalline nature such as fat globules, but some of these have some higher degree of organisation in that they are liquid crystals showing bire-fringence. The liquid crystals inside cells have not been very much studied, but may play a large part in fat and sterol metabolism. The only particles about which there is some beginning of understanding of structure are those of the so-called microsomes — the small particles which are found either free or attached to the intracellular membranes. Microsomes have been shown to consist largely of nucleic acid, usually of ribonucleic acid. They are of the same dimensions as the smaller virus particles, that is from 100–200 Å in diameter, and there is some evidence that the nucleic acids in these structures are arranged in one of the helical forms. They also seem to contain protein and may be analogous to the structure of the smaller viruses.

(b) Fibres

The only fibres which are known to exist in most cells are those which are associated with the mitotic division, the so-called spindle fibres which, attaching themselves at one end to the chromosomes and at the other to the polar bodies or their equivalents, seem to contract and pull the micro-somes apart by their central attachment or centromeres, in the later stages of metaphase and telophase. Electron microscope and optical studies seem to show these as protein fibres, but whether they contract by some method of intrinsic shortening, or whether there is some sliding mechanism similar to that which occurs in muscle, is not yet known. Protein fibres can be found on the lining of the cell membrane and again may be responsible for cell membrane movements or for the movements of cell contents inside the cell itself.

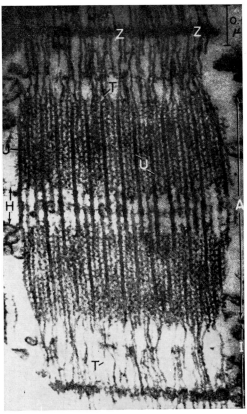

Fig. 33. Striated muscle. (a) Longitudinal section showing short, thick and long, thin fibres.

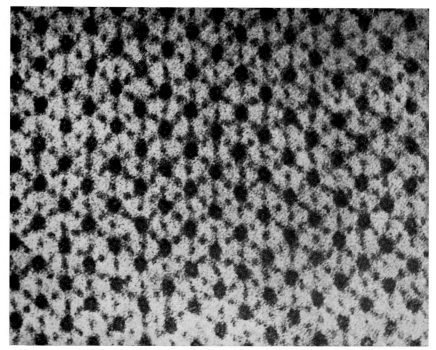

Fig. 33 (b). Cross section showing mutual position of thick and thin fibres in hexagonal net. (*Sci. Am.*, 199 (1950) 67.)

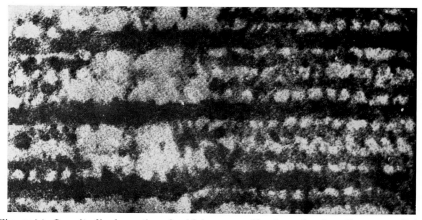

Fig. 33(c). Longitudinal section in higher magnification showing the cross links responsible by their racket action for contraction. (H. STANLEY BENNETT, *Rev. Mod. Phys.*, 31 (1959) 394.) (Magnification: 400,000 ×)

The other intracellular fibres are developed mostly in specialised cells. Most clearly understood of these are the fibres of muscle, where a combination of X-ray and electron microscope studies have shown that here there is an arrangement which may be considered as a multiplication of a liquid crystal compound between two fibrous proteins—myosin and actin, the so-called actomyosin complex. As Huxley and others have shown, these form together an arrangement of equidistant fibres with the myosin fibres in the corners of the hexagonal cells and two actomyosin fibres in the two central triangles of the arrangement (Fig. 33). The movement of the muscle is carried out by the relative stepping past each other by the actin and the myosin fibres, but here a part of the process may be due to small bridges which join them along their length. The major features, however, are essentially similar to the tactoids found in all elongated soluble molecules and most carefully studied in the case of tobacco mosaic virus. The characteristic feature is the equidistant hexagonal arrangement of the fibres in a medium which is largely water—a normal muscle contains about 80 %. Indeed, the whole internal architecture of the cell on this level of size, *i.e.* 100 Å and more, seems to be maintained by the long range forces already discussed.

(c) Chromosomes

Not only proteins but also nucleic acid can form fibres in cells. The structure of the chromosomes are almost certainly essentially fibrous, but here, despite the amount of study to which they have been subjected, it is impossible to give sufficient molecular detail. The main bulk of the chromosomes seems to consist of nucleic acid, but it may have as well a protein element which preserves its mechanical strength and ensures a double and sometimes a triple coiling of the thread. The degree of extension to which chromosomes can be subjected, either naturally in the processes of division or in abnormal division, or when passively extended in the resting state of the nucleus, indicates that we have here to deal with very long fibres indeed, which may be coiled two or more times to form microscopically visible helices. The only evidence that these contain nucleic acid in the form of helices is furnished by the sperm heads of sepia where the X-ray diffraction pattern is identical with that found in artificial preparation of nucleic acid.

(d) Flagellae and cilia

One fibrous adjunct to nearly all cells, including bacteria, is seen in so-called flagellae or cilia-mobile threads. These seem to exist in two levels of organisation, the first being that of the bacterial flagellae which are simple or comparatively simple protein threads about 150 Å in thickness, and giving a pattern corresponding to that of the typical alpha protein. The other, which corresponds to the flagellae of the protozoa and of all other animals and a number of plants as well as to the so-called cilia of the higher animals and the tails of the spermatozoa, seems to have a more complicated but remarkably standardized structure. This consists of an arrangement of 11 long fibres, 2 in the centre and 9 surrounding them, itself embedded in a long helical thread, the whole being of some 3000 Å thick, and capable of wavy movements which produce either the passing by of the liquid or the propulsion of the cell (Fig. 34). For reasons which still elude us, the centrioles or polar bodies that seem to regulate mitosis are structures indistinguishable from the basal bodies of cilia. Further, they are the first organelles where duplication is seen to occur as the budding out and subsequent growth of a daughter centriole at right angles to its parent.

(e) Intracellular membranes

Membranous structures, mostly of a lipid nature although they may be

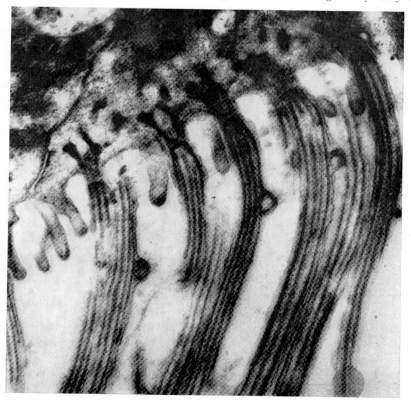

Fig. 34. *Cilia*, from freshwater mussel. (a) Longitudinal section showing basal bodies. (P. SATIR, *Sci. Am.*, 204, No. 2 (1961) 108.) (Magnification: 30,000 ×)

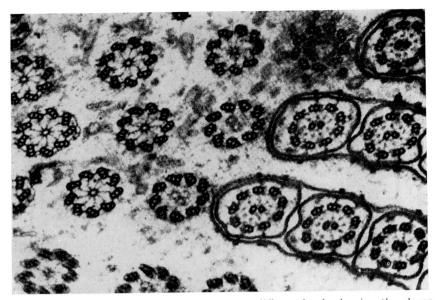

Fig. 34(b). From pseudotrichonympha sections at different levels showing the eleven double sub filaments passing into treble filaments in basal sections. (I. R. GIBBONS AND A. V. GRIMSTONE, *J. Biophys. Biochem. Cytol.*, 7 (1960) 697.) (Magnification: 82,500 ×)

reinforced by protein, seem to be universal in cells, and in fact they probably serve in the first place to define the volume of such a cell. The membranes seem remarkably uniform. Whether they are membranes of the cell itself, of the nucleus or of the various organelles which build the cell up, they seem to consist of double lipid layers of about 80 Å thick on which are adsorbed other substances, in certain cases nucleic acid microsomes and others of proteins. The shape of the membranes indicates two possible conditions under which they are found. But here a certain caution must be introduced and these membranes have only been seen in any detail in electron microscope preparations where certain amounts of the structure may be an artefact due to the forces involved in the fixing or drying. However, there can be no doubt that in certain cases the membranes form a closed vesicle with a curved surface, indicating a difference in osmotic pressure in at least the ionic regime on one side or the other. This is the case, of course, for the cell itself, for its nucleus and for a number of smaller vesicular bodies, found inside cells (Fig. 35 a–b).

In other cases the membrane seems to have a generally wavy character although it may be folded, and this seems to indicate that there is no essential difference between the medium on one side or the other. It should be noted that the membrane itself is symmetrical, being double, and has no intrinsic tendency to curl.

The simplest arrangement of membranes seems to be that of the endoplas-micreticulum already mentioned, which fills a large volume of all cells. Specialised arrangements, however, can be more clearly seen in the mitochondria. Here the structure seems to be that of an in-folding continuous membrane without any holes but in which the in-folds make a kind of bag or cisternae containing, presumably, the enzymic material. The folding is so close that in some cases there would not be room for protein molecules if they were of the thickness observed in crystals, and it is very likely that the protein molecules are extended in the folds of the lipid membrane and they are active in this position.

An even closer apposition of lipid membranes is found in the plastids which are responsible for the photosynthesis of plants. Here the layers are packed together in even larger numbers and more closely, and this is probably

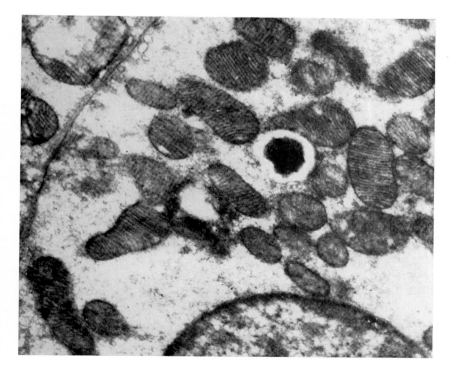

Fig. 35. Intracellular structures. (a). Mitochondria showing parallel lipid layer cisternae.

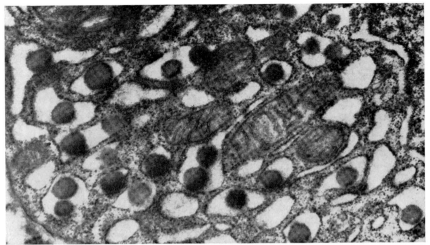

Fig. 35(b). Endoplasmic structures. Ribosome lined cavities containing digestive protein and some mitochondria from guinea pig pancreas. (Photograph by G. E. PALADE in paper by M. B. HOAGLAND, *Sci. Am.*, (1959) 55.) (Magnification: 23,500 ×)

connected with the light absorbing requirements of the so-called grana (Fig. 36a).

Similar arrangements are also found in the active light-receptors in the eyes of both arthropods and vertebrates; in both cases the lipid layers seem an essential part of the absorption and possibly also of the biochemical subsequent reactions to light (Fig. 36b).

One further specialised type of lipid layer is found in nerve sheaths, particularly those of the vertebrates where there is a thick myelinic sheath. The essential fact here is that the process of making this thick sheath is now known to be one of slow rolling by the rotation of a specialised cell. In other words, most of the lipid arrangements in cells are produced by very detailed mechanisms most of which are not yet properly elucidated.

(f) Supporting structures

A large number of molecular products are to be found in the supporting structures of plants and animals. In the former, as well as in some bacteria and in the tunicates or sea squirts, and as a pathological product in mammalia including man, cellulose is the particular material and seems to be laid down in layers of fibres containing a large number of cellulose chains, and of the same order of magnitude as many other biological structures, about a 100 Å in diameter. These are laid down in a very ordered way, imitating the pattern laid down by, presumably, a previously formed

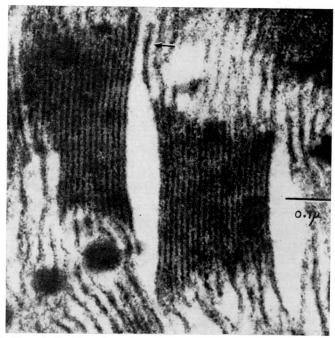

Fig. 36(a). Mesophyll chloroplasts from Zea showing closely packed lipid lamellae in grana. (A. L. HODGE, *Rev. Mod. Phys.*, 31 (1959) 331.) (Magnification: 123,000 ×)

protein fibre or protein layer system. In cases that have been studied in some detail, such as the cell wall of the alga, valonia, and those of the tracheids of pines, there seems to be an alternating process of laying down layers in two different directions, making a kind of web or tissue. But this seems to be a purely biological formation and the cellulose itself is largely undifferentiated although it is oriented in respect to the surface of the cell, as well as in respect to its length. The *b* face of the cellulose crystal is parallel to the cell and the *c* direction lies along the length of the fibre. The linking of these cellulose chains together by other materials such as the lignins has already been described.

Related to cellulose is chitin, an amino-sugar polymer which is the basis of the outer structures of most of the arthropods, particularly of the insects. This substance has the possibility of existing in two forms — soft, without cross-linking, and cross-linked. The cross-linking can be effected very rapidly by means of a type of coloured polyphenol, a process which is set off by exposure to air, or in certain cases to light. The typical insect metamorphosis starts with a soft inner chitin skin which can be withdrawn from the finer

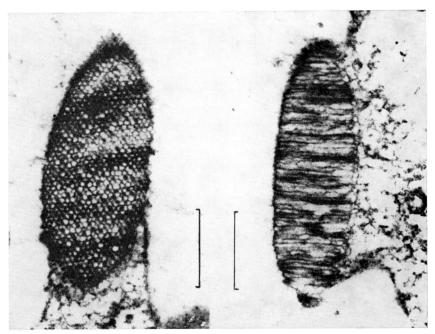

Fig. 36(b). Rhabdomere from eye of drosophila showing hexagonal lamellar structure. (J. J. WOLKEN, J. CAPENOS AND A. TURANO, *J. Biophys. Biochem. Cytol.*, 3 (1957) 441.) (Magnification: 21,300 ×)

parts of the structure and then in a few minutes this turns into a black hard material which acts as the exoskeleton of the insect.

In animal tissues, right down to the protozoal level, another supporting material is collagen, the triply wound specialised protein containing a large number of proline groups (p. 172). This intrinsic or secondary structure of collagen is complicated by a very wide spread higher order structure giving a regularity at very large distances of about 630 Å. But the nature of this repeat has not yet been fully elucidated. Similar to collagen in function, though structurally more related to the alpha-type of proteins, is elastin, the yellow or elastic tissue of ligament and skin. Both collagen and elastin have peculiar relations to temperature, being solubilised in different ways, but this does not strictly speaking belong so much to biochemistry as to industrial chemistry.

Another supporting protein which belongs definitely to the alpha group is keratin, the hard substance of the epidermis of nails, hair, horn, and other hardened tissue. This seems to be a generalised modification of the cell-wall protein, which is laid down in layers with a certain number of variations.

The essential feature of the keratin is that it is a fibrous protein which has been cross-linked or vulcanised by means of the S–S link between cystein residues.

Still further hardening of tissues can be provided by the inclusion of mineral elements. The relation between the deposition of calcium carbonate, as shell, or of calcium phosphate, as bone, is intimately connected with the structure of the organic substrate, originally a protein of the collagen variety, although chitin may also be involved in the arthropods. This is shown by the parellelism of the crystals as they lay down both in shell and in bone. In a particular case even the variety of the crystals is determined biologically — the hard portion being made of calcium phosphate. This is laid down either in the form of the hard fluoroapatite, which is the basis of the enamel of teeth, or of the relatively softer hydroxy-apatite, which is the main inorganic constituents of bone and dentine.

This completes the general picture, of the relation of the structures of molecules to the corresponding biological structure. Brief as it is, it should suffice to show a definite progression from the simplest molecules to the most complicated. In the simple molecules, the bearing of structure is largely on the determination of types of chemical reaction. As the structures get more complicated, especially as they come to depend on higher order structures and conformations, the biological considerations mingle with the physical–chemical conditions such as solubility, osmotic pressure, with colloidal properties in the larger molecule proteins and finally with actual mechanical structure in the tissues of plants and animals.

Chapter IV

Stereoisomerism*

KURT MISLOW

Department of Chemistry, New York University, N.Y. (U.S.A.)

Introduction

The sequential arrangement of atoms in molecules regardless of direction in space defines the constitution of the molecule. Molecules having the same constitution may still differ in the spatial arrangement of their atoms and may thus give rise to stereoisomers. Stereoisomers are described at two levels by the terms configuration, the relative position or order of arrangement of the atoms in space characteristic of the particular isomer, and conformation, the actual disposition in terms of bond distances and angles of the atoms in space. In another (operational) sense, sanctioned by usage, the distinction is made between conformational isomers (rotamers, conformers), *i.e.* non-superimposable isomers which can be interconverted by rotation around single bonds (without excessive angle strain or non-bonded interaction), and configurational isomers, whose interconversion requires bond breaking and making.

In the following, an attempt will be made to answer in brief outline the questions: (*1*) what are the structural features responsible for the occurrence of configurational and conformational stereoisomerism, (*2*) how are stereoisomers individually obtained, and (*3*) how are the configurations of stereoisomers determined.

A. STEREOISOMERIC TYPES

1. Enantiomers and diastereomers

Stereoisomers are sensibly classified as enantiomers (optical antipodes) and diastereomers (diastereoisomers). Enantiomers are stereoisomers which differ as object and mirror image: a molecule may have only one enantiomer. Diastereomers are non-enantiomeric stereoisomers and a molecule may consequently have many diastereomers.

---

* This review was completed in March 1960, with additional references added in May 1961.

(a) Enantiomers

To exist in enantiomeric forms, a molecule must be dissymmetric, *i.e.* it must lack reflection symmetry. Dissymmetric molecules lack mirror axes (alternating axes of symmetry), such axes being defined as passing through object and mirror image at right angles to the mirror plane and as having an order *n* determined by the angle $360°/n$ required to bring the mirror image into a position indistinguishable from that of the original object. Accordingly, a plane of symmetry corresponds to a one-fold and a point of symmetry to a two-fold mirror axis. Conformations having a plane or point of symmetry are thus not dissymmetric, but the absence of these symmetry properties may not be taken as evidence for dissymmetry. Fig. 1 shows an ion which has a

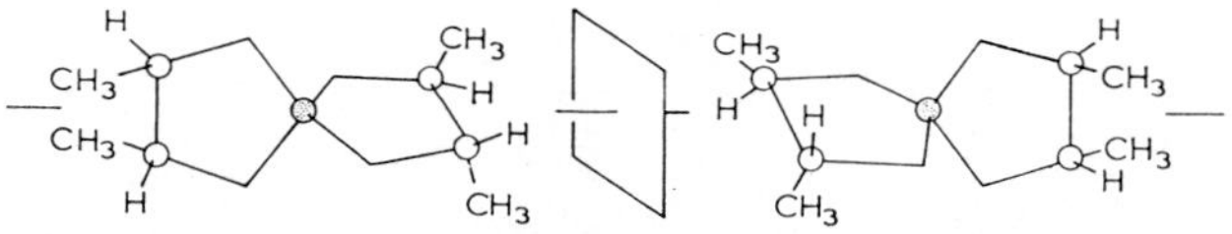

Fig. 1. *meso*-Tetramethylspirobipyrrolidinium ion and its mirror image as an example of a four-fold alternating axis of symmetry.

four-fold mirror axis only, *i.e.* one which is not dissymmetric though it lacks plane or point of symmetry[1].

Use of the term asymmetric (*i.e.* lacking *all* symmetry properties) is frequently inappropriate, since dissymmetry does not preclude the presence of simple symmetry axes[2]. A number of naturally occurring substances or their derivatives are dissymmetric while some of their conformations possess two-fold symmetry axes. A few examples are α-onocerin (I)[3], *cis*-dimethyl-diketopiperazine (II), (+)-tartaric acid (III), mannosaccharic dilactone (IV) and α-isosparteine (V)[4].

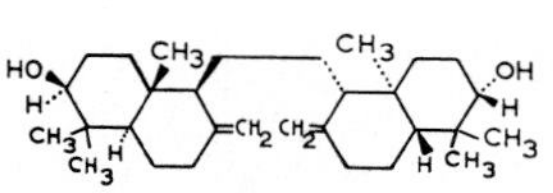

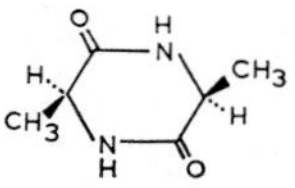

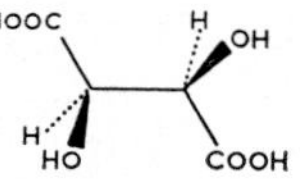

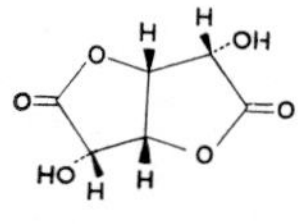

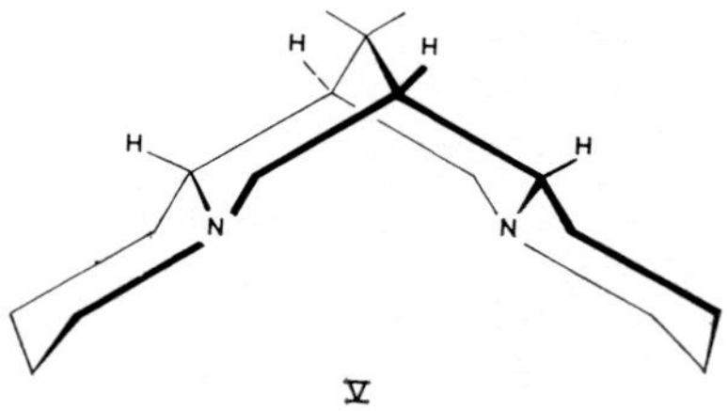

The relationship between enantiomers is most simply that between right- and left-handed helices[5]; the screw sense (handedness, chirality) of the helix defines its configuration. It is characteristic of the enantiomeric relationship that neither isomer can be identified without comparison to a standard which is itself dissymmetric. Thus only common agreement on what constitutes a right-handed helix (*i.e.* a model of the helix itself) forms the basis of the term *absolute configuration*. The stated comparison creates a diastereomeric interaction or relationship. Since diastereomers may be distinguished without resort to a dissymmetric standard, a distinction between enantiomers may thus be achieved. This basic principle of stereochemistry is illustrated in Fig. 2 for the generalized case involving helices.

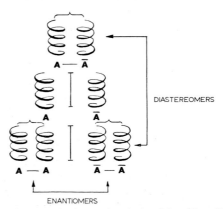

Fig. 2. Schematization of the basic stereoisomeric relationships. Enantiomeric helices A and Ā are characterized by comparison of either helix with another (A or Ā). The resulting diastereoisomeric combinations (A–Ā *versus* either A–A or its enantiomer Ā–Ā) are descriptively distinguished without reference to a helical standard. The vertical bar symbolizes the mirror plane.

The operational distinctions between enantiomers by physical methods, the methods used to separate them, and the usual marked differences in biological activity are all a consequence of this principle. For example, crystals of sodium ammonium tartrate exhibit a dissymmetric habit. The crystals can be mechanically separated into two kinds, since each is either like or unlike another. The direct or indirect comparison of each separate crystal with a dissymmetric standard is implicit in the appropriate "manual separation" of enantiomers.

(b) Optical activity

The rotatory power of dissymmetric substances[6] can be qualitatively understood in terms of the principle just stated. Plane polarized light may be regarded the resultant of two circularly polarized (*i.e.* helical and thus dissymmetric) beams of opposite chirality (*dextro* and *levo*) which are in phase and which are themselves the resultants of two wave trains of the same amplitudes in mutually perpendicular planes and $\lambda/4$ out of phase (Fig. 3). The interactions of the electrons in the dissymmetric field of the molecule with *dextro-* and *levo*-circularly polarized light are in effect diastereomeric, with the result that the refractive indices of the two helical beams differ in this medium (circular birefringence). It follows that one beam will be slowed more than the other and that a change in angle of the resultant plane of polarized light, *i.e.* optical activity, is produced; the change in angle is directly proportional to the difference in refractive indices. In the neighborhood of an absorption band, one helical beam is absorbed

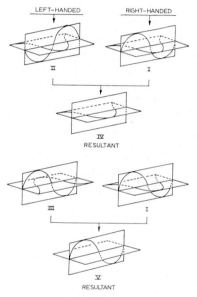

Fig. 3. Result of interaction of plane polarized light with a hypothetical dissymmetric medium. The plane-polarized beam IV, the resultant of right- and left-handed circularly polarized beams I and II, is turned 90° (V) as a consequence of slowing the left-handed beam by 180° (III).

more than the other (circular dichroism) resulting in a change from plane to elliptically polarized light. Here again, it is possible to speak of diastereomeric interactions.

The actual measurement of optical activity (polarimetry) involves large aggregates of molecules, usually in the fluid state, and requires time. Optical activity is therefore observed when a given enantiomer remains in excess over the other during the period of measurement.

Specific rotation, $[\alpha]$, expresses the rotation (α, in degrees) of a sample per unit path length (l, in dm) and concentration (c, in g/100 ml solution) for solutions or density (d, in g/ml) for pure liquids (*i.e.* "neat"). For some purposes, the molecular rotation, $[M]$ or $[\phi]$, is reported. The mean residue rotation, $[R]$, appears to be a useful expression for optically active polymers. Temperature (T), wavelength (λ) and solvent are always specified.

$$[\alpha]_\lambda^T = \frac{\alpha \times 100}{l \times c}, \quad [\alpha]_\lambda^T = \frac{\alpha}{l \times d}$$

$$[\phi]_\lambda^T \equiv [M]_\lambda^T = \frac{M[\alpha]_\lambda^T}{100}, \quad [R]_\lambda^T = \frac{[M]_\lambda^T}{n}$$

M = molecular weight, n = number of monomer units or mean residues per mole of polymer.

The specific rotation is in principle independent of l and c. However, since any observed values of $\alpha \pm 180\,n$ ($n = 0, 1, 2, \ldots$) are indistinguishable, misleading results may sometimes be obtained, as illustrated[7] for the last four entries in Table I.

TABLE I

OPTICAL ROTATION OF (S)-4',1"-DIMETHYL-1,2,3,4-
DIBENZCYCLOHEPTA-1,3-DIENE-6-ONE IN BENZENE

365 mμ, 25°

c	l	Observed α		Calculated	
		+	−	actual α	$[\alpha]$
0.103	0.5	357.3, 177.3	2.7, 182.7	− 2.7°	− 5240°
0.103	1	354.6, 174.6	5.4, 185.4	− 5.4°	− 5240°
0.103	2	349.1, 169.1	10.9, 190.9	− 10.9°	− 5290°
1.04	2	249.8, 69.8	110.2, 290.2	− 110.2°	− 5293°
4.26	2	260.3, 80.3	99.7, 279.7	− 459.7°	− 5396°
6.09	2	256.4, 76.4	103.6, 283.6	− 643.6°	− 5284°
8.26	2	199.7, 19.7	160.3, 340.3	− 880.3°	− 5328°
9.99	2	203.8, 23.8	156.2, 336.2	− 1056.2°	− 5284°

In another sense, specific rotation is dependent on concentration, as it is on temperature, when various species in an association equilibrium are changed. Marked concentration- or temperature-dependence is therefore generally expected with hydrogen-bonding solutes and solvents. Solvent-dependence of specific rotation (including sign) is also often encountered.

The dependence of rotational sign and magnitude on wavelength (rotatory dispersion, plotted as the RD-curve) in regions of low absorption is given by the Drude equation. The equation may be simple (one term) or complex (two or more terms) and has the general form

$$[\alpha]_\lambda^T = \sum_i \frac{A_i}{\lambda^2 - \lambda_i^2} = \frac{A_0}{\lambda^2 - \lambda_0^2} + \frac{A_1}{\lambda^2 - \lambda_1^2} + \cdots$$

where the dispersion constant, λ_i, lies approximately at the center of the ith absorption band corresponding to an optically active electronic transition and A_i is a rotation constant. The several constants in the Drude equation may be determined graphically from appropriate plots[8].

When optical rotation is followed through the absorption bands, anomalous RD-curves (Cotton effect curves) are obtained. A single Cotton effect curve of idealized form is shown in Fig. 4. The active chromophore lies roughly in the middle between the extrema, $i.e.$ between peak and trough, at λ_0. The algebraic difference between the extrema is the amplitude of the curve. The curve shown in the illustration is a positive Cotton effect curve since the peak lies at a longer wavelength than the trough; the curve corresponding to the enantiomer would be a negative one.

When λ_0 is situated at wavelengths much shorter than $ca.$ 220 mμ, as for example in the case of simple hydrocarbons, olefins and alcohols, the Cotton

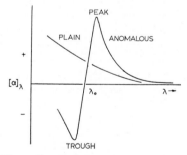

Fig. 4. Types of rotatory dispersion curves.

effect curve is instrumentally inaccessible and only its tail end is observed in the form of a plain curve; the case of a positive plain curve is illustrated in Fig. 4.

Monochromatic measurements are usually made at the sodium D-line (589 mμ) and the sign of rotation at 589 mμ is used to characterize the enantiomer, as by the prefix $(+)$-, d- or $(dextro)$-, resp. $(-)$-, l- or $(levo)$-.

Solvent has to be specified if the sign is strongly solvent-dependent. On occasion, when no rotation is observed at 589 mμ, the enhancement of rotatory power at shorter wavelengths may be used to find the long-wavelength sign. A case in point is the vitamin B_{12} degradation[9] product VI, a 5 % solution of which shows no detectable rotation at 589 mμ but has $[\alpha]_{365} - 68.6°$. VI is therefore the (—)-isomer.

VI

(c) Racemic forms

A racemic form is one composed of equimolar parts of the (+)- and the (—)-forms. Racemic forms (dl-pairs, (±)-pairs) result from direct synthesis in the absence of dissymmetric influences. They also result from either enantiomer by racemization, i.e. reversible interconversion, often but not necessarily[10] through a symmetrical intermediate or transition state. The driving force for racemization is the entropy of mixing ($R \ln 2 = 1.4$ cal/mole degree), which lowers the free energy of the dl-pair by about 0.4 kcal/mole (at room temperature) relative to that of the components.

Enantiomers, in general, mix virtually ideally in the liquid state[11], but the solid racemic forms may be mixtures (conglomerates), solid solutions, or compounds (racemates) of the component enantiomers. Racemate formation is often detected by thermal analysis, i.e. by the appearance of a binary compound in the phase diagram of the component enantiomers. Alternatively, if the X-ray powder diagram or infrared spectrum[12] of the solid racemic form differs from that of the enantiomeric components, racemate formation is indicated. Occasionally racemates form solvates while the component enantiomers do not, and sometimes the crystal habits differ, but these differences are not generally encountered and are not to be depended on for diagnostic testing.

(d) Diastereomers

Since diastereomers are non-enantiomeric, the intramolecular interactions between non-bonded atoms of diastereomeric conformations must be different. It follows that conformational diastereomers as well as configurational diastereomers, which consist of conformational mixtures, differ in free energy content and hence in all physical and chemical properties (in degree if not in kind).

For example, diastereomers differ in melting and boiling point, solubility, density, dipole moment, infrared, ultraviolet and n.m.r. spectra, dielectric constant, crystal structure, and adsorptivity. While their functional chemistry will be the same, rates of reaction and hence ratio of products in competing reactions will be different. Diastereomeric acids or bases will have different values of pK_a.

Diastereomers may, but need not, be dissymmetric; if dissymmetric they will differ in magnitude and possibly sign of optical rotation.

In the present discussion, geometric isomers will be regarded a structural subclass of diastereomers, despite the common classification of diastereomers as non-enantiomeric optical isomers. Though an occasionally useful distinction may be made between optical isomers, *i.e.* isomers which differ in the configuration of dissymmetric groupings, and geometric isomers, *i.e.* isomers which do not, such a distinction is limited in principle. Thus, ricinoleic acid VII[13] has one enantiomer (VIII) and two diastereomers (IX and X). While

VII and VIII (or IX and X) are optical isomers, and while VII and IX (or VIII and X) are geometric isomers, VII and X (or VIII and IX) are both. There seems to be little advantage in such a subclassification. *Optical-geometric* isomerism[14] in Co(III) complexes presents a similar situation.

2. Stereoisomers resulting from hindered or restricted rotation

(a) Conformational stereoisomers

The various rotamers of butane illustrate some basic types of conformational stereoisomerisms (Fig. 5). The staggered (gauche or syn-skew[15]) 60°- and 300°-isomers are enantiomers and form a conformational *dl*-pair. The staggered 180°-isomer (trans or anti-parallel[15]) is a diastereomer of the syn-skew rotamers.

The eclipsed or opposed anti-skew[15] 120°- and 240°-conformations are also enantiomeric and the eclipsed syn-parallel[15] 0°-conformation diastereomeric to the others, but these conformations have no life-time and are to be regarded as transition states separating the staggered isomers rather than as isomers in themselves.

Anti-parallel butane is more stable than the syn-skew isomers by about 0.8 kcal/mole, since repulsive non-bonded interaction effects are minimized in the point of symmetry conformation of the former. This concept cannot

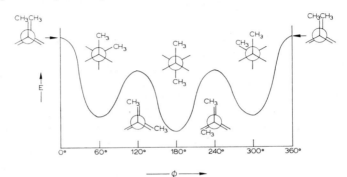

Fig. 5. Rotamerization of butane. Potential energy (E) as a function of dihedral angle (ϕ). Projection convention according to M. S. NEWMAN, *J. Chem. Educ.*, 32 (1955) 344.

be generalized; for example there is support for the contention that the syn-skew isomers of $(CHCl_2)_2$ and $(CHBr_2)_2$ are more stable than the anti-parallel isomers[16].

The barrier heights separating the isomers are of the order of 3 kcal/mole. While there can thus be no question of free rotation, interconversion is far too rapid to permit separation of stereoisomers. The origin of the barrier is not fully understood[17].

Conformational isomerism due to "partial double bond character" is encountered in the s-*cis* and s-*trans* forms of 1,3-dienes, esters, nitrites, amides and the like, *e.g.* the s-*cis* and s-*trans* forms of butadiene (XI and XII). Physical separation of such stereoisomers is prevented by the low barrier to interconversion[18].

XI   XII

(b) Atropisomers

Repulsive non-bonded interaction in the transition state for interconversion may provide barriers large enough for the ready separation of stereoisomers. Restricted rotation of this type (atropisomerism) is illustrated by

the isolation of enantiomeric forms XIII–XIV and XV–XVI; space-filling
models according to Stuart-Briegleb[19] or Robinson (Courtauld)[20] reflect
with reasonable faithfulness the overcrowding encountered in the interconversion of such stereoisomers.

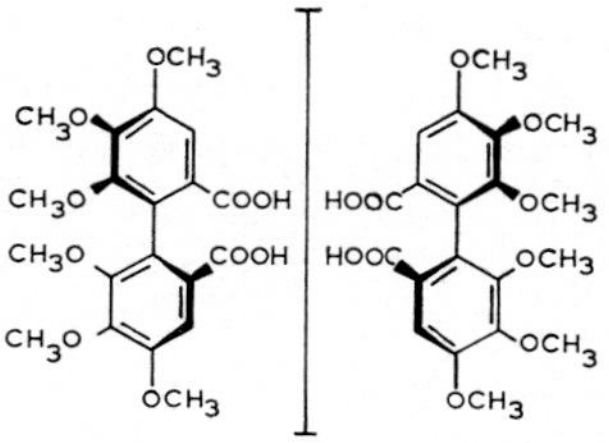

XIII XIV 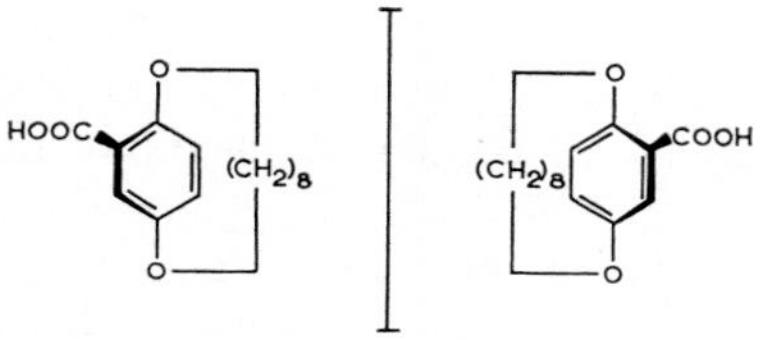 XV XVI

Interestingly, XIII and XIV are derivatives of the naturally occurring
ellagitannins[21]; the (+)-form derives from corilagin and the (—)-form from
valonea tannin. Atropisomerism has been recognized[22] in phenyldihydrothebaine (XVII) and suspected[23] in isocolchicine (XVIII). In aporphine
alkaloids, e.g. isocorydine (XIX)[24], atropisomerism is a consequence of the
fused ring system:

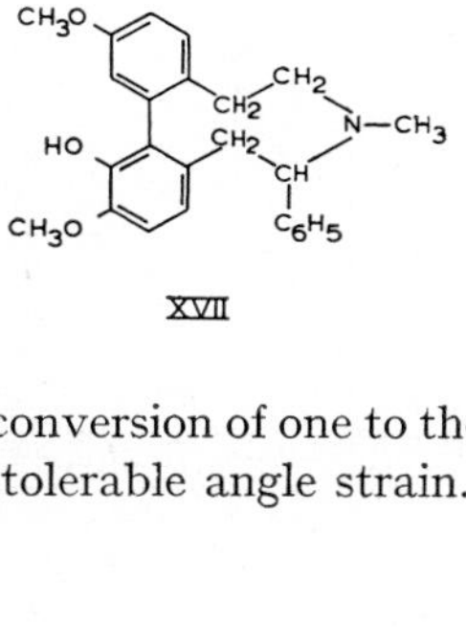

XVII 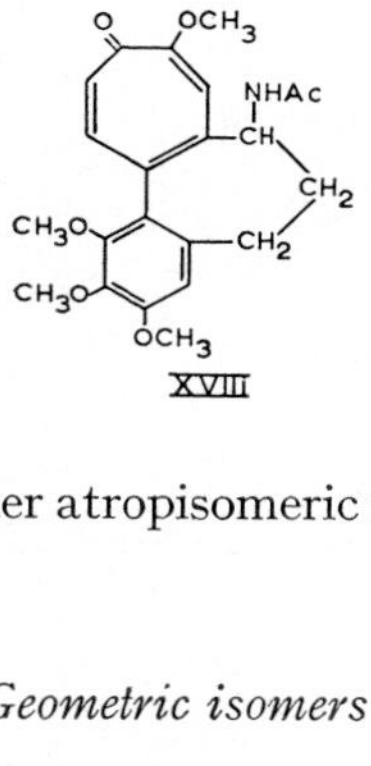 XVIII 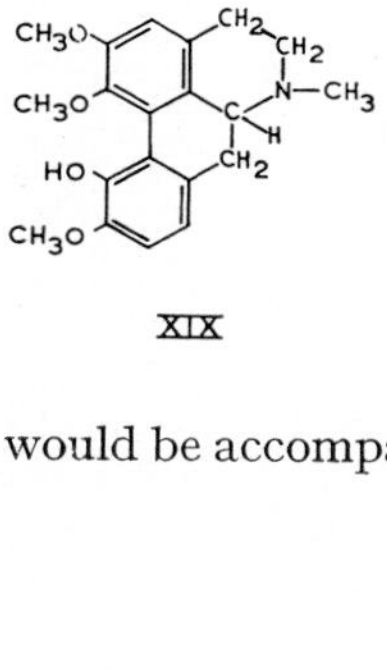 XIX

interconversion of one to the other atropisomeric form would be accompanied
by intolerable angle strain.

(c) Geometric isomers

Geometric or *cis-trans* (*syn-anti*) isomers[25] are made possible by the presence
of a formal or essential[26] double bond in the molecule. Generally, the double
bond links two carbon atoms, less frequently a carbon and a nitrogen atom
(*e.g.* Schiff bases, oximes, hydrazones) or two nitrogen (*e.g.* azo compounds)
atoms. Formally, stereoisomerism of this type is possible only when interchange of substituents on either atom does not result in the identical isomer.

Rotation about the double bond is restricted by an activation energy
barrier of usually not less than 20 kcal/mole which makes interconversion

References p. 239

(stereomutation) an energetically costly process under ordinary conditions and in the absence of catalysts. The barrier is a result of the decrease in overlap of double-bond π-electrons, but even when the energy is lowered by a singlet–triplet transition[27], the concomitant lessening of the probability factor keeps the rate of stereomutation small. Only special structural features which serve to increase the "single-bond character" of the double bond seem to have the effect of substantially lowering the potential barrier[28]. As a result, diastereomers differing in configuration around the double bond are physically separable and ordinarily shown no tendency to stereomutate.

In principle, 2^n diastereomers are possible for constitutionally unsymmetrical acyclic olefins with n double bonds, as illustrated in Table II for $n = 1$–4. The *cis*-isomer generally predominates among naturally occurring non-conjugated fatty acids (compounds which constitutionally belong to this class); thus oleic, linoleic, linolenic and arachidonic are *cis*-, *cis,cis*-, *cis,cis,cis*- and *cis,cis,cis,cis*-isomers of olefins derived from octadecanoic acid.

The number of diastereomers for constitutionally symmetrical acyclic olefins[29] is $2^{n-1} + 2^{(n-2)/2}$ when n is even and $2^{n-1} + 2^{(n-1)/2}$ when n is odd. Squalene (XX) and lycopene (XXI), both all-*trans*-isomers, illustrate these two categories; other examples abound in the terpenoids.

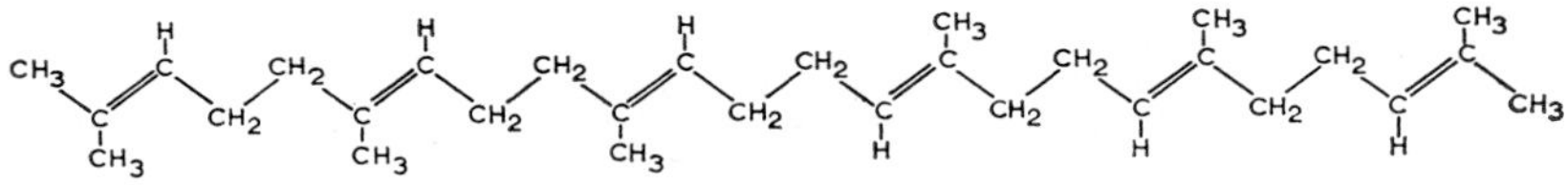

XX

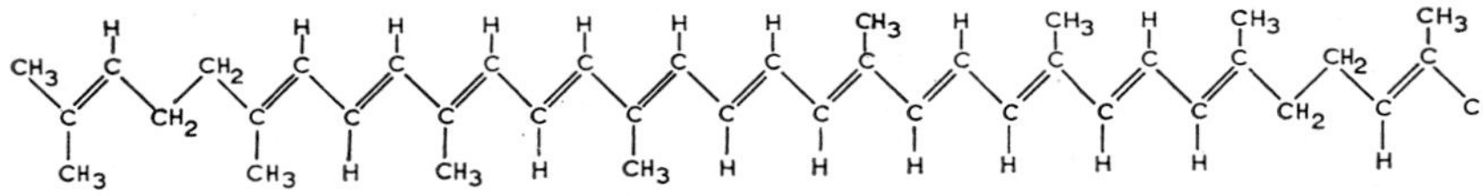

XXI

Since the smallest ring known to accommodate a *trans*-double bond is eight-membered[30], stereoisomerism of the geometric type is not possible in cyclic systems containing fewer than eight carbons. Larger rings, *e.g.* the isomers of civetone (XXII, XXIII)[31] and caryophyllene (XXIV, XXV)[32], are exempt from this restriction; indeed, in rings larger than cyclodecene, as in acyclic systems, the *trans*-isomer is the thermodynamically more stable[33] one.

TABLE II

DIASTEREOMERS POSSIBLE FOR CONSTITUTIONALLY UNSYMMETRICAL OLEFINS

No. of double bonds (n)	Configuration							
	CIS (C)				TRANS (T)			
1	C				T			
2	CC	CT			TC	TT		
3	CCC	CCT	CTC	CTT	TCC	TCT	TTC	TTT
4	CCCC CCCT CCTC CCTT CTCC CTCT CTTC CTTT				TCCC TCCT TCTC TCTT TTCC TTCT TTTC TTTT			

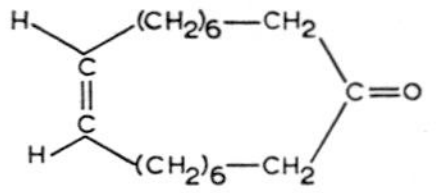

XXII

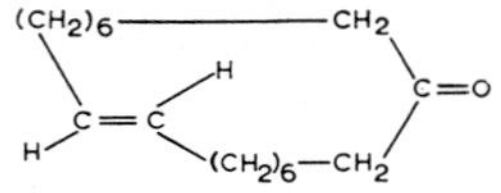

XXIII

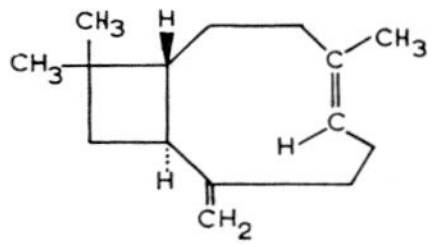

XXIV

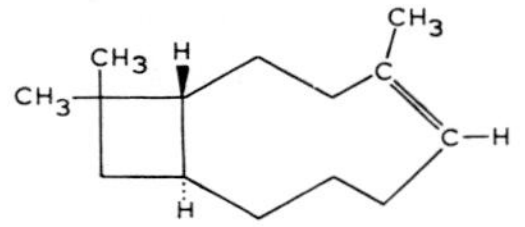

XXV

Cumulenes are geometrically analogous to simple olefins, since the four substituents lie in a plane:

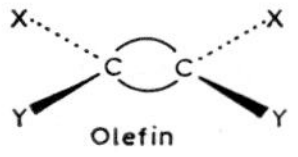

Olefin

Cumulene

For example, stereoisomers XXVI and XXVII have been separated[34].

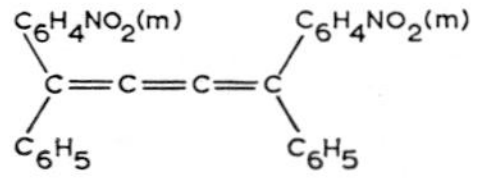

XXVI

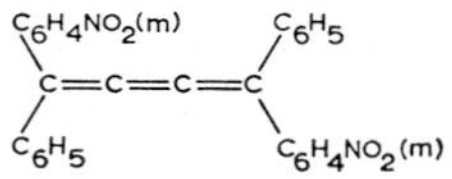

XXVII

(d) Allenes

The four substituents in allene are arranged at the corners of a tetragonal bisphenoid, *i.e.* a tetrahedron stretched along one of the three two-fold rotational axes:

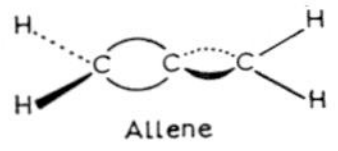

Allene

Suitably substituted allenes (*e.g.* XXVIII) may therefore exhibit dissymmetry and optical activity. The structural criterion for optical activity is the same as that for *cis–trans* isomerism: interchange of substituents on either atom may not result in the identical isomer.

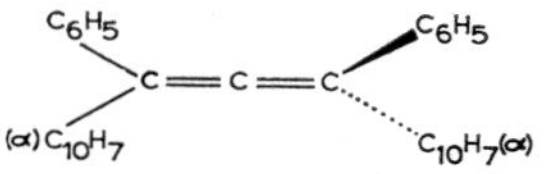

XXVIII

The double bond is geometrically equivalent to a ring, so that the stereo-chemistry of the allene system is not essentially changed when we go to systems having one (*e.g.* XXIX) or two (*e.g.* XXX) rings (spirans) in place of double bonds.

Mycomycin[35] is a naturally occurring allene which also has a *cis-* and a *trans*-double bond and two acetylenic bonds. In the arbitrary absolute con-figuration shown (XXXI), it is one of eight possible stereoisomers.

3. Stereoisomers resulting from asymmetric atoms

(a) Asymmetric atoms

Stereoisomerism, especially enantiomerism, most commonly arises from the presence of one or more asymmetric atoms whose substituents differ in the sense that exchange of any two gives a new stereoisomer. The familiar asymmetric carbon atom illustrates the general definition. The four sub-stituents usually differ constitutionally; whenever this is the case, dis-symmetry results and optical activity is in principle observable. The difference may merely be an isotopic one, as in optically active ethanol-1-d and similar compounds[36]. Molecules with asymmetric tetracoordinate silicon[37] and group V elements[38] (nitrogen, phosphorus, arsenic) are similarly known to give rise to optical activity. An unshared electron pair is regarded as a substituent, and although the carbanion $[R_1R_2R_3C:]^-$ is not expected to maintain configuration over a significant period of time, rapid inversion of the isosteric nitrogen pyramid $R_1R_2R_2N:$ having been demonstrated[39], numerous compounds are known which owe their optical activity to the configurationally stable tricoordinate asymmetric arsenic, antimony, sulfur, and phosphorus[39a].

When a molecule has n asymmetric atoms, $\frac{1}{2}(2^n)$ diastereomeric racemic pairs or altogether 2^n stereoisomers may exist. The sixteen aldohexoses are a familiar illustration for $n = 4$. The ephedrines [(+)-ephedrine, XXXII; (—)-ephedrine, XXXIII; (—)-ψ-ephedrine, XXXIV; (+)-ψ-ephedrine, XXXV)] are shown as specific examples for $n = 2$.

XXXII   XXXIII   XXXIV   XXXV

The above formula may not be properly applied to camphor, which can only exist in two enantiomeric forms (XXXVI, XXXVII) and has no diastereomers. It is thus seen that the number of bridgehead diastereomers possible in bicyclic systems is limited by ring size in the same way and for the same reason as the number of *cis–trans* isomers in cyclenes.

XXXVI   XXXVII

A number of natural products combine the stereochemical features of atomic asymmetry and restricted rotation. Sulforaphene[40], shown in the arbitrary absolute configuration XXXVIII, like ricinoleic acid (VII) is one of four stereoisomers; a compound of the same type, sphingosine[41] (XXXIX), is one of eight stereoisomers. Nemotinic acid[42], shown in the arbitrary absolute configuration XL, combines allenic with atomic asymmetry and is one of four possible isomers.

XXXVIII   XXXIX   XL

(b) Meso isomers

Constitutionally symmetrical molecules containing asymmetric atoms have fewer than 2^n stereoisomers, $2^{n-1} + 2^{(n-2)/2}$ when n is even and 2^{n-1} when n is odd. Of these, some, the *meso*-isomers, will be optically inactive diastereomers. For example, there are only three tartaric (tetraric) acids (Table III). Two of these, the (+)- and (—)-isomers, are mixtures of conformational diastereomers. The *meso*-isomer is a mixture of one symmetric anti-parallel and two interconvertible enantiomeric syn-skew conformers. As a result, the *meso*-isomer is optically inactive[10].

TABLE III

STEREOCHEMISTRY OF THE TARTARIC ACIDS

Configurational isomer	Conformers
(+)	
(—)	
meso	

The pentahydroxypimelic (heptaric) acids are particularly instructive (Table IV), in that they represent all the various stereochemical possibilities for a carbon (C-4) containing two constitutionally identical substituents. In asymmetric and optically active diastereomers XLI–XLIV, the two groupings are *diastereomeric* and the central atom is asymmetric. In asymmetric and optically active diastereomers XLV and XLVI, the two groupings are *configurationally identical* and the central atom is not asymmetric since exchange of any two groups will not lead to a new stereoisomer. In symmetric and optically inactive diastereomers XLVII–L, the central atom is attached to two *enantiomeric* groupings and is *pseudoasymmetric*; exchange of any two groups on the pseudoasymmetric atom leads to a new

LI

TABLE IV

STEREOCHEMISTRY OF THE HEPTARIC ACID

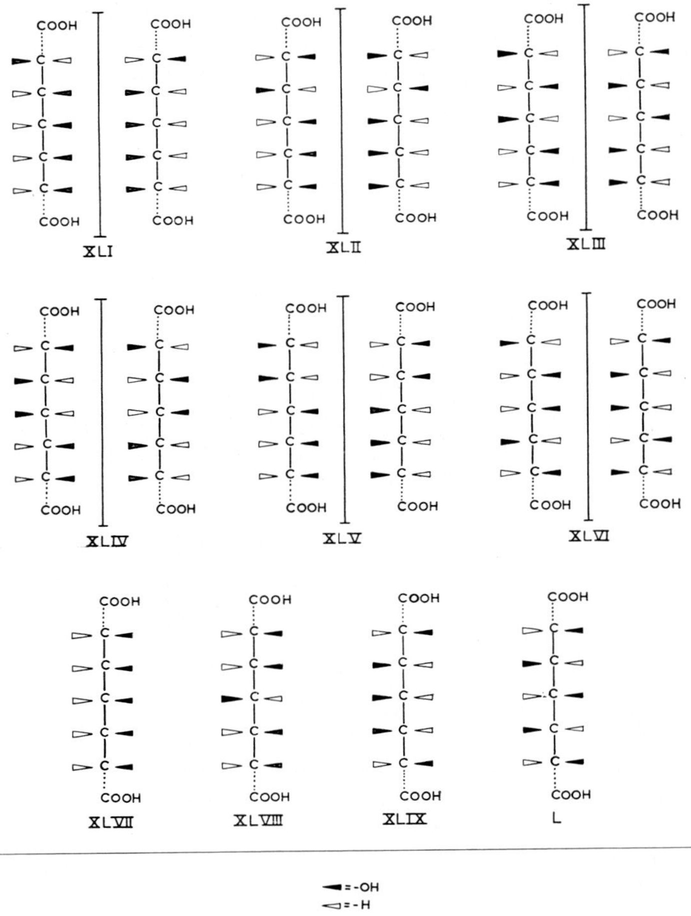

XLI   XLII   XLIII

XLIV   XLV   XLVI

XLVII   XLVIII   XLIX   L

◄ = -OH
◁ = -H

optically inactive diastereomer[43]. The case of LI is akin to that of XLI–XLIV: the substituents are diastereomeric and the central atom as well as the whole molecule is therefore asymmetric.

The term *epimer* can also be clearly illustrated by reference to the heptaric acids. Epimers are diastereomers differing in the configuration of any *one* of several dissymmetric groupings; thus XLI is epimeric with XLIII, XLV, XLVI, XLVII and XLIX. In carbohydrate chemistry, the term has come to mean configuration at C-2 only, while *anomers* refers to diastereomers differing in configuration at C-1.

When all four substituents on carbon have the same constitution and differ in configuration, the meso-isomer has a four-fold mirror axis only[1].

4. Stereoisomerism in cyclohexanes

Stereochemical features peculiar to this, the most ubiquitous of the ring systems in natural products, prompt a separate discussion. It will prove helpful to consult models suitable for conformational analysis[44].

(a) Cyclohexane

Two conformational isomers can be distinguished in cyclohexane which are formally free of angle strain; the chair (rigid) and the flexible form.

The chair form has favorable staggering (dihedral angle 60°) of bonds. Two bond arrangements are distinguished: the axial (*a*) arrangement (LII), so called because the bonds are parallel to the three-fold symmetry axis, and the equatorial (*e*) arrangement (LIII). Thus, diastereomeric conformers of chair-methylcyclohexane may exist, the axial (LIV) and equatorial (LV) isomers. The two additional (net) syn-skew butane-like non-bonded interactions (arrows) render LIV less stable than LV by about 1.6 kcal/mole, so that the equilibrium mixture at room temperature contains about 94 % of LV.

That interconversion readily takes place is demonstrated by the observation[45] that conversion of acid ester LVI leads to the same ester amide LVIII whether by path A (via the acid amide LVII) or directly, by path B. Interconversions of the type discussed take place by way of the intermediate flexible form of cyclohexane. The various conformations of this isomer all involve some repulsive interaction of the butane type. The most unfavorable of these, the boat conformation (LIX), is actually a transition state conformation in which the most opposed (*flagpole*) hydrogens bear geometric

LIX

resemblance to the 2,2'-hydrogens in planar biphenyl. As a result, the flexible form is less stable than the chair form by about 5 kcal/mole[45a]. The activation energy barrier for the conversion of chair to flexible form is low (about 10 kcal/mole) since only a slight amount of bond bending and compression is involved; consequently the interconversion of chair *a*- and *e*-isomers is most facile.

(b) Inositol

The configurational–conformational analysis of the inositols[46] (Table V) shows up the various stereochemical possibilities in polysubstituted cyclohexanes.

Of the eight configurational diastereomers, only one, the (±)-form, is racemic. At the conformational level, it is only the *allo*-isomer which has (interconvertible) enantiomers; all the other conformers have planes of symmetry. It is illuminating in this respect to compare the inositols to the dimethylcyclohexanes, where only the *cis*-1,2-isomer exists as a conformational *dl*-pair.

The *cis*- and *muco*-isomers exhibit no conformational stereoisomerism, in analogy with *trans*-1,3- and *cis*-1,4-dimethylcyclohexanes, since the interconvertible conformers are identical. All other inositol conformers exist as mixtures of diastereomers, in analogy with *trans*-1,2-, *cis*-1,3- and *trans*-1,4-dimethylcyclohexanes.

It is occasionally asserted that the optically active isomers of inositol lack an asymmetric carbon. However, each carbon contains two substituents which differ in being diastereomeric. As was seen in the case of heptaric acids XLI–XLIV, such carbons are asymmetric.

Much of the stereochemistry of the carbohydrates is closely related to inositol stereochemistry[47]; *cf. e.g.* the anomeric α- and β-glucopyranosides (LX and LXI) which are heterocyclic analogs of cyclohexane derivatives.

LX   LXI

TABLE V

STEREOCHEMISTRY OF THE INOSITOLS

Configuration		Conformers
Designation	Isomer ◀ = –OH up ◁ = – H up	Conformers (Lines indicate bonds to —OH)

Cis		
Epi		
Allo		
Myo		
Muco		
Neo		
(+)		
(−)		
Scyllo		

(c) Decalin

Cyclohexanes may be fused 1,4, as in bicyclo[2,2,2]octane (LXII) where boat conformations must be assumed, or 1,3, as in bicyclo[3,3,1]nonane (LXIII), or 1,2, as in the decalins. Some natural products combine several types, *e.g.* α-isoparteine (V), which has both 1,2- and 1,3-fusions.

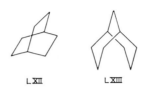

LXII   LXIII

The decalins can exist in diastereomeric *cis*- and *trans*-forms (Table VI). The *trans*-system is locked, but two enantiomeric (dissymmetric but not asymmetric) *cis*-conformers are possible; the enantiomers interconvert

TABLE VI

STEREOCHEMISTRY OF THE DECALINS

Configuration		Conformers
Designation	*Isomer*	
Trans		
Cis		

through flexible forms. One of the consequences is that the conformation (*a* or *e*) of a substituent in the 1- or 2-position of decalin remains unaltered in the *trans*-isomer but is interconvertible in the *cis*-isomer, as for example in stereoisomers LXIV and LXV of 2-methyldecalin.

The *cis*-isomer is less stable than the *trans*-isomer by about 2.4 kcal/mole as a result of three net syn-skew butane-like interactions (arrows). The difference is lessened when an angular methyl group is introduced[48]. In 9-methyl-*cis*- and *trans*-decalins (LXVI and LXVII), two resp. four net skew

TABLE VII

STEREOCHEMISTRY OF THE PERHYDROPHENANTHRENES

Heavy dot signifies hydrogen projecting toward observer

Configuration		Conformers	
Designation	*Isomer*	*Designation*	*Isomer*
Cis-syn-cis		*ea–ae–ea*	
Cis-syn-trans		*ea–ae–ee*	
Cis-anti-trans		*ee–ee–ea*	
Cis-anti-cis		on the left *ae–ee–ea* on the right *ea–aa–ae*	
Trans-syn-trans		boat	
Trans-anti-trans		*ee–ee–ee*	

interactions of the angular methyl group (arrows) reduce the energy difference between the diastereomers to 0.8 kcal/mole, while the difference is

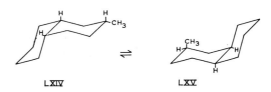

reduced (in principle) to zero in 9,10-dimethyl-*cis*- and *trans*-decalins (LXVIII and LXIX) where five resp. eight net skew interactions are ascribable to the angular methyls (arrows). In heterocyclic analogs, the effect of angular methyl may actually cause the *cis*-isomer to be more stable than the *trans*[49].

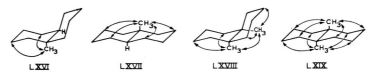

(d) Perhydrophenanthrene

The stereochemistry of the perhydrophenanthrenes[50] is summarized in Table VII. Configurational and conformational nomenclature refers to the geometry of the central ring-junctions.

The *cis–syn–cis*-isomer has interconvertible conformational enantiomers each having three net skew plus one 1:3-diaxial interaction; the total interaction energy is about 7 kcal/mole. The *cis–syn–trans*- and *cis–anti–trans*-isomers are *dl*-pairs, one conformation corresponding to each configuration with four net skew interactions. The *trans–anti–trans*-isomer has a similar stereochemistry with only one net skew interaction.

The *cis–anti–cis*-isomer is also a *dl*-pair, but each enantiomer exists as a mixture of two diastereomeric conformers, the *ae–ee–ea*-isomer with seven net skew interactions and the *ea–aa–ae*-isomer with six.

The *trans–syn–trans*-isomer would have to have the *aa–ae–ee*-conformation to remain all-chair. However, since a chair ring cannot be fused to an *aa*-junction, the central ring necessarily assumes the boat-conformation.

5. Stereoisomerism in macromolecules

Stereoisomerism resulting from addition polymerization of unsymmetrical olefins may become quite complex[51]. Of particular interest are the ordered polyvinyl diastereomers which may result from stereospecific polymeriza-tion[52]. The *isotactic* (LXX) and *syndiotactic* (LXXI) diastereomers of (—CH$_2$CHR—)$_n$ differ in configuration as shown; assuming chains of infinite length, every other carbon in both isomers is pseudoasymmetric, for LXX may be regarded an extension in type of XLVII, and LXXI an extension in type of L. Since the chains are finite and the terminal groups undoubtedly not the same, each alternate carbon is asymmetric and the polymers are *dl*-pairs.

A relatively stable crystal lattice is a distinguishing mark of the isotactic polymers. The same is true of optically active polymers which have dis-symmetric units of the same configuration. An example of the last type is polypropylene oxide, (—CH$_2$CH(CH$_3$)O—)$_n$, formed by polymerization of optically active propylene oxide[53].

The naturally occurring poly-1,4-isoprenes (—CH$_2$C(CH$_3$) = CHCH$_2$—)$_n$, are also diastereomeric: rubber is the all-*cis* isomer (LXXII) while gutta percha is the all-*trans* isomer (LXXIII).

The biologically most important macromolecules, *i.e.* the polysaccharides, polypeptides, proteins, polynucleotides and nucleic acids are all dissymmetric and optically active since their constituent units are dissymmetric.

Macromolecules may possess a *secondary structure*, a term reserved for the conformation or coil of the main-chain[54]. When the conformation is helical, as in (—CF$_2$CF$_2$—)$_n$, an element of dissymmetry has been introduced; the two helices in this case are interconvertible enantiomers. Hexahelicene[55] (LXXIV) is an example of an optically active helical conformation, here stabilized by *molecular overcrowding*.

Main-chains which do not contain dissymmetric elements form right- and left-handed helices in equal amounts. If the main chain units are dissymmetric, the twist of the helix will introduce diastereomerism. As a result of the difference in free energy of the diastereomers, one of the enantiomeric helices will predominate in the equilibrium *dextro*-helix ⇌ random coil ⇌ *levo*-helix.

LXXIV

The polypeptide α-helix, for example, may either be right- or left-handed, but the right-handed α-helix of a given poly-L-amino acid and that of the corresponding poly-D-amino acid (for nomenclature, see below) cannot possibly have the same stability; the same is true of the left-handed α-helix. It is found that rotatory dispersion affords an answer to the question of helical identity and stability[56]. In the Moffitt equation the second term

$$[R]_\lambda^{\overline{T}}\left(\frac{3}{n^2 + 2}\right) = \frac{a_0 \lambda_0^2}{\lambda^2 - \lambda_0^2} + \frac{b_0 \lambda_0^4}{(\lambda^2 - \lambda_0^2)^2}$$

gives the rotatory contribution of the helix and the coefficient b_0 a measure of helical content: b_0 varies from zero to *ca.* ± 600 as helical content varies from zero to 100 %. The sign of b_0 reflects the sense of the helix. For example, poly-benzyl-L-glutamate has a negative b_0 of about 600, the contribution of what is presumably a right-handed helix, while poly-benzyl-L-aspartate has a positive b_0 of about 600, presumably because the sense of the helix is opposite. The optical rotation of proteins and synthetic polypeptides is thus made up of two components: the residue rotation of the dissymmetric amino acid units, which would persist even in a randomly coiled main-chain, and the rotational contribution of the helical conformation, *e.g.* the α-helical polyglycine conformation in the case of polypeptides.

The axis of the α-helix need not be linear but may itself describe a helix (compound helix, superhelix, coiled coil) of the same sense as the α-helix but of larger pitch. Resulting *tertiary structures* formed by twisting such helical strands about one another to form ropes and cables have been proposed for compound α-proteins[57] and for the deoxyribonucleoproteins[58], the last pictured as fully extended polypeptide chains wrapped helically around the open helical groove of the DNA double helix (itself a result of two interlocking polynucleotide helices[59]).

The conformational dissymmetry discussed for macromolecules closely resembles the dissymmetry resulting from the helical arrangement of atoms in the lattice of optically active quartz.

6. Configurational nomenclature

Proper and unequivocal identification of stereoisomers is essential. Until recently, nomenclature has been solely genetic in character and such designations are still in use. Thus, in the carbohydrates, the designation D- or D_g-applies to (+)-glyceraldehyde (LXXV) and to all compounds obviously relatable to it, e.g. (—)-lactic acid (LXXVI); L- or L_g- applies to the enantiomers. Similarly, L- or L_s-refers to (—)-serine (LXXVII) and obviously related compounds, e.g. (+)-alanine (LXXVIII). Ambiguities arise, however, as soon as the genetic relationship is no longer clear. This is the case with

CHO	COOH	COOH	COOH
H—C—OH	H—C—OH	H₂N—C—H	H₂N—C—H
CH₂OH	CH₃	CH₂OH	CH₃
LXXV	LXXVI	LXXVII	LXXVIII

(—)-tartaric acid (LXXIX), which can either be synthesized[60] from LXXV or be degraded[61] via (—)-malic acid (LXXX) to (+)-glyceric acid (LXXXI), itself produced from the enantiomer of LXXV, (—)-glyceraldehyde (LXXXII).

These difficulties have been overcome by the use of nongenetic systems, of which one[62] appears to find general acceptance. According to this system, the groups attached to the asymmetric atom are arranged according to a sequence rule in a priority order of decreasing atomic number and, for the same atomic number, decreasing atomic weight. The lone pair, as in asymmetric sulfur atoms, has the lowest priority. If the atoms which are directly linked to the asymmetric atom are the same, priority order is determined by the nature of the atoms attached further away. Multiple linkages are treated as duplicates (for double bonds) or triplicates (for triple bonds) of the attached groups. Thus, in decreasing priority: I, Br, Cl, F, O, N, C, [$COOCH_3$, COOH, $CONH_2$, $COCH_3$, CHO, CH_2OH, CN, CH_2NH_2, C_6H_5, $C(CH_3)_3$, C≡CH, $CH(CH_3)_2$, CH=CH_2, C_2H_5,CH_3], D, H, lone pair.

According to a conversion rule, the group of lowest priority is viewed through the triangle formed by joining the other three; the triangle interposes itself between the observer and the group of lowest priority, which is viewed in a line with the bond joining it to the asymmetric atom. If the observed decreasing priority order of the three groups is clockwise, the (R)-configuration is specified, otherwise the (S)-configuration. Hence, LXXV and LXXVI have (R)-configurations, and LXXVII, LXXVIII, LXXX, LXXXI and LXXXII have (S)-configurations, while LXXIX is unambiguously named(—)-(S, S)-tartaric acid.

In the naming of diastereomers, this system has the advantages of precision and generality. Prefixes often used to differentiate diastereomers, such as *epi-*, *allo-*, *pseudo-* and *iso-*, have no significance outside the narrow area within which they are applied. Less narrow but still limited are the prefixes *threo-* and *erythro-* (suggesting a similarity in type to threose and erythrose) which are used for diastereomers with two asymmetric carbons. The designating prefixes for the 1-phenyl-2-methylamino-1-propanols XXXII, XXXIII, XXXIV and XXXV, are thus most precisely (1S, 2R), (1R, 2S), (1R, 2R) and (1S, 2S) rather than L$_g$-*erythro*, D$_g$-*erythro*, D$_g$-*threo* and L$_g$-*threo*. Similarly, XXXIX becomes (2S, 3R)- rather than D-*erythro*-sphingosine.

Where no genetic precedent has been set, the present system can be easily applied; thus XXXVIII has the (S)-configuration. Names such as α-OH$_{L_s}$-β-^{2}H$_{L_s}$-malic acid[63] are more simply expressed as (2S, 3R)-2-hydroxysuccinic-3-d acid. The system can also be applied to allenic and atropisomeric stereoisomerism. Only in cases where the genetic relationship is clear, unequivocal and applied to very large families is continued usage of "corresponding configuration", denoted by D- and L-, desirable. Thus it may be said that L-serine has the (S)-configuration while L-cysteine has the (R)-configuration. Similar considerations apply to the prefixes α- and β- in the carbohydrates and steroids.

XXXII a   XXXIII a   XXXIV a   XXXV a

The problem of proper representation of configurational stereoisomers is related to the problem of nomenclature. The method employed in this chapter is self-explanatory and unequivocal. Alternatively, the Fischer convention may be employed, according to which the main-chain of an acyclic stereoisomer, written vertically, is imagined in or below the plane of the paper, with the side-chains, written horizontally, imagined projecting toward the observer. For example, XXXII–XXXV could be written as XXXIIa–XXXVa.

B. PREPARATION OF STEREOISOMERS

The central object in the preparation of individual stereoisomers is the production of diastereomerically pure products, intermediates, transition states or, in the broadest sense, interactions. Syntheses which yield predominantly one of several possible diastereomers in the above sense are called stereospecific or stereoselective[63].

1. Diastereomers

The synthesis of geometric isomers of the dialkylethylene type illustrates the preparation of diastereomerically pure products. The acyclic *cis*-isomers being the less stable, their formation is therefore the outcome of special driving forces in the transition state of the reaction; the products are "kinetically controlled". For example, the semihydrogenation of the triple bond over specially prepared catalysts[64] affords *cis*-isomers, as in the preparation of oleic[65] and linoleic[65] acids from the corresponding acetylenic precursors, presumably because hydrogen is added to the face adsorbed on the catalyst. *Trans*-isomers on the other hand may result as the *thermodynamically* as well as the kinetically controlled products from *cis–trans* equilibrations, exemplified[65] by the stereomutation of oleic to elaidic acid (elaidinization) in the presence of catalysts such as iodine, selenium and nitrogen oxides. Generally, in the absence of special constraining features, most reactions capable of yielding both geometric isomers will give the *trans*-isomer in predominance.

Stereospecific elimination reactions may also lead to individual geometric isomers. Thus the debromination by iodide ion of *meso-* and *dl-*2,3-dibromobutane leads to *trans-* and *cis-*2-butene respectively[67]; by extension *erythro* (LXXXIII)- and *threo* (LXXXIV)- lead to *trans* (LXXXV)- and *cis* (LXXXVI)-diastereomers respectively. The reverse steps, addition of bromine, are equally stereospecific.

The cited sequences are examples of *trans-elimination* and *trans-addition*. Other examples of *trans*-addition (*trans → erythro, cis → threo*): addition of performic acid and halogens. Examples of *cis*-addition (*trans → threo-*,

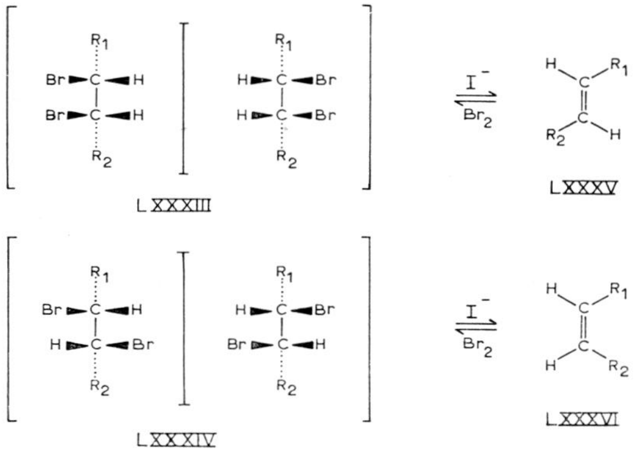

$$\left[\begin{array}{c} R_1 \\ Br \blacktriangleright C \blacktriangleleft H \\ Br \blacktriangleright C \blacktriangleleft H \\ R_2 \end{array} \quad \begin{array}{c} R_1 \\ H \blacktriangleright C \blacktriangleleft Br \\ H \blacktriangleright C \blacktriangleleft Br \\ R_2 \end{array} \right] \quad \overset{I^-}{\underset{Br_2}{\rightleftarrows}} \quad \begin{array}{c} H \\ C \\ R_2 \end{array}\!\!\!\begin{array}{c} R_1 \\ C \\ H \end{array}$$

LXXXIII   LXXXV

$$\left[\begin{array}{c} R_1 \\ Br \blacktriangleright C \blacktriangleleft H \\ H \blacktriangleright C \blacktriangleleft Br \\ R_2 \end{array} \quad \begin{array}{c} R_1 \\ H \blacktriangleright C \blacktriangleleft Br \\ Br \blacktriangleright C \blacktriangleleft H \\ R_2 \end{array} \right] \quad \overset{I^-}{\underset{Br_2}{\rightleftarrows}} \quad \begin{array}{c} H \\ C \\ H \end{array}\!\!\!\begin{array}{c} R_1 \\ C \\ R_2 \end{array}$$

LXXXIV   LXXXVI

cis → erythro): hydroxylation with alkaline permanganate or osmium tetroxide, addition of dienes (Diels–Alder reaction). The intimate inter-relationship of alkene and alkane diastereomers is perhaps best illustrated by the highly stereospecific interconversion[68] of *cis* (LXXXVII)- and *trans* (LXXXVIII)-3-hexanes.

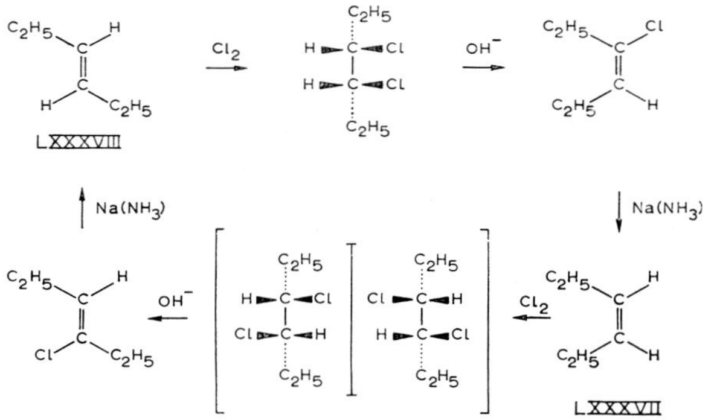

LXXXVIII

Na(NH₃)

LXXXVII

By a similar path, tiglic has been converted[69] into angelic acid.

In a further approach to the stereospecific synthesis of diastereomers, use is made of precursors whose stereochemistry is maintained in the product, as in the Kolbe synthesis[70] of erucic and brassidic acids from oleic and elaidic acids.

Asymmetric synthesis

This term refers to the stereospecific creation of a new element of dis-symmetry. One of numerous examples is the lithium aluminium hydride reduction of estrone (LXXXIX) which affords[71] exclusively 17β-estradiol

(XC) and none of the 17α-epimer (XCI). To rationalize such results, it is only necessary to consider that the transition states leading to various dia-stereomers are themselves diastereomeric and thus differ in free energy.

XC   LXXXIX   XCI

Further, the ratio of diastereomeric products is determined by the ratio of rates and thus in this case by the ratio of rate constants. Since that ratio is a function of the difference in free energy ($\Delta\Delta F^{\pm} = -RT \ln k/k'$) it follows that the ratio of diastereomeric products is directly governed by $\Delta\Delta F^{\pm}$. Hence a 97 % yield of one diastereomer (for example) as against 3 % of the other could follow from a $\Delta\Delta F^{\pm}$ of only 2.1 kcal/mole, a figure readily accounted for by relatively minor differences in structural features.

2. Optical activation

Optical activation[72] refers to the process of securing an excess of one enantiomer over the other; in the ideal case, one enantiomer is obtained completely free from the other. When the starting material is racemic, the process is called resolution.

Optical activation rests on the principle stated in the discussion of enantiomer relationships, that diastereomeric interactions form the basis on which enantiomers may be distinguished.

(a) Resolution

In its most general terms, the above principle is illustrated by three types of resolution. The first is the manual separation of enantiomeric crystals already referred to. The second is the preferential destruction of the enantio-mers (partial asymmetric destruction, a kind of kinetic resolution) by circularly polarized light[73]. The third is optical activation by preferential crystallization of one of the enantiomers from an optically active solution of the racemic modification[55, 74].

Many cases are known of resolution by chromatography on an optically active adsorbent such as lactose or cellulose[75]. In these cases, the difference in energy of the diastereomeric topological interactions (R)-adsorbent/(S)-enantiomer and (R)-adsorbent/(R)-enantiomer is sufficient to result in a difference in R_F for the two enantiomers.

The method of resolution *via* inclusion compounds[76] similarly depends on differences in topological interaction. If enantiomers become guest molecules in a hole of the host lattice or molecule and if that hole has dissymmetric walls, the diastereomeric topological interactions may differ to such an extent that the complexes (R)-host/(S)-guest and (R)-host/(R)-guest have widely differing solubilities and stabilities. A handle for resolution is thus provided, for the complexes may be separated and the guest molecules isolated in optically active form. Both lattice hosts (desoxycholic acid[77], urea[78], tri-*o*-thymotide[79] and 2,3,4,6-tetraacetylglucose[80]) and molecular hosts (β-dextrin, *i.e.* cycloheptaamylose[81]) have been thus employed.

The most common method of resolving a *dl*-pair (R)-A/(S)-A requires a functionally specific dissymmetric reagent (B). Diastereomers are formed, separated (usually by fractional crystallization though occasionally by other methods such as fractional distillation, chromatography etc.) and decomposed according to the scheme [(S)-B could have been used as well]:

$$(R){\rm —A}/(S){\rm —A} + (R){\rm —B} \Biggl\lceil \begin{array}{l} \rightarrow (R){\rm —A}\cdot(R){\rm —B} \rightarrow (R){\rm —A} \\ \rightarrow (S){\rm —A}\cdot(R){\rm —B} \rightarrow (S){\rm —A} \end{array}$$

The nature of the resolving agent depends on the functionality of the compound to be resolved. Since they are easily and rapidly formed and decomposed, salts are the preferred diastereomers. Thus amines are resolved by salt formation with optically active acids (*e.g.* malic, camphor-10-sulfonic, pyroglutamic, dibenzoyltartaric) and acids similarly by amines (*e.g.* alkaloids). When salts cannot be directly formed, the compound is sometimes converted into an acid derivative which is then resolved by salt formation. Alcohols may thus be resolved as the acid phthalates[82] and ketones as the 4-(4-carboxyphenyl)-semicarbazones[83]. These handles (H) are removed at the end of the resolution:

$$(R){\rm —A}/(S){\rm —A} + {\rm H} \rightarrow (R){\rm —AH}/(S){\rm —AH}$$

$$(R){\rm —AH}/(S){\rm —AH} + (R){\rm —B} \Biggl\lceil \begin{array}{l} \rightarrow (R){\rm —AH}\cdot(R){\rm —B} \rightarrow (R){\rm —AH} \\ \rightarrow (S){\rm —AH}\cdot(R){\rm —B} \rightarrow (S){\rm —AH} \end{array}$$

$$(R){\rm —AH} \rightarrow (R){\rm —A} + {\rm H}$$

$$(S){\rm —AH} \rightarrow (S){\rm —A} + {\rm H}$$

Appropriate non-ionic derivatives have also been used as diastereomeric intermediates in resolution. These derivatives may be classical (esters, hydrazones etc.) or dependent on secondary forces, as in the charge–transfer complexes formed by nitroaromatics[84].

In the method of kinetic resolution, a *dl*-pair is subjected to a dissymmetric influence, almost always an optically active catalyst or reagent (sometimes circularly polarized light). Diastereomeric transition states result which differ in free energy. Since $\Delta\Delta F^{\pm} = -RT \ln k/k'$, one of the enantiomers will initially react faster than the other so that at any time other than zero or infinity one enantiomer is in excess over the other; interruption of the reaction thus leads to a mixture richer in one of the enantiomers. As in asymmetric synthesis to which kinetic resolutions are obviously related, a relatively small $\Delta\Delta F^{\pm}$ may lead to high enantiomeric purity (*i.e.* the ratio of (R)–A $-$ (S)–A to (R)–A $+$ (S)–A) as expressed by the optical purity (*i.e.* the ratio of the rotation of the mixture to that of the pure enantiomer).

Kinetic resolutions are popular in cases where handles are difficultly accessible. For instance, alkyl halides are almost invariably resolved by partial asymmetric decomposition with brucine[85]. Kinetic resolutions are also valuable when the efficiency of the process ($\Delta\Delta F^{\pm}$) is extremely high, as in the enzymatic resolution of amino acids[86]; mechanistically, these kinetic resolutions by dissymmetric catalysis have their non-biochemical counterpart in the partial asymmetric decomposition of camphor carboxylic acid in the presence of amino acids or alkaloids[87].

The principle of reciprocity *cannot* hold in resolutions. The mixture (R)–A $\cdot$ (R)–B/(S)–A $\cdot$ (R)–B obtained in the resolution of (R)–A/(S)–A by (R)–B *must* be diastereomeric with the mixture (R)–A $\cdot$ (R)–B/(R)–A $\cdot$ (S)–B obtained in the resolution of (R)–B/(S)–B with (R)–A, or with the mixture (S)–A $\cdot$ (R)–B/(S)–A $\cdot$ (S)–B obtained in the resolution of (R)–B/(S)–B with (S)–A. Therefore different energy relationships obtain in the two resolutions and results, though they may be very similar, necessarily cannot be identical.

(b) Asymmetric synthesis

Optical activation is often achieved by allowing compounds of the type CXXYZ to interact with dissymmetric reagents or catalysts[88], where CXXYZ stands for a carbon attached to four groups two of which are *identical*, or for carbon attached to three groups, one of which is joined by a double bond. When one of the groups X reacts *even under symmetric conditions* it becomes different (X') from the other so that dissymmetry (CXX'YZ) must have been introduced at some stage of the reaction. It follows that when the reagent or catalyst (E) is dissymmetric, diastereomeric products, intermediates or transition states must result:

$$\text{CXXYZ} + (R)\text{—E} \begin{cases} \rightarrow (R)\text{—CXX'YZ} \cdot (R)\text{—E} \rightarrow (R)\text{—CXX'YZ} \\ \rightarrow (S)\text{—CXX'YZ} \cdot (R)\text{—E} \rightarrow (S)\text{—CXX'YZ} \end{cases}$$

Thus, for example, diastereomeric (—)-menthyl hydrogen β-phenylglutarates result from the reaction of (—)-menthol with the symmetric β-phenylglutaric anhydride[89]. Similarly, it is easy to understand why in the degradation of symmetric citric acid to α-ketoglutaric acid two diastereomeric transition states must be considered, since the enzyme is dissymmetric. The experimental evidence in this case has been provided[90] by the degradation of configurationally pure citric acid-2,2-d_2, for quite obviously the —CH_2COOH and —CD_2COOH groups cannot be involved in identical interactions in the diastereomeric complexes symbolized by XCII and XCIII. It must be

$$
\begin{array}{cc}
\overset{\displaystyle OH}{HOOCCH_2 \blacktriangleright C \blacktriangleleft COOH} & \overset{\displaystyle COOH}{HOOCCD_2 \blacktriangleright C \blacktriangleleft OH} \\
\underset{\displaystyle CD_2COOH \cdot E}{} & \underset{\displaystyle CH_2COOH \cdot E}{} \\
\textbf{XCII} & \textbf{XCIII}
\end{array}
$$

stressed that such results do not depend on the nature of the isotopic label but are thermodynamically necessary consequences of the stereochemistry discussed. Structural interpretations, such as the *three-point mechanism*[91], are not essential.

Numerous cases are known of asymmetric addition to ethylene or carbonyl functions. The XX in CXXYZ is here represented by the double bond function. A few examples must suffice.

Reaction with the ethylenic bond is illustrated by the addition of methanol to methylphenylketene in the presence of the optically active acetylquinine. The produced methyl atrolactate is optically active[92]. Among diverse other examples[92a] is the enzymatic hydrogenation of geraniol to (+)-citronellal[93].

Asymmetric additions to the carbonyl function are illustrated by the partial asymmetric atrolactic acid synthesis[94] (which will be discussed in detail below) and by the partial asymmetric reduction of ketones with dialkylmagnesium[95], and with lithium, magnesium or aluminum alkoxides[96]. These reactions have their biochemical equivalent in the microbial asymmetric hydrogenation of ketones with *Curvularia falcata*[97] and in the large scale production of optically active ethanol-1-d by asymmetric enzymatic reduction of acetaldehyde-1-d[98].

Similarly, the asymmetric synthesis of cyanohydrins from HCN and aldehydes may be accomplished in the presence of emulsin[99] or by the equivalent non-biochemical catalysts, alkaloids[100] or cyclodextrin[101].

Asymmetric syntheses and kinetic resolutions have also played an important role in the optical activation of biphenyls and allenes[102].

Finally, it must be pointed out that asymmetric syntheses may be successful if only the solvent is optically active; in such cases, *e.g.* Grignard additions, the solvent enters the transition state of the reaction and diastereoisomers result[103].

(c) Some conjectures concerning origin and maintenance of
optical activity in nature

The transformation of all molecules and organisms on earth into their mirror images should not interfere with continued survival. Thus, a left-handed α-helix composed of D-amino acids in such a hypothetical system should have the same chance for survival as does a right-handed α-helix composed of L-amino acids in the actual systems. In order to explain why vital substances possess the particular configuration they do rather than the opposite, one may for example assume that some statistical fluctuation in a pre-biological reaction resulted in optical activation; simple reactions of optically inactive substances have sometimes been known to lead to products in which one of the enantiomers predominates to the extent of a few percent[104]. Following this, the achievement of optical purity is a matter of time, for a number of processes are conceivable by which the initially minute bias may be translated into overwhelming predominance[105]. The processes involved may be physical fractionation by phase separation, as in the growth of single crystals[106], or simply fractional crystallization, if racemic modification and enantiomer have different solubilities[104]. Additionally, parallel asymmetric syntheses involving both enantiomers may increase the preponderance of one, providing the process is interrupted, as in a kinetic resolution: the rate constants of the competing processes cannot be the same, for the asymmetric synthesis occurs in a slightly optically active medium and diastereomeric interactions with the medium will affect the free energies of activation. The effect will be enhanced if the reaction is of order greater than one. Furthermore, such a mixture may also act as an optically active catalyst for asymmetric synthesis in other systems.

By a combination of asymmetric synthesis and physical fractionations, the most effective expression of which is the total asymmetric transformation[107], the quantitative gap between the rival enantiomers may increasingly widen and total reversal become increasingly improbable. Thus, in a natural selection process, one enantiomer will eventually become the dominant hand. It must be emphasized, however, that this consequence does not *necessarily* follow from the initial slight bias; many of the asymmetric syntheses and physical fractionations may lead once more to racemic material, and many "false starts" may thus have occurred in time. The successful combination of favorable environment (reaction conditions) and special reaction type again becomes obviously a matter of chance. By implication, the opposite chirality may be dominant in some extraterrestrial biological system.

The substances most characteristically involved in vital processes, *i.e.* the macromolecules (proteins, carbohydrates, nucleic acids) and their component units (amino acids, monosaccharides) are in fact almost without exception of one configurational type and configurationally pure. In the sense discussed above, maintenance of configurational integrity is essential for the survival of the organism; mechanisms for maintaining the requisite degree of optical purity have been discussed above.

Both enantiomeric forms of a number of naturally occurring substances of varied structural types are sometimes found. These substances—frequently terpenoids—do not seem to be intimately involved in the higher vital processes. An example is citronellal, which occurs in oil of eucalyptus as the (+)-form and in Java oil of citronella as the (—)-form. Similarly, D-amino acids are found to an important extent only in the lower organisms[108].

C. DETERMINATION OF CONFIGURATION

1. Diastereomers

Configurations may be assigned directly in the course of total structure determination by X-ray or electron diffraction. The stereochemistry of numerous substances of biochemical interest (steroids, vitamins, alkaloids, macromolecules etc.) have been elucidated by this method[109]. Alternatively, the physical or chemical differences between diastereomers may serve to characterize each, for the differences in properties may be interpreted as resulting from differences characteristic of molecular topology in ground or transition state. Since diastereomers differ in all of their physical and chemical characteristics, any physical property or chemical reaction could in principle serve as a basis for configurational assignment.

Among physical properties[110], density, refractive index and boiling point have been used in assigning configuration to the diastereomeric disubstituted cyclohexanes (Von Auwers–Skita Rule)[111]. Heats of hydrogenation[112] or combustion are useful in characterizing olefinic diastereomers since these quantities are greater for the less stable of two stereoisomers. Differences in ultraviolet[113], infrared[113], and n.m.r.[114] spectra have been extensively used to characterize stereoisomers. Dipole moments[115] and rotatory dispersions[116] have been similarly exploited.

The gamut of chemical differences has served in configurational assignments of diastereomers. The difference may be subtle, *e.g.* the characteristic values of ΔpK_a[117] employed in the elucidation of the stereochemistry of abietic acid[118] and of the cinchona alkaloids[119], or it may be as gross as that exhibited by the diastereomeric 3-hydroxycyclohexanecarboxylic acids (XCIV and XCV) of which only the *cis*-form (XCIV) yields a lactone (XCVI)[120]. In the same sense, the highly stereospecific and mechanistically understood addition and elimination reactions discussed previously serve to identify the particular diastereomer involved.

Between these two extremes lies the assignment of configurations by comparison of reaction rate constants (kinetic method). For example, under comparable conditions the *erythro*-isomer (LXXXIII) of vicinal acyclic dibromides is generally more rapidly debrominated by iodide ions than the

XCⅥ   XCⅣ   XCⅤ

threo-isomer (LXXXIV) and the *cis*-isomer of carboxylic α-glycols generally more rapidly cleaved by lead tetraacetate than the *trans*-isomer[121]. A well known example in biochemistry is the specific action of glycosidases on the α- resp. β-glycoside linkages.

Demonstration of enantiomerism is sometimes an unequivocal chemical method for assigning diastereomeric configurations. The resolvability of *trans*-1,2-cyclopropanedicarboxylic acid is sufficient proof of its diastereomeric identity.

2. Absolute and relative configurations of enantiomers

When the relative position or order of arrangement of the atoms in space can be described in terms of a macroscopic standard of dissymmetry (*i.e.* a hand or a helix), the absolute configuration of a molecule is known. Two approaches have been employed. In one of these, absolute configurations have been assigned to some simple molecules such as (—)-2,3-epoxybutane as the result of theoretical considerations based on suitable models for optical activity[6]. The experimental method of anomalous X-ray scattering[123] has, however, been regarded as more reliable. The elucidation of the absolute configurations of (+)-tartaric acid (III) and of (—)-isoleucine (XCVII), a particularly important application of this method, has provided the key

XCⅦ

substances in the correlation of many organic compounds of biochemical interest, as discussed below.

Configurations of dissymmetric groupings may be determined relatively, *i.e.* by comparison to another dissymmetric grouping either intra- or intermolecularly. Configurational correlation[124] may thus serve to establish the absolute configuration of an unknown grouping if that of the comparison grouping is known.

Two approaches to the realization of configurational correlations have been employed. In one, chemical reactions form the basis of the correlation, while in the other physical methods are employed.

(a) Correlations by chemical methods

Configurations may be unequivocally correlated by reactions which cannot affect the stereochemical integrity of the dissymmetric grouping, e.g., in the case of asymmetric atoms, reactions which do not directly affect the bonds to the asymmetric atom. For example, sequences discussed above unequivocally establish the configurations of (—)-malic acid (LXXX) and of (+)-glyceraldehyde (LXXV), both relative to that of (—)-tartaric acid (LXXIX). Since the absolute configuration of III is known, those of its enantiomer LXXIX and of the correlated LXXX and LXXV are also known; such substances thus become secondary configurational standards.

Many such correlations form link chains which connect several biochemically important families. As an illustration, the terpenoids and steroids which have in common the feature of the asymmetric methine carbon (RR'R"CH) have both been unequivocally correlated to (—)-2-methyl-1-butanol ("active amyl alcohol", XCVIII) and therefore to each other. The correlations of Δ^{14}-cholestenyl benzoate (XCIX), (+)-citronellal(C), (+)-1-menthene (CI), and (+)-camphor (XXXVI) are shown. Since XCVIII has been correlated to (+)-isoleucine (CII), the enantiomer of the primary standard XCVII, the absolute configuration of all of these compounds is known[124,125]. Note that the non-existence of diastereomers in camphor uniquely correlates *both* asymmetric carbons.

Another important body of correlations interlinks members of the carbinol series (asymmetric RR'CHOH); an example from the carbohydrates[126] is the establishment of the configuration of (+)-xylose (CIII) as D-xylose. Oxidation of (+)-xylose gives an optically inactive xylaric acid which therefore can only have configuration CIV or CV. It follows that (+)-xylose can only have configuration CIII or CVI or their mirror images. Since degradation of (+)-xylose (to (—)-threose, CVII) followed by oxidation gives (—)-tartaric acid (LXXIX) rather than *meso*-tartaric acid (CVIII), xylaric acid must be CIV rather than CV, (+)-xylose CIII rather than CVI (which corresponds to (—)-ribose) and the absolute configurations must be as shown.

The methine and carbinol families have been bridged in several instances, as shown for the correlation of the simple representatives (+)-CIX and

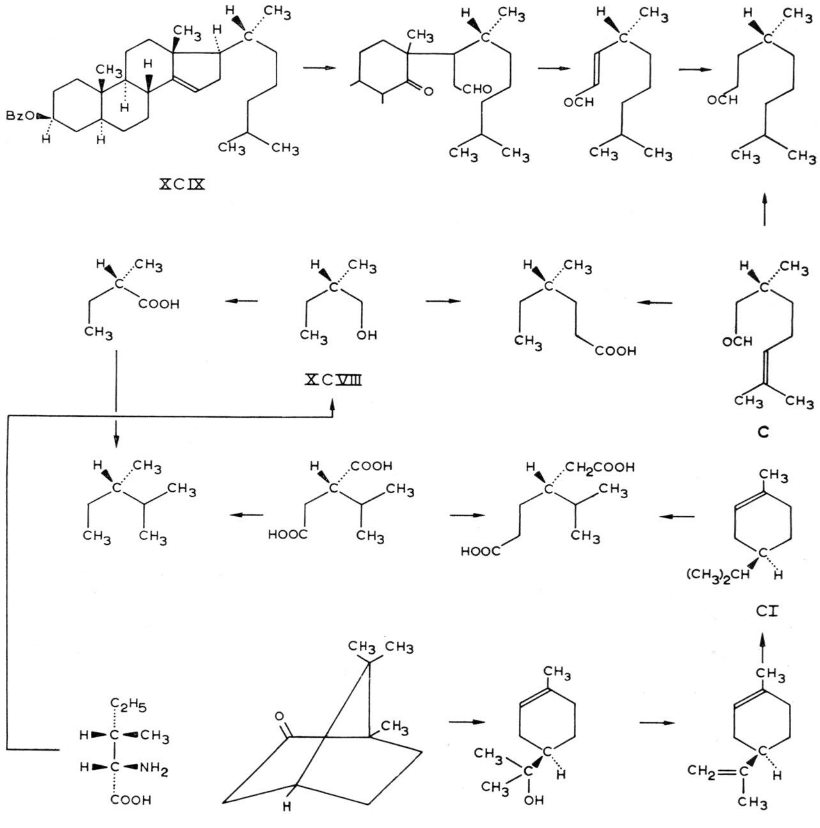

XCIX

XCVIII

C

CI

CII

XXXVI

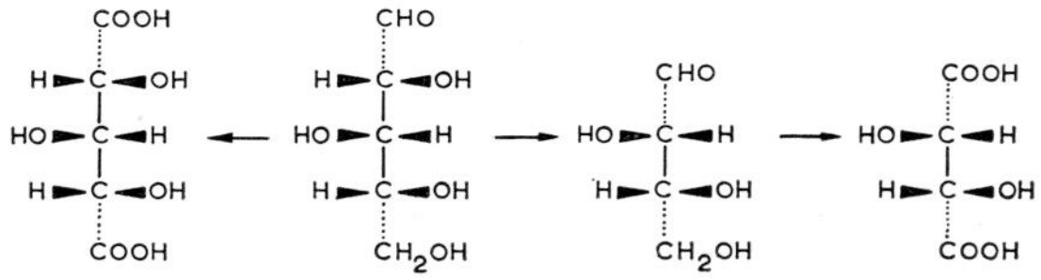

CIV

CIII

CVII

LXXIX

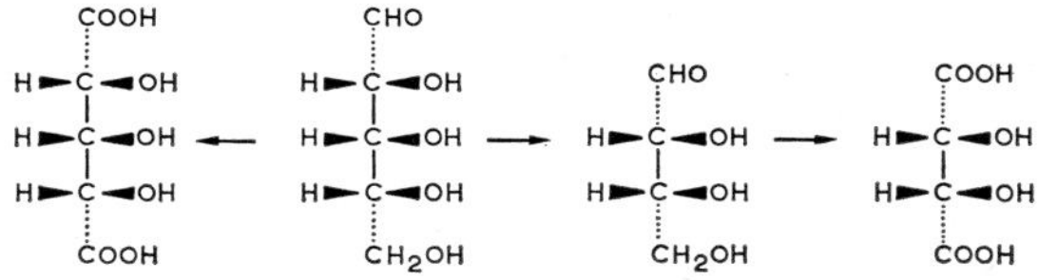

CV

CVI

CVIII

References p. 239

(—)-CX[124, 127]. The central point is the recognition that the hydroxyl and carbonyl groups in (—)-XCIV must bear a *cis*-relationship, as discussed before. The independent and unambiguous correlations of CX to (—)-tartaric acid (LXXIX) and of (+)-citronellal(C) to (+)-isoleucine (CII) confirm the relationships and define the absolute configurations of the compounds shown.

When bond-making and -breaking reactions at the asymmetric atom are unavoidable, reactions may be resorted to whose stereochemical course is mechanistically understood and predictable by analogy with a wealth of related data. Thus, diverse families of compounds have been correlated[128] by nucleophilic displacement reactions at saturated carbon (S_N2) which are under kinetic control, and by stereospecific 1,2-shifts in which the migrating group maintains configuration. A notable example is the correlation of (+)-lactic acid (CXI) with (+)-alanine (LXXVIII).

In principle, any method of resolution is capable of yielding information on the configuration of the enantiomers since the dissymmetric resolving agent functions by virtue of differences in diastereomeric interactions; these may in principle be accounted for by characteristic differences in molecular shape and hence configuration of the enantiomers. Kinetic resolutions and asymmetric syntheses or destructions have in fact been made to serve this purpose. For example, α-hydroxy and α-amino acids have been correlated on the basis that substrates with corresponding configurations behave similarly in enzymatic reactions[124]; a non-biochemical variant of this approach rests on the observation that (+)-camphorcarboxylic acid decarboxylates more rapidly than the (—)-isomer in the presence of L-α-amino acid ethyl esters[129].

The partial asymmetric atrolactic acid synthesis[94] in particular has found extensive use in configurational assignments, *e.g.* to steroids, terpenoids and catechins[130]. It is observed that the diastereomeric atrolactates resulting from the Grignard addition of methylmagnesium iodide to the phenyl-glyoxylate of an optically active alcohol are produced in unequal amounts, as shown by the fact that saponification yields almost always optically active atrolactic acid. When the optically active alcohol has three differently sized residues (S = small, M = medium, L = large) arranged as in CXII, (—)-(R)-atrolactic acid (CXIII) is produced in excess over the (+)-(S)-isomer (CXIV); the direction of the asymmetric synthesis is evidently governed by differences in the free energies of the diastereomeric transition states deriving from differences in non-bonded interactions. From the sign of the atrolactic acid and a judgement of relative sizes S, M and L in CXII, it is

possible to use this generalization in the assignment of configurations. For example, the phenylglyoxylates of (—)-borneol (CXV), (—)-isoborneol (CXVI), cholestan-7α-ol (CXVII) and (—)-epicatechin tetramethyl ether (CXVIII) all give CXIII. It follows that these alcohols all belong to type CXII. Conversely, the phenylglyoxylate of cholestan-7β-ol (CXIX), an epimer of CXVII, yields CXIV; it follows that CXVII and CXIX, though diastereomers, are *enantiomeric types* as far as the neighborhood of the alcohol function is concerned.

(b) Correlations by physical methods

X-ray analysis of a molecule which contains two dissymmetric groupings provides a direct physical method, for the relative disposition of the atoms in space of the two groupings can be ascertained and the relative configurations determined. If the absolute configuration of one is known, the absolute configuration of the other can be deduced[131], a striking example being the elucidation of the absolute configuration of asymmetric sulfur in the natural product[132] (+)-S-methylcysteine-S-oxide[133] (CXX).

$$CH_3\cdots S—CH_2—C\cdots COOH$$

CXX

The more common indirect methods involve comparisons of molecules of known with those of unknown configurations.

One of these is the method of quasi-racemates[134]. In this method, any differences in phase behavior between the diastereomeric binary mixtures (R)-known/(R)-unknown and (R)-known/(S)-unknown (or their equivalent) are held to be reflections of differences in molecular shape and hence relative configuration. The method is limited to comparisons of molecules of similar size and shape. When an equimolar compound (quasi-racemate) is formed in one diastereomeric mixture and not in the other, it is concluded that the components (quasi-enantiomers) have *opposite* corresponding configurations because their shapes are close to being enantiomeric. By the same token, solid solution formation bespeaks a similarity in shape and therefore corresponding configurations which are the *same*. For example, the key step in the link chain relating α-lipoic acid to the configurational standard, isoleucine, is the observation[135] that (+)-3-methyloctanedioic (CXXI) and (—)-3-thiooctanedioic (CXXII) acids form solid solutions while CXXI and (+)-3-thiooctanedioic acid (CXXIII) do not.

Any method suitable for detecting racemate formation is suitable also for the detection of quasi-racemates. Thermal analysis, the examination of solid I.R. spectra, and examination of X-ray powder diagrams of diastereomeric mixtures have all been employed with success.

The remaining important indirect methods involve comparisons of optical rotations, either at a single wavelength or at many.

Measurements at a single wavelength, usually the D-line, have given rise to two types of *monochromatic* rules[136], the rule of superposition and the rule of shift.

In the rule of superposition the assumption is made that the optical rotation of a compound with several dissymmetric groupings is approximately the algebraic sum of the rotations of the constituent groupings. Obviously, rotatory contributions of dissymmetric groupings cannot be strictly determined, for the chemical environment of the groupings varies from molecule to molecule; furthermore, the intramolecular interactions of dissymmetric groupings are diastereomeric in type and will cause deviations in the calculated sum of group contributions (vicinal effect). Granted their approximate nature, appropriate rules have been applied with success in the steroids and terpenoids[124] and, classically, in the carbohydrates as Hudson's Rules of Isorotation. In these rules, the anomeric grouping is considered to contribute to the total rotation independently of the rest of the molecule, thus allowing a distinction to be made between α- and β-anomers. To a first approximation this is generally correct, and the principle has been extended to steroid glycosides[136].

An important variant of the rule of superposition is based on the hypothesis that each dissymmetric grouping in a molecule is in effect describable as a screw pattern of electron polarizability[137]. For compounds with a single asymmetric atom X, this concept leads to the rule that an arrangement of absolute configuration CXXIV is dextrorotatory at the D-line when the

$$A \blacktriangleright \overset{B}{\underset{D}{X}} \blacktriangleleft C$$

CXXIV

polarizabilities of the substituent atoms decrease in the order $A > B > C > D$. This and related rules have been successfully applied[137] in the carbohydrates, steroids and terpenoids.

The rule of shift[138] states that two compounds have corresponding configurations when their molecular rotations undergo parallel changes in direction under changed conditions (including derivatization). This rule has

References p. 239

proven extraordinarily fruitful, an example being the Freudenberg Amide Rule[139] according to which an acid RCHOHCOOH has the (R)-configuration if $\Delta M_D(CONH_2\text{-}COOH)$ is positive, as in the case of the aldonic acids.

Comparisons of RD-curves has provided a further basis for configurational correlations[116]. It is desirable though not always essential that there be present in the molecule a suitable chromophore, generally though not necessarily a carbonyl group, which permits measurement of optical rotation through the weakly absorbing band and gives rise to Cotton effect curves. The sign and shape of the Cotton effect curve is held to be characteristic of the stereochemical environment of the chromophore. It follows that when two comparison substances exhibit curves of the same sign and shape, the configurations of the dissymmetric groupings near the chromophoric groups correspond. On the other hand, curves of opposite sign and mirror image shape signify *enantiomeric types*, as for example in the case of the epimeric pregnan-3α-ol-20-one acetates, where the 17α-isomer CXXV has a negative and the 17β-isomer CXXVI a positive Cotton effect curve, the two curves being essentially mirror images[140].

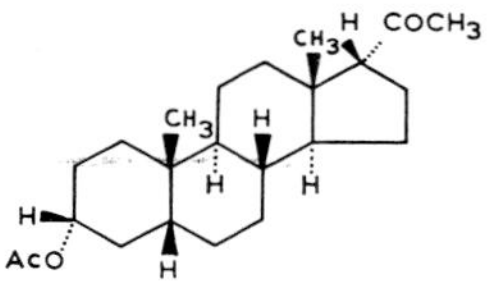

CXXV 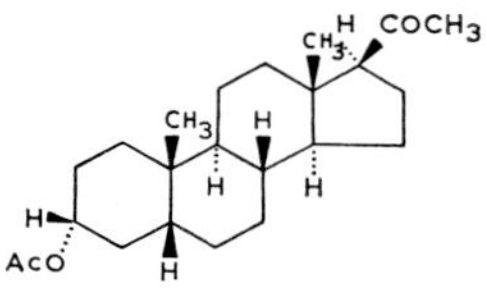   CXXVI

This method has been extremely useful in the steroids and terpenoids, but it is not restricted to these areas. Thus, it has been observed[141] that the dithiocarbamates of L-α-amino acids (CXXVII) and the dithiocarbonates (xanthates) of L-α-hydroxyacids (CXXVIII) all feature positive Cotton effect curves.

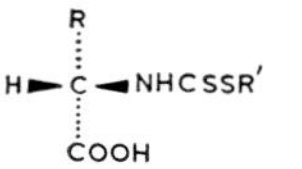

CXXVII 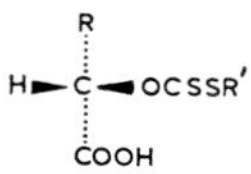   CXXVIII

(c) The configuration of mandelic acid

The independent elucidation of the absolute configuration of mandelic acid by several of the methods discussed in the preceding sections illustrates how the same stereochemical information may be obtained in various different ways.

The direct chemical correlation of (—)-mandelic acid (CXXIX) and

(—)-glyceraldehyde (LXXXII)[142, 124] unequivocally establishes the (R)-configuration for CXXIX since the absolute configuration of LXXXII is known. The indirect methods bear out this conclusion.

The asymmetric synthesis of (+)-atrolactic acid (CXIV) from the phenylglyoxylate of (—)-phenylmethylcarbinol (CXXX)[94] provides evidence that

CXXX and CXII are enantiomeric types. This conclusion is in harmony with the identification of C_6H_5-, CH_3- and H- in (S)-CXXX as L, M and S respectively. Accordingly, since CXXX has been correlated with CXXIX, the (R)-configuration may be assigned to the acid.

The method of quasi-racemates has been successfully employed[143]. The comparison compound is (—)-(S)-2-thienylglycolic acid (CXXXI), whose absolute configuration has been established by direct correlation of the enantiomer (CXXXII) with CXXXIII, which has in turn been correlated[144]

with (—)-malic acid (LXXX) of known absolute configuration. The comparison is made possible by the isomorphism of benzene and thiophene. It is observed that the infrared spectrum and X-ray powder photograph of an equimolar solid mixture of CXXXI and CXXIX is additively composed of the spectra or lines of the components, while a similar mixture of CXXXI and (+)-mandelic acid (CXXXIV) gives a different infrared spectrum and powder photograph. It follows that a quasi-racemate is formed in the last case, that CXXXI and CXXXIV are quasi-enantiomers and that the (R)-configuration may be assigned to CXXIX.

Among optical rules, the simplest to apply is the monochromatic polarizability rule[137]. Since the polarizability order is $C_6H_5 > COOH > OH > H$, it follows from the identification of these groups in CXXXIV with the generalized groups in CXXIV that (S)-CXXXIV is dextrorotatory, and that CXXIX has the (R)-configuration.

Use of the rules of shift also leads to the correct result[145]. The Amide Rule, for example, has been employed in a comparison of CXXIX with the corresponding derivative obtained on hydrogenation, (—)-hexahydromandelic acid (CXXXV), and with (—)-lactic acid (LXXVI). The absolute (R)-configuration of the last compound may be deduced from the direct correlation of its enantiomer with LXXXII. Table VIII provides strong evidence that all

TABLE VIII

$[M]^{20}_{578}$ OF R—CHOH—COR′

R′	R		
	C_6H_5 (CXXIX)	C_8H_{11} (CXXXV)	CH_3 (LXXVI)
OH	— 239	— 40	— 3.5
NH$_2$	— 137	+ 76	+ 20

three compounds have the (R)-configuration, in harmony with the previous conclusions. The rule of shift as applied to the parallel changes in molecular rotation observed upon lengthening the alcohol chain of corresponding esters leads to the same result (Table IX).

TABLE IX

$[M]_D$ OF R—CHOH—COOR′ DERIVED FROM (—)-ACIDS

R	R′						
	CH_3	C_2H_5	$n\text{-}C_3H_7$	$n\text{-}C_4H_9$	$n\text{-}C_5H_{11}$	$n\text{-}C_6H_{13}$	$n\text{-}C_7H_{15}$
C_6H_{11}	— 36.8	— 24.4	— 15.5	— 15.4	— 9.7	— 9.3	— 9.1
C_6H_3	+ 8.6	+ 13.4	+ 17.4	+ 19.6	+ 20.2	+ 21.3	+ 21.3

Finally, the method of rotatory dispersion has yielded results consistent with the preceding conclusions. The ethyl dithiocarbonates of (+)-lactic and

(+)-mandelic acid have positive Cotton effect curves[116, 141] which are strikingly similar in shape (Fig. 6). These compounds are thus of the type represented by CXXVIII, *i.e.* they both have the (S)-configuration. Hence CXXIX has the (R)-configuration.

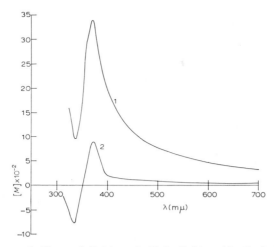

Fig. 6. *RD*-curves of (S)-mandelic(1) and (S)-lactic(2) acid ethyl dithiocarbonate.

BIBLIOGRAPHY

Advances in general stereochemistry reported in *Ann. Reports on Progr. Chem. (London)*: N. V. SIDGWICK, *ibid.*, 29 (1933) 64; P. MAITLAND, *ibid.*, 36 (1940) 236; M. P. BALFE AND J. KENYON, *ibid.*, 39 (1943) 115; M. M. JAMISON, M. S. LESSLIE AND E. E. TURNER, *ibid.*, 43 (1947) 155; H. N. RYDON, *ibid.*, 47 (1951) 147; I. G. M. CAMPBELL, *ibid.*, 48 (1952) 135; 50 (1954) 152; R. C. COOKSON, *ibid.*, 54 (1958) 170; J. McKENNA, *ibid.*, 56 (1960) 187.

E. A. BRAUDE AND F. C. NACHOD, *Determination of Organic Structures by Physical Methods*, Academic Press, New York, 1955.

C. DJERASSI, *Optical Rotatory Dispersion*, McGraw-Hill, New York, 1960.

E. L. ELIEL, *Stereochemistry of Carbon Compounds*, McGraw-Hill, New York, 1962.

K. FREUDENBERG, *Stereochemie*, F. Deuticke, Leipzig and Vienna, 1932.

J. H. VAN'T HOFF, *The Arrangements of Atoms in Space*, 2nd ed. (translated by A. EILOART), Longmans, Green and Co., London, 1898.

F. M. JAEGER, *Spatial Arrangements of Atomic Systems and Optical Activity*, McGraw-Hill, New York, 1930; *idem, Lectures on the Principles of Symmetry*, Elsevier, Amsterdam, 1917.

W. KLYNE, *Progress in Stereochemistry*, Vol. I, Academic Press, New York, 1954.

W. KLYNE AND P. B. D. DE LA MARE, *Progress in Stereochemistry*, Vol. II, Academic Press, New York, 1958.

S. MIZUSHIMA, *Structure of Molecules and Internal Rotation*, Academic Press, New York, 1954.

M. S. NEWMAN, *Steric Effects in Organic Chemistry*, J. Wiley and Sons, New York, 1956.

R. L. SHRINER, R. ADAMS AND C. S. MARVEL, in Chapter 4 of H. GILMAN, *Organic Chemistry*, Vol. I, 2nd ed., J. Wiley and Sons, New York, 1943.

G. W. WHELAND, *Advanced Organic Chemistry*, 3rd ed., J. Wiley and Sons, New York, 1960.

REFERENCES

[1] G. E. McCasland and S. Proskow, *J. Am. Chem. Soc.*, 78 (1956) 5646; *cf.* also G. E. McCasland, R. Horvat and M. R. Roth, *ibid.*, 81 (1959) 2399; S. A. Buckler and V. P. Wystrach, *ibid.*, 83 (1961) 168.

[2] W. v. Engelhardt, *Die Chemie*, 57 (1944) 133.

[3] D. H. R. Barton and K. H. Overton, *J. Chem. Soc.*, (1955) 2639.

[4] M. Przybylska and W. H. Barnes, *Acta Cryst.*, 6 (1953) 377.

[5] L. Pasteur, *Recherches sur la dissymétrie moléculaire des produits organiques naturels*, in *Leçons de chimie professées en 1860*, Paris, 1861, p. 25.

[6] W. Kuhn, *Ann. Revs. Phys. Chem.*, 9 (1958) 417; W. Kauzmann, *Quantum Chemistry*, Academic Press, 1957, pp. 616–635 and 703–725; A. Moscowitz, Ch. 12 of C. Djerassi, see Bibliography.

[7] R. E. O'Brien, *Ph.D. thesis*, New York University, 1960.

[8] W. Heller, *J. Phys. Chem.*, 62 (1958) 1569.

[9] V. M. Clark, A. W. Johnson, I. O. Sutherland and A. Todd, *J. Chem. Soc.*, (1958) 3283.

[10] K. Mislow and R. Bolstad, *J. Am. Chem. Soc.*, 77 (1955) 6712; K. Mislow, *Trans. N.Y. Acad. Sci.*, [II] 19 (1957) 298.

[11] H. Mauser, *Chem. Ber.*, 90 (1957) 299, 307.

[12] P. Sensi and O. Fagioli, *Gazz. chim. ital.*, 83 (1953) 73; E. L. Eliel and J. T. Kofron, *J. Am. Chem. Soc.*, 75 (1953) 4585; A. Rosenberg and L. Schotte, *Acta Chem. Scand.*, 8 (1954) 867; N. Wright, *J. Biol. Chem.*, 120 (1937) 641; 127 (1939) 137.

[13] K. Serck-Hanssen, *Chem. & Ind. (London)*, (1958) 1554.

[14] W. E. Cooley, C. F. Liu and J. C. Bailar Jr., *J. Am. Chem. Soc.*, 81 (1959) 4189.

[15] V. Prelog, in A. Todd, *Perspectives in Organic Chemistry*, Interscience, New York, 1956, p. 97.

[16] R. E. Kagarise and D. H. Rank, *Trans. Faraday Soc.*, 48 (1952) 394.

[17] E. B. Wilson Jr., *Proc. Natl. Acad. Sci. U.S.*, 43 (1957) 816; L. Pauling, *ibid.*, 44 (1958) 211; H. Eyring, G. H. Stewart and R. P. Smith, *ibid.*, 44 (1958) 259.

[18] *e.g.* J. A. Pople, W. G. Schneider and H. J. Bernstein, *High-Resolution Nuclear Magnetic Resonance*, Chapter 13, McGraw-Hill, New York, 1959.

[19] H. A. Stuart, *Die Struktur des freien Moleküls*, Springer-Verlag, Berlin, 1952, pp. 101–106.

[20] C. Robinson, *Trans. Faraday Soc.*, 48 (1952) 847; C. Robinson and E. J. Ambrose, *ibid.*, 48 (1952) 854.

[21] O. Th. Schmidt, in L. Zechmeister, *Progress in the Chemistry of Organic Natural Products*, Springer-Verlag, Berlin, 1956, Vol. 13, pp. 70–136.

[22] R. Robinson, *Nature*, 160 (1947) 815.

[23] H. Rapoport and J. B. Lavigne, *J. Am. Chem. Soc.*, 78 (1956) 2455.

[24] A. Rüegger, *Helv. Chim. Acta*, 42 (1959) 754.

[25] L. Crombie, *Quart. Revs. (London)*, 6 (1952) 101.

[26] H. C. Longuet-Higgins, *J. Chem. Phys.*, 18 (1950) 265.

[27] C. Reid, *Quart. Revs. (London)*, 12 (1958) 205.

[28] G. W. Wheland, *Resonance in Organic Chemistry*, J. Wiley and Sons, New York, 1955, pp. 196–199.

[29] R. Kuhn and A. Winterstein, *Helv. Chim. Acta*, 11 (1928) 87.

[30] H. Ziegler and H. Wilms, *Liebigs Ann. Chem.*, 567 (1950) 1.

[31] M. Stoll, J. Hulstkamp and A. Rouvé, *Helv. Chim. Acta*, 31 (1948) 543.

[32] D. H. R. Barton and P. de Mayo, *Quart. Revs. (London)*, 11 (1957) 189.

[33] A. C. Cope, P. T. Moore and W. R. Moore, *J. Am. Chem. Soc.*, 82 (1960) 1744. 1,2-Dihaloethylenes are not included in this generalization (H.-G. Viehe, *Chem. Ber.*, 93 (1960) 1697).

[34] R. Kuhn and D. Blum, *Chem. Ber.*, 92 (1959) 1483.

[35] W. D. Celmer and I. A. Solomons, *J. Am. Chem. Soc.*, 75 (1953) 1372.

[36] *e.g.* E. L. ELIEL, *J. Am. Chem. Soc.*, 71 (1949) 3970; F. A. LOEWUS, F. H. WEST-HEIMER AND B. VENNESLAND, *ibid.*, 75 (1953) 5018; G. K. HELMKAMP AND N. SCHNAUTZ, *Tetrahedron*, 2 (1958) 304; A. STREITWIESER JR., J. R. WOLFE JR. AND W. D. SCHAEFFER, *ibid.*, 6 (1959) 338; K. MISLOW, R. E. O'BRIEN AND H. SCHAEFER, *J. Am. Chem. Soc.*, 82 (1960) 5512; Y. POCKER, *Proc. Chem. Soc. (London)*, (1961) 140.

[37] *e.g.* C. EABORN AND C. PITT, *Chem. & Ind. (London)*, (1958) 830; H. L. SOMMER AND C. L. FRYE, *J. Am. Chem. Soc.*, 81 (1959) 1013.

[38] F. G. MANN, Chapter 6 of W. KLYNE AND P. B. D. DE LA MARE, see Bibliography.

[39] A. T. BOTTINI AND J. D. ROBERTS, *J. Am. Chem. Soc.*, 78 (1956) 5126; 80 (1958) 5203.

[39a] I. G. M. CAMPBELL AND J. K. WAY, *J. Chem. Soc.*, (1960) 5034; L. HORNER, H. WINKLER, A. RAPP, A. MENTRUP, H. HOFFMANN AND P. BECK, *Tetrahedron Letters*, (1961) 161.

[40] H. SCHMID AND P. KARRER, *Helv. Chim. Acta*, 31 (1948) 1017, 1497.

[41] C. A. GROB, *Record Chem. Progr.*, 18 (1957) 55.

[42] J. D. BU'LOCK, E. R. H. JONES AND P. R. LEEMING, *J. Chem. Soc.*, (1955) 4270.

[43] *cf. e.g.* S. P. FINDLAY, *J. Am. Chem. Soc.*, 75 (1953) 3204.

[44] A. S. DREIDING, *Helv. Chim. Acta*, 42 (1959) 1339.

[45] W. A. WIGHTMAN, *J. Chem. Soc.*, (1926) 2541.

[45a] N. L. ALLINGER AND L. A. FREIBERG, *J. Am. Chem. Soc.*, 82 (1960) 2393; W. S. JOHNSON, J. L. MARGRAVE, V. J. BAUER, M. A. FRISCH, L. H. DREGER AND W. N. HUBBARD, *ibid.*, 82 (1960) 1255; 83 (1961) 606.

[46] S. J. ANGYAL, *Quart. Revs. (London)*, 11 (1957) 212.

[47] R. E. REEVES, *Advances in Carbohydrate Chem.*, 6 (1951) 107; A. KJAER AND B. LINDBERG, *Acta Chem. Scand.*, 13 (1959) 1713.

[48] *e.g.* R. B. TURNER, *J. Am. Chem. Soc.*, 74 (1952) 2118.

[49] W. E. BACHMANN, A. ROSS, A. S. DREIDING AND P. A. S. SMITH, *J. Org. Chem.*, 19 (1954) 222.

[50] W. S. JOHNSON, *J. Am. Chem. Soc.*, 75 (1953) 1498.

[51] C. L. ARCUS AND D. W. WEST, *J. Chem. Soc.*, (1959) 2699 and references cited.

[52] G. NATTA, *Chem. & Ind. (London)*, (1957) 1520.

[53] C. C. PRICE, M. OSGAN, R. E. HUGHES AND C. SHAMBELAN, *J. Am. Chem. Soc.*, 78 (1956) 690.

[54] J. D. BERNAL, *Discussions Faraday Soc.*, 25 (1958) 7; A. RICH, *Revs. Mod. Phys.*, 31 (1959) 50, 191; E. J. AMBROSE, Chapter 7 of W. KLYNE, see Bibliography.

[55] M. S. NEWMAN AND D. LEDNICER, *J. Am. Chem. Soc.*, 78 (1956) 4765.

[56] E. R. BLOUT, Chapter 17 in C. DJERASSI, see Bibliography.

[57] F. H. C. CRICK, *Acta Cryst.*, 6 (1953) 689; L. PAULING AND R. B. COREY, *Nature*, 171 (1953) 59.

[58] M. FEUGHELMAN, R. LANGRIDGE, W. E. SEEDS, A. R. STOKES, H. R. WILSON, C. W. HOOPER, M. H. F. WILKINS, R. V. BARKLAY AND L. D. HAMILTON, *Nature*, 175 (1955) 834.

[59] J. D. WATSON AND F. H. C. CRICK, *Nature*, 171 (1953) 737, 964.

[60] A. WOHL AND F. MOMBER, *Ber. deut. chem. Ges.*, 50 (1917) 455.

[61] K. FREUDENBERG, *Ber. deut. chem. Ges.*, 47 (1914) 2027; K. FREUDENBERG AND F. BRAUNS, *ibid.*, 55 (1922) 1339.

[62] R. S. CAHN, C. K. INGOLD AND V. PRELOG, *Experientia*, 12 (1956) 81.

[63] H. ZIMMERMAN, L. SINGER AND B. S. THYAGARAJAN, *J. Am. Chem. Soc.*, 81 (1959) 108.

[64] H. LINDLAR, *Helv. Chim. Acta*, 35 (1952) 446; K. HOFMANN AND S. M. SAX, *J. Biol. Chem.*, 205 (1953) 55; B. B. ELSNER AND P. F. M. PAUL, *J. Chem. Soc.*, (1953) 3156.

[65] W. F. HUBER, *J. Am. Chem. Soc.*, 73 (1951) 2730.

[66] R. A. RAPHAEL AND F. SONDHEIMER, *J. Chem. Soc.*, (1950) 2100; H. M. WALBORSKY, R. H. DAVIS AND D. R. HOWTON, *J. Am. Chem. Soc.*, 73 (1951) 2590.

[67] S. WINSTEIN, D. PRESSMAN AND W. G. YOUNG, *J. Am. Chem. Soc.*, 61 (1939) 1645.

[68] M. C. HOFF, K. W. GREENLEY AND C. E. BOORD, *J. Am. Chem. Soc.*, 73 (1951) 3329.

[69] R. E. BUCKLES AND G. V. MACK, *J. Org. Chem.*, 15 (1950) 680.

[70] D. G. BOUNDS, R. P. LINSTEAD AND B. C. L. WEEDON, *J. Chem. Soc.*, (1953) 2393.

[71] G. PAPINEAU-COUTURE, E. M. RICHARDSON AND G. A. GRANT, *Can. J. Research*, 27B (1949) 902.

[72] W. THEILACKER, in HOUBEN-WEYL, *Methoden der organischen Chemie*, Part 4/2, 4th ed., Thieme-Verlag, Stuttgart, 1955, pp. 505-538.

[73] *e.g.* W. KUHN AND E. KNOPF, *Z. physik. Chem.*, B7 (1930) 292.

[74] A. MCKENZIE, *J. Chem. Soc.*, 107 (1915) 440; A. MCKENZIE AND N. WALKER, *ibid.*, 121 (1922) 349; M. D. ARMSTRONG, *J. Am. Chem. Soc.*, 73 (1951) 4456; A. LÜTTRING-HAUS AND D. BERRER, *Tetrahedron Letters*, No. 10 (1959) 10.

[75] L. ZECHMEISTER, *Ann. N.Y. Acad. Sci.*, 49 (1948) 220; E. LEDERER AND M. LEDERER, *Chromatography*, Elsevier, Amsterdam, 1957, p. 420 ff.; H. KREBS, J. DIEWALD, R. RASCHE AND J. A. WAGNER, *Die Trennung von Racematen auf chromatographischem Wege*, Forschungsber. Wirtschafts- und Verkehrsmin., Nordrhein-Westf., No. 270, Westdeutscher Verlag, Köln, 1956.

[76] F. CRAMER, *Einschlussverbindungen*, Springer-Verlag, Berlin, 1954.

[77] H. SOBOTKA AND A. GOLDBERG, *Biochem. J.*, 26 (1932) 905.

[78] W. SCHLENK JR., *Experientia*, 8 (1952) 337.

[79] A. C. D. NEWMAN AND H. M. POWELL, *J. Chem. Soc.*, (1952) 3747.

[80] B. HELFERICH AND W. PORTZ, *Chem. Ber.*, 86 (1953) 1034.

[81] F. CRAMER AND W. DIETSCHE, *Chem. Ber.*, 92 (1959) 378.

[82] A. W. INGERSOLL, in *Organic Reactions*, Vol. II, Ch. 9, John Wiley and Sons, New York, 1944.

[83] J. K. SHILLINGTON, G. S. DENNING JR., W. B. GREENOUGH III, T. HILL JR. AND O. B. RAMSAY, *J. Am. Chem. Soc.*, 80 (1958) 6551.

[84] M. S. NEWMAN AND W. B. LUTZ, *J. Am. Chem. Soc.*, 78 (1956) 2469; M. GREEN AND R. F. HUDSON, *J. Chem. Soc.*, (1958) 3129.

[85] H. J. LUCAS AND C. W. GOULD JR., *J. Am. Chem. Soc.*, 64 (1942) 601; S. J. CRISTOL, F. R. STERMITZ AND P. S. RAMEY, *ibid.*, 78 (1956) 4939; S. J. CRISTOL, *ibid.*, 71 (1949) 1894; R. K. SUMMERBELL AND H. E. LUNK, *ibid.*, 79 (1957) 4802; E. F. JENNY AND J. D. ROBERTS, *ibid.*, 78 (1956) 2005.

[86] J. P. GREENSTEIN, *Advances in Protein Chem.*, Vol. 9, Academic Press, New York, 1954, p. 121 ff.

[87] G. BREDIG AND K. FAJANS, *Ber. deut. chem. Ges.*, 41 (1908) 752, *Z. physik. Chem.*, 73 (1910) 25; W. KUHN, *Ergeb. Enzymforsch.*, 5 (1936) 1, *Angew. Chem.*, 49 (1936) 215.

[88] H. HIRSCHMANN, in S. GRAFF, *Essays in Biochemistry*, John Wiley and Sons, New York, 1956, p, 156 ff; A. G. OGSTON, *Nature*, 181 (1958) 1462.

[89] R. ALTSCHUL, P. BERNSTEIN AND S. G. COHEN, *J. Am. Chem. Soc.*, 78 (1956) 5091.

[90] C. MARTIUS AND G. SCHORRE, *Liebigs Ann. Chem.*, 570 (1950) 143.

[91] A. G. OGSTON, *Nature*, 162 (1948) 963.

[92] H. PRACEJUS, *Angew. Chem.*, 71 (1959) 577; *Ann. Chem., Liebigs*, 634 (1960) 9.

[92a] V. Prelog and H. SCHERRER, *Helv. Chim. Acta*, 42 (1959) 2227; F. J. IMPASTATO, L. BARASH AND H. M. WALBORSKY, *J. Am. Chem. Soc.*, 81 (1959) 1514; H. M. WALBORSKY, T. SUGITA, M. OHNO AND Y. INONYE, *ibid.*, 82 (1960) 5255; C. L. ARCUS, L. A. CORT, T. J. HOWARD AND L. B. LOC, *J. Chem. Soc.*, (1960) 1195; H. C. BROWN AND G. ZWEIFEL, *J. Am. Chem. Soc.*, 83 (1961) 486; C. L. ARCUS AND T. J. HOWARD, *J. Chem. Soc.*, (1961) 670.

[93] F. G. FISCHER, *Angew. Chem.*, 53 (1940) 465.

[94] A. MCKENZIE, *Ergeb. Enzymforsch.*, 5 (1936) 49; V. PRELOG, *Bull. soc. chim. France*, (1956) 987.

[95] H. S. MOSHER *et al.*, *J. Am. Chem. Soc.*, 72 (1950) 3994 *et seq.*

[96] W. v. E. DOERING AND R. W. YOUNG, *J. Am. Chem. Soc.*, 72 (1950) 631; A. BOTHNER-BY, *ibid.*, 73 (1951) 846; A. STREITWIESER JR. *et al.*, *ibid.*, 75 (1953) 5014 *et seq.*

[97] P. BAUMANN AND V. PRELOG, *Helv. Chim. Acta*, 41 (1958) 2362 *et seq.*

[98] H. R. LEVY, F. A. LOEWUS AND B. VENNESLAND, *J. Am. Chem. Soc.*, 79 (1957) 2949.

[99] L. ROSENTHALER, *Biochem. Z.*, 14 (1908) 238 *et seq.*

[100] G. BREDIG AND P. S. FISKE, *Biochem. Z.*, 46 (1912) 7 *et seq.*

[101] F. CRAMER AND W. DIETSCHE, *Chem. Ber.*, 92 (1959) 1739.

[102] *e.g.* K. Mislow, *Angew. Chem.*, 70 (1958) 683; S. R. Landor and R. Taylor-Smith, *Proc. Chem. Soc.*, *(London)*, (1959) 154; E. R. H. Jones, J. D. Loder and M. C. Whiting, *ibid.*, (1960) 180; E. L. Eliel, *Tetrahedron Letters*, [8] (1960) 16.

[103] H. L. Cohen and G. F. Wright, *J. Org. Chem.*, 18 (1953) 432 *et seq.*

[104] R. C. Ferreira, *Nature*, 171 (1953) 39; K. Vogler and M. Kofler, *Helv. Chim. Acta*, 39 (1956) 1387.

[105] W. H. Mills, *J. Soc. Chem. Ind. (London)*, 51 (1932) 750; W. Kuhn, *Experientia*, 11 (1955) 429, *Advances in Enzymology*, Vol. 20, Interscience, New York, 1958, p. 1; E. Havinga, *Biochim. et Biophys. Acta*, 13 (1954) 171.

[106] *e.g.* L. Velluz and G. Amiard, *Bull. soc. chim. France*, 20 (1953) 903.

[107] H. M. Powell, *Nature*, 170 (1952) 155; M. M. Harris, Chapter 5, in W. Klyne, see Bibliography.

[108] *e.g.* C. M. Stevens, R. P. Gigger and S. W. Bowne Jr., *J. Biol. Chem.*, 212 (1955) 461.

[109] J. M. Robertson, *Organic Crystals and Molecules*, Chapters 10 and 11, Cornell University Press, 1953.

[110] L. L. Ingraham, Chapter 11 in M. S. Newman, see Bibliography.

[111] W. G. Dauben and K. S. Pitzer, Chapter 1 in M. S. Newman, see Bibliography.

[112] *e.g.* R. B. Turner *et al.*, *J. Am. Chem. Soc.*, 79 (1957) 4116, 4122, 4127, 4133.

[113] E. A. Braude and E. S. Waight, Chapter 4 in W. Klyne, see Bibliography; E. A. Braude, Chapter 4 in E. A. Braude and F. C. Nachod, see Bibliography; R. C. Gore, Chapter 5 in E. A. Braude and F. C. Nachod, see Bibliography; A. R. H. Cole, in L. Zechmeister, *Progress in the Chemistry of Natural Products*, Vol. 13, Springer-Verlag, 1956, pp. 1–69.

[114] L. M. Jackman, *Applications of NMR Spectroscopy in Organic Chemistry*, Pergamon Press, London, 1959, pp. 119–125; Ref. 18, Chapter 14.

[115] L. E. Sutton, Chapter 9 in E. A. Braude and F. C. Nachod, see Bibliography.

[116] C. Djerassi, see Bibliography.

[117] H. C. Brown, D. H. MacDaniel and O. Häfliger, Chapter 14 in E. A. Braude and F. C. Nachod, see Bibliography.

[118] D. H. R. Barton and G. A. Schmeidler, *J. Chem. Soc.*, (1948) 1197.

[119] V. Prelog and O. Häfliger, *Helv. Chim. Acta*, 33 (1950) 2021.

[120] W. H. Perkin Jr. and G. Tattersall, *J. Chem. Soc.*, 91 (1907) 480.

[121] E. A. Braude and L. M. Jackman, Chapter 15 in E. A. Braude and F. C. Nachod, see Bibliography.

[122] H. Baumann and W. Pigman, Chapter 10 in W. Pigman, *The Carbohydrates*, Academic Press, New York, 1957.

[123] J. M. Bijvoet, *Endeavour*, 14 (1956) 145; R. Pepinsky, *Record Chem. Progr.*, 17 (1956) 145.

[124] J. A. Mills and W. Klyne, Chapter 5 of W. Klyne, see Bibliography.

[125] J. Trommel and J. M. Bijvoet, *Acta Cryst.*, 7 (1954) 703; B. Riniker, D. Arigoni and O. Jeger, *Helv. Chim. Acta*, 37 (1954) 546; K. Freudenberg, W. Lwowski and W. Hohmann, *Liebigs Ann. Chem.*, 594 (1955) 76.

[126] C. S. Hudson, *J. Chem. Ed.*, 18 (1941) 353.

[127] D. S. Noyce and J. H. Canfield, *J. Am. Chem. Soc.*, 76 (1954) 3630.

[128] C. K. Ingold, *Structure and Mechanism in Organic Chemistry*, Cornell University Press, Ithaca, 1953, pp. 386–397, 500–528.

[129] P. Pratesi, L. Arpesella and A. La Manná, *J. Am. Chem. Soc.*, 75 (1953) 5476.

[130] V. Prelog *et al.*, *Helv. Chim. Acta*, 36 (1953) 308, 320, 325, 1178; A. J. Birch, J. W. Clark-Lewis and A. V. Robertson, *J. Chem. Soc.*, (1957) 3586.

[131] A. M. Mathieson, *Acta Cryst.*, 9 (1956) 317.

[132] R. L. M. Synge and J. C. Wood, *Biochem. J.*, 64 (1956) 252; C. J. Morris and J. F. Thompson, *J. Am. Chem. Soc.*, 78 (1956) 1605.

[133] R. Hine and D. Rogers, *Chem. & Ind. (London)*, (1956) 1428.

[134] J. Timmermans, *J. Chim. Phys.*, 49 (1952) 162; A. Fredga, in *The Svedberg*, Almqvist and Wiksells, Uppsala, 1944, p. 261 ff.; *Tetrahedron*, 8 (1960) 126.

[135] K. Mislow and W. C. Meluch, *J. Am. Chem. Soc.*, 78 (1956) 5920.

[136] W. Klyne, Chapter 3 in E. A. Braude and F. C. Nachod, see Bibliography.

[137] J. H. Brewster, *J. Am. Chem. Soc.*, 81 (1959) 5475, 5493, 5483.

[138] *e.g.* K. Freudenberg, *Monatsh. Chem.*, 85 (1954) 537.

[139] K. Freudenberg, F. Brauns and H. Siegel, *Ber. deut. chem. Ges.*, 56 (1923) 193.

[140] C. Djerassi, *Bull. soc. chim. France*, (1957) 741.

[141] B. Sjöberg, A. Fredga and C. Djerassi, *J. Am. Chem. Soc.*, 81 (1959) 5002.

[142] K. Mislow, *J. Am. Chem. Soc.*, 73 (1951) 3954.

[143] S. Gronowitz, *Arkiv Kemi*, 13 (1958) 87.

[144] D. H. S. Horn and Y. Y. Pretorius, *J. Chem. Soc.*, (1954) 1460.

[145] K. Freudenberg and L. Markert, *Ber. deut. chem. Ges.*, 58 (1925) 1753; G. W. Clough, *J. Chem. Soc.*, (1925) 2808.

SUBJECT INDEX

Absolute configuration, of enantiomers, definition, 194
—, determination of — of (+)-tartaric acid and (—)-isoleucine, 227
—, and relative configurations of enantiomers, determination, 227–238
Acetylene in MO and VB theory, 72, 73
Actin, globular–fibrous transformation, 146
Active proteins, 168
Actomyosin fibres, 184
Aggregated polymer, definition, 144
(+)-Alanine, configurational correlation with (+)-lactic acid, 230
Aldohexoses, number of stereoisomers, 205
Alkaloids, table of — of which structure is known, 162
Allene, geometry of molecule based on consideration of orbitals, 70
Allenes, stereoisomerism, 204, 205
Alternant hydrocarbons, 77
D-Amino acids found in lower organisms, 226
Amino acids, planarity of the amide groups, 154
—, structure, 151, 153
—, whose structures have been accurately determined by X-ray studies, 153
Amyrins, 157
Angelic acid, conversion of tiglic acid to —, 220
Angle of isocline in flow birefringence, definition, 147
Angular momentum, intrinsic, of electron, 27
—, orbital, of electron, 7, 27
Anomers, definition, 209
Antibonding orbital, definition, 49
— wave function, definition, 38
Aporphine alkaloids, atropisomerism, 201
Argon, atomic structure, 32
Aromatic molecules, electronic theory, 73–103

Asymmetrical additions, to carbonyl function, 224
—, to ethylene function, 224
Asymmetrical atoms, 205
— atrolactic acid synthesis, 224
— enzymatic reduction of acetaldehyde-1-d, 224
— hydrogenation of ketones with *Curvularia falcata*, 224
— molecules, definition, 193
— reduction of ketones with dialkylmagnesium, lithium, magnesium or aluminium oxides, 224
— synthesis, 220, 223, 224
— — of cyanohydrins from HCN and aldehydes, 224
— — of 17β-oestradiol, 220, 221
— — with optically active solvents, 224
— —, partial asymmetrical atrolactic acid synthesis, use in configurational assignments to steroids, terpenoids and catechins, 231
Atomic core, definition, 31
— number, definition, 29
— spectra, investigations of J. J. Balmer, 4
— structure, earlier ideas, 5, 6
— —, of helium, lithium, beryllium, boron, carbon, nitrogen, oxygen, fluorine, sodium, argon, potassium, 31, 32
ATPase, 168
Atropisomers, 200, 201

Back donation, definition, 101
Baker–Nathan effect, 91
Balmer series, in hydrogen spectrum, 4, 9
Basket-like molecules, 139
Bent bonds, 72, 101
—, definition, 72
Benzene, Dewar structures, 90
—, energy levels, 89
—, ionic structures, 90
—, Kekulé structures, 90
—, MO's in —, 87

Benzene (*continued*)
— in MO theory, 85–90
—, resonance energy, 90
— in VB theory, 90, 91
Benzphenanthrene, structure, actual atomic positions in molecule, 124
Beryllium, atomic structure, 32
Bicyclo[3,3,1]nonane, stereoisomerism, 212
Bicyclo[2,2,2]octane, stereoisomerism, 212
Bimolecular sheets, hydrogen bonds in formation of —, 128, 129
Biotin, structure and shape of molecule, 140
Birefringence, flow — of polymer molecules in solution, 147
— of polymers depending on stress, 147
Black body radiation, 2
Boat conformation of cyclohexane, 210
Bohr, quantum condition, 7, 12
— theory of the hydrogen atom, 4–10
Bond order, π, definition, use, 79
— in resonance theory, 85
Bonding orbital, definition, 49
— wave function, definition, 38
Bonds, bent, 72, 101
—, —, definition, 72
—, essential double, definition, 76
—, — single, definition, 76
—, partial multiple, conditions for the formation, 105
—, — triple, definition, 105
—, π, definition, 71
—, σ, definition, 70
—, three-electron, 58
Bone, structure, 191
(—)-Borneol, configuration, 231
Boron, atomic structure, 32
Butadiene, electronic structure of ground state, 77
—, energy levels, 77
—, MO's, 76
— in MO and VB theory, 73–85
—, total energy of π electrons, 77
— in VB theory, 82–85
Butane, rotamers, 199, 200

Calciferol iodoacetate, structure and shape of molecule, 137
Camphor, stereoisomers, 206
—, *trans-d-α-*, basket-like molecule, 139
Carbon, atomic structure, 32
Carotenoids, structure, 159
Caryophyllene, geometric isomerism, 202, 204
Cellular reticulum, 187
Cellulose, structure, 157
— in supporting structures of plants and animals, 188

Centre of inversion of hydrogen molecule, 40
Centrioles, 185
Chair conformation of cyclohexane, 209
Charge density at an atom, definition, use, 78
— in resonance theory, 85
Chitin in supporting structures of arthropods, 189
Cholestan-7α-ol, configuration, 231
Cholesteric phenomena, 160
Cholesteryl iodide, structure and shape of molecule, 137
Chromosomes, 184
Cilia, 185
Circular dichroism, definition, 195
Cis addition, 219
Cis–trans or geometric (*syn–anti*) isomers, 201
Citric acid, diastereomeric transition states in the degradation of — to α-ketoglutarate, 224
Citronellal, enantiomers in oil of eucalyptus and in oil of citronella, 226
Civetones, geometric isomerism, 202, 204
CO, energy level diagram, 62
— in MO theory, 61, 62
— in VB theory, 63
Coacervates, 150
Coiled coil arrangement of polymer molecules, 143, 144
— —, definition, 216
Coiling of polymer molecules, 142, 143
Collagen proteins, twined protein chains, 172
Collagen, structure, 171
— in supporting structures of animals, 190
Complex atoms, model of structure, 29
—, theory of structure, 26–33
Complexes of transition metals, covalent, 110
—, inner orbital, 110
—, ionic, 110
—, ligand field theory, 108
—, MO treatment, 106–112
—, outer orbital, 110
Compound helix, definition, 216
— molecules, oligomers and polymers, conformation, 141–144
Configuration, absolute, definition, 194
—, *cis* and *trans*, 123
—, determination, 226–237
— of enantiomers, correlations by chemical methods, 228–232
— —, — by physical methods, 232–234
—, Freudenberg Amide Rule for determination of enantiomer —, 234
—, of mandelic acid, determination, 234–237

Configuration (*continued*)
— of molecule, definition, 192
—, rule of shift in determination of enantiomer —, 233
Configurational correlations, comparison of RD curves as basis, 234
— isomers, definition, 192
— nomenclature, genetic and non-genetic systems, 217–219
— stereoisomers, representation, 219
Conformation and conformational properties of molecules, definition, 121
Conformation, determination for an isolated molecule, 123
—, influence of environment, 123
— of molecule, definition, 192
—, role of attractive part of Van der Waals forces (London–Van der Waals forces), 126
—, — of hydrogen bonds, 126–129
—, — of repulsive factor of Van der Waals forces, 124
Conformational isomerism due to partial double bond character, 200
— isomers, definition, 192
— stereoisomers, 199, 200
Conformers, definition, 192
Conjugated molecules, electronic theory, 73–103
— systems, substituted, in MO and VB theory, 92–100
Constitution of molecule, definition, 192
Convoluted polymer, definition, 144
Coordination numbers of transition metals, 106, 108
Cotton effect curves (anomalous RD curves), 197
Coulson–Longuet-Higgins perturbation method, 95–97
Covalent complexes of transition metals, 110
Cumulenes, geometric isomerism, 204
Crystal field theory, 108–111
Crystalline proteins, 169
—, definition, 168
Cyclobutane, MO treatment, 103
Cyclohexane(s), boat conformation, 210
—, chair (rigid) and flexible form, 209
—, determination of configuration of diastereomeric disubstituted —, 226
—, stereoisomerism, 209–215
Cyclopropane, in MO theory, 101, 102
trans-1,2-Cyclopropanedicarboxylic acid, determination of diastereomeric identity, 227
Cytidine, structure, 116

De Broglie, determination of amplitude of — waves (ψ), 18

De Broglie (*continued*)
—, hypothesis of wave nature of matter, 15–21
Decalins, stereoisomerism, 212, 214
Degenerate states, definition, 23
— wave functions, definition, 40
Denaturation of proteins, 169
Deoxyribonucleoproteins, tertiary structure, 216
Dewar perturbation method, 98
— structures of benzene, 90
Dianthrolidene, structure, actual atomic positions in molecule, 125
Diastereomers, determination of configuration, 226, 227
—, — from chemical differences, 226
—, — by kinetic methods, 227
— (diastereoisomers), definition, 192
—, difference in physical and chemical properties, 198, 199
— possible for constitutionally symmetrical and unsymmetrical olefins with *n* double bonds, 202, 203
Dibenzene chromium in MO theory, 103
dl-2,3-Dibromobutane, formation of *cis*-2-butene by debromination, 219
meso-2,3-Dibromobutane, formation of *trans*-2-butene by debromination, 219
Dichroism, circular, definition, 195
Dilithium (Li_2) in molecular orbital and valence bond theory, 50–52
Dimeric molecules, definition, 130
(S)-4′,1″-Dimethyl-1,2,3,4-dibenzcyclo-hepta-1,3-dien-6-one, optical rotation in benzene, 196
cis-Dimethyldiketopiperazine, stereo-isomerism, 193
Dioxane as acceptor of hydrogen bonds, 127
Disaggregation, reversible, of larger protein molecules, 170
Dissymmetrical catalysis, kinetic resolution of racemic material, 223
— grouping in a molecule describable as screw pattern of electron polarizability, 233
Dithiocarbamates of L-α-amino acids, determination of configuration, 234
Dithiocarbonates (xanthates) of L-α-hydroxyacids, determination of configuration, 234
Di-*p*-xylene, structure, actual atomic positions in molecule, 125
DNA chain, arrangements of purine and pyrimidine nucleotides in part of DNA chain, 173–175
—, linking of purines and pyrimidines by H bonds to form double chain, 174

DNA, character of double helical chains, 177
— structure, Crick and Watson model, 175
Drude equation for rotatory dispersion, 197
Dynamic or localization method in MO descriptions, 81

Einstein, quantization of energy and photoelectric effect, 3
Elasticity, long-range or rubber-like, 126
Elastin in elastic tissue, 190
Elastomers, definition, 126
Electron in a box, 99
— path, along conjugated system, 99
— —, potential energy function, 99
— repulsions, effect in ligand field theory, 110
— volt, definition, 9
Electronic theory of conjugated and aromatic molecules, 73–103
— of organic molecules, 34–112
— — and geometry of molecules, 68–70
Electrons as atomic radiators, 5
—, binding energy in H atom, 9
—, d, role in structure of molecules, 103–112
—, —, in transition metals, 106
—, frontier, 98
—, π, definition, 71
—, shell, definition, 30
—, spin, definition, 27
Elimination reactions, stereospecific, 219
Ellagitannins, atropisomerism, 201
Enantiomers, absolute and relative configurations, 227–237
—, definition, 192
—, relationship of — compared with that between right- and left-handed helices, 194
Energy, atomic — levels and radiation, 10–15
—, binding — of electron in H atom, 9, 47
— levels of Li_2, 51
— of a "normal" hydrogen molecule (binding energy), 48, 49
Ephedrines, stereoisomers, 205
Epicatechin tetramethyl ether, configuration, 231
Epimer, definition, 208
Equidistant structures, 150
Ethane in MO theory, 66
Ethylene bromonium ion in VB and MO theory, 101
— in MO and VB theory, 71, 72
— oxide, MO treatment, 102

Ethylene–transition metal complex, MO's, 101, 102
Exchange effects, definition, 29
— and Pauli exclusion principle, 29
Exclusion principle, Pauli, 29

Ferrocene, in MO theory, 103
Fibres, intracellular, 182–184
—, spindle, 182
— in striated muscle, 182, 183
Fibrinogen–fibrin transformation, 146
Fibrous proteins, 171–174
—, α-type, 172
—, β-type, 167, 172
—, collagen type, 172
—, transformations between α- and β-type, 172
Flagellae, animal, 184, 185
—, bacterial, 184
Flexible and rigid molecules, 123
Flow birefringence, angle of isocline, 147
Fluorine, atomic structure, 32
— molecule, electronic structure, 57
— — in VB theory, 57, 58
Four-membered rings in MO theory, 103
Franck and Hertz, demonstration of existence of allowed energy levels, 11
Free electron method (FEM), 98, 99
Free valence, definition, 79, 80
— in resonance theory, 85
Freudenberg Amide Rule for determination of enantiomer configuration, 234
Frontier electrons, 98

Gels, iridescent, 150
Geometric or cis–trans (syn–anti) isomers, 201
— description of molecular structures, value in biochemistry, 120
— isomers, definition, 199
— stereoisomerism in ring systems, 202, 203
Geometry of long chains, 142
— of molecules and electronic theory of organic molecules, 68–70
Gerade character, definition, 40
Geranylamine, structure, 160
Globular–fibrous transformation of polymers, 146, 147
Globular proteins, 165–168
α- and β-Glucopyranosides, stereoisomerism, 210
α-D-Glucose, structure and shape of molecule, 136
L-Glutamine molecule, structure, 151
Glutathione, structure, 163
Glutinous proteins, structure, 172

Glyceraldehyde, determination of
    absolute configuration, 228
Glycine molecule, structure, 151
β-Glycylglycine, structure, 163
Gramicidin, 163
Ground state of atom, definition, 10
Gutta percha, stereoisomerism, 215
—, structure, 159

H–H bond, ionic character, 37
Haemoglobin molecule, structure, 166,
    169, 170
Heisenberg uncertainty principle, 43
Helical identity and stability, and rotatory
    dispersion, 216
Helices, diastereomerism, 216
Helium, atomic structure, 31
Helix, compound, definition, 216
—, α-, of polypeptide chain, 165
—, super-, definition, 216
Heptaric acids, stereoisomerism, 207,
    208
Heteroatom(s), 92–94
—, carbon, 92
—, Coulomb integrals, 93
—, electronegativity, 93
—, ionization potential, 93
— resonance integral between carbon
    atom and —, 94
Heteromeric (heteromorphous) molecules,
    126, 130, 140
Hexahelicene, stereochemistry, 215, 216
Hudson's rules of isorotation, 233
Hybridization, energetics of — of N_2
    orbitals, 56
Hydrocarbons, alternant, 77
—, lath-shaped, 139
Hydrogen atom, application of quantum
    mechanics to theory of —, 21–26
—, Bohr theory, 4–10
—, comparison between models of — pre-
    dicted by Bohr theory and by quantum
    mechanics, 23–26
Hydrogen bonds, bond distance, 127
— in formation of bimolecular sheets,
    128
—, role in determination of conformation
    of molecules, 126–129
—, — in secondary structure of peptides
    and proteins, 129
—, strength, 127
Hydrogen peroxide, geometry of molecule
    based on consideration of orbitals, 70
Hydrogen molecule, graphic representa-
    tions of wave functions, 45
Hydrogen molecule ion and hydrogen
    molecule, energies, 46–49
— — in MO and VB theory, 35–50

Hyperconjugation in VB and MO theory,
    91, 92

Inner shell repulsion, definition, 52
Inositols, stereoisomerism, 210, 211
Insulin, globular–fibrous transformation,
    146, 168
Intracellular structures, relation to molec-
    ular structures, 181
Ionic character of H–H bond, 37
Ionization potential (IP) of hydrogen
    molecule, 48, 49
Iridescent gels, 150
(—)-Isoborneol, configuration, 231
Isocolchicine, atropisomerism, 201
Isocorydine, atropisomerism, 201
(—)-Isoleucine, determination of absolute
    configuration, 227
Isomerism, conformational, due to partial
    double bond character, 200
Isomers, atropisomers, 200
—, cis-trans, 201
—, configurational, definition, 192
—, conformational, definition, 192
—, geometric, 201
—, —, definition, 199
—, meso-, 206–209
—, optical, definition, 199
—, syn-anti, 201
Isoprenoid molecules, structure, 158
α-Isosparteine, stereoisomerism, 193, 212
Isotactic polymers, definition, 147
— polyvinyl diastereomers, 215

Kekulé structures of benzene, 90
Keratin in supporting structures of
    animals, 190
K-shell, definition, 30

(+)-Lactic acid, configurational correla-
    tion with (+)-alanine, 230
Lath-shaped molecules, 139
LCAO (linear combination of atomic
    orbitals), 35
Lewis octet rule, 104
— for compounds of second row elements,
    104
Ligand field splitting, 109
Ligand field theory, 108–111
—, effect of electron repulsions, 110
Lignins, structure, 156, 157
Lipid substances, shape of molecules and
    packing, 134, 135
Lipids and discriminatingly permeable
    membranes, 158
—, structure, 122, 128, 157–160
α-Lipoic acid, determination of absolute
    configuration, 232

Lipoproteins, structure, 172
Liquid crystal forms among lipid substances, 158
Lithium, atomic structure, 32
— hydride, energy levels, 60
— — in MO and VB theory, 58–61
— molecule, energy levels, 51
— — in MO and VB theory, 50–52
Localization or dynamic method in MO descriptions, 81
— energy, definition, 81
Long-chain organic molecules, branched chains, 135, 136
— (linear), lipid-like, shape and packing, 134
Long chains, geometry, 142
Long-range forces between polymer molecules, 149
Lorentz, H. A., identification of the electrons as the atomic radiators, 5
L-shell, definition, 31
Lycopene, number of diastereomers, 202
Lyman series, correlation between frequencies of the lines in the spectrum of a given element, 10
L-Lysine molecule, structure, 151

Macromolecules, secondary structure, definition, 215
—, stereoisomerism, 214–217
Magnetic moment of an atomic system, 13
Malic acid, determination of absolute configuration, 228
Mandelic acid, determination of configuration, 234–237
Mannosaccharide dilactone, stereoisomerism, 193
Matter waves, physical significance, 16–21
Maxwell's equations describing interactions of charged particles, 1
Mean residue optical rotation, 196
Membranes, intracellular, 185, 186
—, lipid intracellular, 185–188
—, lipids and discriminatingly permeable —, 158
Mendeleyev, 29
(—)-Menthyl hydrogen β-phenylglutarates, formation of diastereomeric — from reactions of (—)-menthol with symmetrical phenylglutaric anhydride, 223
Meso isomers, 206–209
Methane, electronic structure, 64
— in MO theory, 63, 64
— in VB theory, 66
(+)-S-Methylcysteine-S-oxide, determination of absolute configuration, 232
Microsomes, 181

Millikan, R. A., photoelectric effect, 3
Mirror axes (alternating axes of symmetry), definition, 193
Mitochondria, 187
MO method (molecular orbital method), definition, 35
MO and VB theories, comparison, 67
— of unsaturated compounds, 70
Molecular aggregates, definition, 144
— compounds, definition, 144
— double sheets, 134
— optical rotation, definition, 196
— orbital method (MO method), definition, 35
— orbitals, equivalent, definition, 65
— —, localized and non-localized, definition, 65
— shapes, classification, 129–145
— sheets, 128, 134
— skeleton, classification of molecule shapes based on —, 131, 132
— structure, modern refined concept, 116, 117
— — of polymers, variability imposed by medium, 148
— — in relation to cells or tissues, 181–191
— —, value of geometrical description for biochemistry, 120
Molecule(s), asymmetrical, definition, 193
—, basket-like shape, 139
—, compound, see Compound molecules
—, configuration, definition, 192
—, conformation, definition, 192
—, constitution, definition, 192
—, constitutional formula, definition, 115
—, dimeric, definition, 130
—, heteromorphous, 140
—, lath-shaped, 139
—, long-chain (see also Long-chain molecules), 134–136
—, monocyclic, shape, 136, 137
—, oligomeric and heteromeric type, 124
—, polycyclic, shape, 137–139
—, rigid and flexible, 122–124
—, simple, see Simple molecules
—, small or quasi-spherical, 133, 134
—, stereochemical formula, definition, 116
—, stretched out and curled up form, 123
—, structural formula, definition, 115
—, structure in the physical sense, 113–191
—, structures of the major classes of biochemical —, 151–191
—, unipolar, surface activity, 127

Monochromatic optical rotation rules for determination of enantiomer configuration, 233, 236
Morphine, structure, 161
Mucoproteins, structure, 172
Mycomycin, stereoisomerism, 205
Myoglobin molecule, structure, 166, 169, 170

Nemotinic acid, allenic and atomic asymmetry, 206
Nerve sheaths, lipid layers, 188
Newton's laws, describing the motion of particles, 1
Nitrogen, atomic structure, 32
Nitrogen molecule, electronic structure, 54, 56
—, energy level diagram, 62
—, energy levels, 53
—, molecular orbitals, 52–57
—, in VB theory, 57, 58
Nomenclature, configurational, genetic and non-genetic systems, 217–219
Non-bonding orbitals, definition, 81
Nucleic acids, stereoisomerism, 215
—, structure (see also DNA and RNA), 176, 177
Nucleophilic attacking reagent, definition, 81
Nucleoproteins, structure, 178
—, virus —, structure, 178
Nucleotide-containing co-enzymes (ATP, DPN, FAD, co-enzyme A), conformation of molecules, 175, 176
Nucleotides, structure, 174, 175

Occupation number, definition, 78
Odd alternant hydrocarbon, 96
17β-Oestradiol, formation from oestrone by reduction with lithium aluminium hydride, 220, 221
Oestrone, reduction by lithium aluminium hydride, asymmetrical synthesis of 17β-oestradiol, 220, 221
Oleanolic acids, structure and shape of molecule, 138
Olefinic diastereomers, determination of configuration, 226
Olefins, constitutionally symmetrical and unsymmetrical — with n double bonds, number of diastereomers possible, 202, 203
Oligomeric type of molecule, 124
Oligomers, definition, 130
—, distinction between — and polymers with respect to method of biochemical formation, 141
α-Onocerin, stereoisomerism, 193

Optical activation, of biphenyls and allenes, 224
—, definition, 221
Optical activity, 194–198
—, some conjectures concerning origin and maintenance in nature, 225
Optical-geometric isomerism in Co(III) complexes, 199
Optical isomers, definition, 199
Optical rotation, of compounds with several dissymmetrical groupings, rule of superposition, 233
—, mean residue —, definition, 196
—, molecular, definition, 196
—, prefixes for designation of rotation, 197
—, specific, definition, 196
Orbitals, antibonding, definition, 49
—, bonding, definition, 49
—, d, role in structure of molecules, 104
—, non-bonding, definition, 81
—, π, definition, 71
Oxygen, atomic structure, 32
Oxygen molecule, electronic structure, 57
—, in VB theory, 57, 58

Partial multiple bond, conditions for formation, 105
— triple bond, definition, 105
Paschen series, correlation between frequencies of the lines in the spectrum of a given element, 10
Pauli exclusion principle, 26–29, 39
Pectins, structure, 157
Penicillin, benzyl-, structure and shape of molecule, 140
Pentahydroxypimelic acids, stereoisomerism, 207, 208
Peptides, structure, 163, 164
Perhydrophenanthrenes, stereochemistry, 214
Perturbation method, Coulson–Longuet–Higgins, 95–97
—, Dewar, 98
Perturbation theory, definition, 94
Phenyldihydrothebaine, atropisomerism, 201
Phosphoric acid in VB and MO theory, 104, 105
Photoelectron, definition, 3
Photon, definition, 3
α-Pimelic acid, molecular dimensions and crystal structure, 135
Planck's constant in black body radiation, 2
Plastids, 187, 189
Polar bodies, 185

Polarimetry, 195–198
Polyalcohols, open chain —, shape of molecules and packing, 136
Polyatomic molecules in MO and VB theory, 63–67
Poly-benzyl-L-aspartate, helical structure, 216
Poly-benzyl-L-glutamate, helical structure, 216
Poly-1,4-isoprenes, stereoisomerism, 215
Polymer(s), aggregated, definition, 144
— aggregates, physical properties, 145–150
—, colloidal properties, 148
—, convoluted, definition, 144
—, definition, 130
—, isotactic, definition, 147
— molecules, coiled coils, 143, 144
— —, coiling, 142–144
— —, cyclic, branched or cross-linked, 146
— —, flow birefringence in solution, 147
— —, molecular aggregates, 144
— —, — compounds, 144
— —, primary structure, definition, 141
— —, secondary structure, definition, 141
— —, tertiary structure, 144
— —, twining, 142, 143
Polymerized substances, amorphous and so-called crystalline regions, 147
Polynucleotides, stereoisomerism, 215
Polypeptide chain, fully extended, 165
—, α-helix, 165
—, uncoiling, 171
Polypeptides, stereoisomerism, 215
Polypropylene oxide, crystal lattice, 215
Polysaccharides, stereoisomerism, 215
Polyvinyl diastereomers, isotactic and syndiotactic, 215
Porphyrins, and porphyrinoid derivatives, structure and shape of molecules, 139, 155
Potassium, atomic structure, 32
Potential energy function along electron path, 99
Pregnan-3α-ol-20-one acetates, configuration of 17α- and 17β-isomer, 234
Primary structure of polymer, definition, 141
Proteins, chemically active, 168
—, crystalline, 168–170
—, —, definition, 168
—, denaturation, 169
—, fibrous, 165–168, 171
—, — β-type, 167, 172
—, globular, 165–168
—, glutinous, structure, 172
—, lipo-, structure, 172

Proteins, muco-, structure, 172
—, primary, secondary and tertiary structures, 169
—, stereoisomerism, 215
—, structural, 168
α-Proteins, tertiary structures, 216
Pseudoasymmetrical carbon, 215
Pseudo-atom, H_3, 91, 92
Purines, structure, 138, 154, 155, 174
Pyrimidines, structure, 154, 155

Quantized states, definition, 7
Quantum mechanics, basic concepts, 15–21
— numbers, n, l, s, definition, 9, 22, 27
— —, standard notation, 22
Quasi-racemates, method of — for determination of enantiomer configuration, 232

Racemate formation, 198
Racemic material, resolution of —, see Resolution of racemic material
— forms, definition, 198
— —, solid, 198
Racemization, entropy of mixing as driving force, 198
RD curves, see Rotatory dispersion curves
Relation between frequencies of the lines in the spectrum of a given element, Balmer series, 4, 9
— — —, Lyman series, 10
— — —, Paschen series, 10
— — —, Ritz Combination Principle, 4, 10
Repulsion, inner shell —, definition, 52
Resolution of racemic material, by chromatography on optically active adsorbent, 221
—, definition, 221
—, with functionally specific dissymmetrical reagent, 222
—, via inclusion compounds, 222
—, kinetic, by dissymmetrical catalysis, 223
Resonance energy, definition, 84
— hybrid, 36, 85
— integral between carbon atom and heteroatom, 94
— —, definition, 47
— theory, definition, 83
Ricinoleic acid, stereoisomerism, 199, 206
Rigid and flexible molecules, 123–124
Rings, four-membered, in MO theory, 103
Ritz Combination Principle, correlation between frequencies of the lines in the spectrum of a given element, 4, 10

RNA, double helical chains in artificial —, 177
Rotamers, definition, 192
Rotatory dispersion constant, 197
Rotatory dispersion curves (RD curves), 197
—, comparison of — as basis for configurational correlations, 234
Rotatory dispersion, definition, 197
—, Drude equation, 197
—, and helical identity and stability, 216
Rubber, stereoisomerism, 215
Rule of shift in determination of enantiomer configuration, 233
Rule of superposition for optical rotation of compounds with several dissymmetrical groupings, 233
Rutherford, nuclear model of the atom, 6

"Sandwich compounds", 103
Schrödinger equation for determination of amplitude of De Broglie wave, 18–20
Screw pattern of electron polarizability, dissymmetrical grouping in a molecule describable as —, 233
Secondary structure, of peptides and proteins, role of hydrogen bonds, 128, 129
—, of polymer, definition, 141
Secular determinant, definition, 59
— equations, definition, 59
Silk, glycine–alanine sequence in —, 167
Simple molecules, classification based on skeleton, 132–141
—, definition, 129
—, types, 132, 133
Singlet state, definition, 40
Small or quasi-spherical molecules, 133, 134
Small ring compounds in MO theory, 100
Sodium ammonium tartrate, dissymmetrical habit of crystals, 194
Sodium, atomic structure, 32
Space quantization, definition, 12
—, experiment of Stern and Gerlach, 13
Specific optical rotation, 196
Sperm nucleoproteins, 178, 184
Spermatozoa tails, 185
Spherulites, formation, 146
Sphingosine, stereoisomerism, 206
Spin functions, antisymmetrical in exchange of electrons of hydrogen molecule, 39
—, of electrons of hydrogen molecule, 39
—, symmetrical in exchange of electrons of hydrogen molecule, 39

Squalene, number of diastereomers, 202
Starches, structure, 157
Stearyl alcohol, crystal structure, 128
Stereoisomeric relationships, schematization of basic —, 194
— types, 192–219
Stereoisomerism, 192–243
— in cyclohexanes, 209–215
— in macromolecules, 214–217
Stereoisomers, configurational, representation, 219
—, conformational, 199, 200
—, preparation, 219–226
—, resulting from asymmetrical atoms, 205–209
—, resulting from hindered or restricted rotation, 199–205
Stereomutation, 201, 202
Stereoselective syntheses, definition, 219
Stereospecific elimination reactions leading to geometric isomers, 219
— interconversion of cis- and trans-3-hexanes, 220
— syntheses, definition, 219
— —, of geometric isomers of dialkylethylene type, 219
Steric hindrance, 124, 126
Stern and Gerlach, demonstration of space quantization, 13, 14
Steroids, determination of absolute configuration, 228
Sterols and sterol derivatives, lath-shaped, 139
Sterols, structure, 160
Structural proteins, 168
Structure of molecules, 113–191
—, difference between physical and chemical approach for study of —, 114
—, stages in the description, 115–120
Structures of the major classes of biochemical molecules, 150–191
Structures, supporting, of plants and animals, 188
Strychnine, structure, 161
Sucrose, structure and shape of molecule, 136
Sugars, noncyclic, shape of molecules and packing, 134
Sulphoraphene, stereoisomerism, 206
Sulphuric acid, structure in VB and MO theory, 104, 105
Superhelix, definition, 216
Svedberg's rule of the multiplicity of protein molecular weights, 170
Symmetry, plane of, definition, 193
—, point, definition, 193
— symbols of wave functions, 40

Syn-anti or geometric (*cis-trans*) isomers, 201

Syndiotactic polyvinyl diastereomer, 215

Synthesis, asymmetrical, 220, 223, 224

—, stereoselective, definition, 219

—, stereospecific, definition, 219

Tactoids, 150

(+)-Tartaric acid, determination of absolute configuration, 227

—, stereoisomerism, 207

—, structure, 136, 156

Tartrate, molecular dimensions and crystal structure, 136

Terpenes, structure, 160

Terpenoids, determination of absolute configuration, 228

Tertiary structures, definition, 216

—, of deoxyribonucleoproteins, 216

—, of α-proteins, 216

meso-Tetramethylspirobipyrrolidinium ion and its mirror image, 193

Thermal radiation, 2

Thomson, G. P., demonstration of matter waves associated with beam of electrons, 16

Thomson, J. J., model of atom, 5, 6

Three-electron bond, 58

Three-point mechanism, 224

Tiglic acid, conversion into angelic acid, 220

Tobacco mosaic virus, structure, 179

Trans-addition, 219

Trans-elimination, 219

Transition metals, complexes, MO treatment, 106–112

—, coordination numbers, 108

—, d electrons, 106

α–β Transition in proteins, 129

Triglycerides, shape of molecules and packing, 135

Triplet state, definition, 40

Twining of polymer molecules, 142, 143

Uncertainty principle, Heisenberg, 43

Uncoiling of polypeptide chains, 171

Ungerade character, definition, 40

Unipolar molecules, surface activity, 128

Unsaturated compounds in MO and VB theory, 70

Valence bond theory (VB theory), definition, 35

Valence, free, definition, 79, 80

Value of knowledge of geometrical structure of molecules for biochemistry, 120

Van der Waals forces, role of attractive part of — in conformation, 126

—, — of repulsive factor of — in conformation, 124

Variational principle, 59

VB and MO theories, comparison, 67

VB theory (valence bond or resonance theory), definition, 35

Vegetable acids, shape of molecules and packing, 136

Vicinal acyclic dibromides, determination of configuration of isomers, 227

Virus nucleoproteins, structure, 178

Virus(es), polyhedral adeno-, electron microphotograph, 180

—, rod-shaped, structure, 179

—, spherical, 180

—, tobacco mosaic —, structure, 179

Vitamin B_{12}, structure, 117–120

— D, structure, 137, 160

Water, electronic structure, 67

— in MO theory, 66, 67

Wave function(s), antibonding and bonding, 38

—, approximate, 47

—, definition, 18

—, exact, 46

—, physical meaning, 43–46

—, total, definition, 36

Wavelength of De Broglie wave of accelerated electron, 16

Wave nature of matter, concept, 15, 16

Wilson–Sommerfeld quantum conditions, 12

(+)-Xylose, determination of absolute configuration, 228

Zeeman effect of strong magnetic field on spectral lines, 5

COMPREHENSIVE BIOCHEMISTRY

SECTION II

Chemistry of Biological Compounds

The volumes of this section contain the following chapters:

Volume 5. *Carbohydrates*

Chapter I. Monosaccharides by Elizabeth Percival (Edinburgh)
Chapter II. Aldonic, uronic, oxoaldonic and ascorbic acids by Elizabeth Percival (Edinburgh)
Chapter III. Amino sugars by H. Egge (Heidelberg)
Chapter IV. Sugar phosphates by L. F. Leloir and C. E. Cardini (Buenos Aires)
Chapter V. Glycosides by J. Conchie and G. A. Levvy (Aberdeen)
Chapter VI. Oligosaccharides by S. Tsuiki, Y. Hashimoto and W. Pigman (New York)
Chapter VII. Polysaccharides
    (a) General considerations by D. Horton and M. L. Wolfrom (Columbus, Ohio)
    (b) Starch, glycogen, dextrins by D. Horton and M. L. Wolfrom (Columbus, Ohio)
    (c) Polyuronides by Z. I. Kertesz (Ithaca, N.Y.)
    (d) Polysaccharides of bacteria, moulds, yeast and protozoa by S. A. Barker (Birmingham)
    (e) Mucopolysaccharides (acidic glycosaminoglycans) by R. W. Jeanloz (Boston, Mass.)
Chapter VIII. Cyclitols by S. J. Angyal (Kensington, N.S.W.)

Volume 6. *Lipids – Amino acids and related compounds*
    Part A. *Lipids*

Chapter I. Fatty acids, long-chain alcohols and waxes by J. F. Mead, D. R. Howton and J. C. Nevenzel (Los Angeles, Calif.)
Chapter II. Neutral fats and oils by J. A. Lovern (Aberdeen)
Chapter III. Phosphoglycerides and sphingolipids by D. J. Hanahan and H. Brocker-hoff (Seattle, Wash.)

    Part B. *Amino acids and related compounds*

Chapter IV. General chemistry of amino acids by M. Winitz (Duarte, Calif.)
Chapter V. Nitrogenous bases by N. van Thoai (Paris)
Chapter VI. Melanins by J. Harley-Mason (Cambridge)
Chapter VII. Peptides: Synthetic methods and applications by G. W. Anderson (Pearl River, N.Y.)
Chapter VIII. Capsular polypeptides by G. Ivánovics (Szeged)
Chapter IX. Synthesis of bacterial glutamyl polypeptides by V. Bruckner (Budapest)

Volume 7. *Proteins, part 1*

Chapter I. Occurrence, classification, preparation and analysis by E. GORDON YOUNG (Halifax)
Chapter II. The chemistry of proteins by H. FRAENKEL-CONRAT (Berkeley, Calif.)
Chapter III. Acid–base properties and electrophoresis of proteins by R. TRAUTMAN (Long Island, N.Y.)
Chapter IV. Reactions of proteins, denaturation by H. A. SCHERAGA (Ithaca, N.Y.)
Chapter V. Thermodynamic properties of proteins found from osmotic experiments by R. L. BALDWIN (Palo Alto, Calif.)
Chapter VI. Sedimentation, diffusion and partial specific volume by K. O. PEDERSEN (Uppsala)
Chapter VII. Spacial configuration in proteins by D. W. GREEN (London)

Volume 8. *Proteins, part 2 – Nucleic acids*

Part A. *Proteins, part 2*

Chapter I. Conjugated proteins
    (a) Lipoproteins by F. R. N. GURD (Indianapolis, Ind.)
    (b) Glycoproteins and glycopeptides by A. GOTTSCHALK (Canberra)
    (c) Non-porphyrin metalloproteins by E. BOERI (Ferrara)
    (d) Haemoglobin and myoglobin by H. LEHMANN AND R. G. HUNTSMAN (London)
Chapter II. Peptide and protein hormones
    (a) Thyroid by J. ROCHE (Paris)
    (b) Parathyroid hormone by H. RASMUSSEN (New York)
    (c) Adenohypophyseal hormones by C. H. LI (Berkeley, Calif.)
    (d) Neurohypophyseal hormones by R. ACHER (Paris)
    (e) Insulin and glucagon by W. W. BREMER AND O. K. BEHRENS (Indianapolis, Ind.)

Part B. *Nucleic acids*

Chapter III. Purines, pyrimidine bases and nucleosides by D. M. BROWN (London)
Chapter IV. Nucleotides, polynucleotides and nucleic acids by D. M. BROWN (London)
Chapter V. Physical properties of nucleic acids
    (a) The three-dimensional configuration of the DNA molecule and its relation to genetic replication and mutation by M. H. F. WILKINS (London)
    (b) Solution properties by J. D. COOMBES (London)
    (c) Spectroscopic properties of nucleic acids by G. R. WILKINSON (London)

Volume 9. *Pyrrol pigments, isoprenoid compounds and phenolic plant constituents*

Part A. *Pyrrol pigments*

Chapter I. Porphyrins and metalloporphyrins by J. E. FALK (Canberra)
Chapter II. Physico–chemical properties of porphyrins by J. N. PHILLIPS (Canberra)
Chapter III. Chlorophyll by ROBERT HILL (Cambridge)
Chapter IV. Bile pigments by C. H. GRAY (London)

Part B. *Isoprenoid compounds*

Chapter V. Isoprenoid compounds by A. J. HAAGEN-SMIT AND C. C. NIMMO (Pasadena, Calif.)
Chapter VI. Vitamin A by J. G. BAXTER (Rochester, N.Y.)
Chapter VII. Vitamins E by ROBERT S. HARRIS (Cambridge, Mass.)
Chapter VIII. Vitamins K by ROBERT S. HARRIS (Cambridge, Mass.)
Chapter IX. Quinones by R. A. MORTON (Liverpool)

Part C. *Phenolic plant constituents*

Chapter X. Flavonoid compounds, tannins, lignins and related compounds by T. A. GEISSMAN (Los Angeles, Calif.)

Volume 10. *Sterols, bile acids and steroids*

Chapter I. Sterols by D. KRITCHEVSKY (Philadelphia, Penn.)

Chapter II. Bile salts by G. A. D. HASLEWOOD (London)

Chapter III. Steroids
    (a) Androgens and other C_{19} steroids by G. I. FUJIMOTO AND R. W. LEDEEN (New York)
    (b) Estrogens by Ph. A. KATZMAN AND W. H. ELLIOTT (St. Louis, Mo.)
    (c) Adrenal hormones by H. J. RINGOLD AND A. BOWERS (Mexico)
    (d) Progestational hormones by J. A. ZDERIC (Stanford, Calif.)

Volume 11. *Water-soluble vitamins, hormones and antibiotics*

    Part A. *Water-soluble vitamins*

Chapter I. Thiamine by E. P. STEYN-PARVÉ AND C. H. MONFOORT (Utrecht)

Chapter II. Riboflavin and closely related flavins by J. P. LAMBOOY (Rochester, N.Y.)

Chapter III. Niacin by G. ARROYAVE AND R. BRESSANI (Guatemala)

Chapter IV. Vitamin B_6 by E. E. SNELL (Berkeley, Calif.)

Chapter V. Pantothenic acid by R. J. WILLIAMS (Austin, Texas)

Chapter VI. Biotin by L. H. STERNBACH (Nutley, N. J.)

Chapter VII. Folic acid and pteridines by W. SHIVE (Austin, Texas)

Chapter VIII. Vitamin B_{12} by A. F. WAGNER AND K. FOLKERS (Rahway, N. J.)

    Part B. *Hormones*

Chapter IX. Plant hormones
    (a) Indole auxins of plants by B. B. STOWE (New Haven, Conn.)
    (b) Synthetic auxins by H. VELDSTRA (Leiden)
    (c) Gibberellins by CH. A. WEST (Los Angeles, Calif.)
    (d) Purines and other compounds by K. MOTHES (Berlin)

Chapter X. Insect hormones by P. KARLSON (Munich)

    Part C. *Antibiotics*

Chapter XI. Antibiotics by E. P. ABRAHAM (Oxford)

DATE DUE

FEB 0 6 1976			
GAYLORD			PRINTED IN U.S.A.